Oil Paintings in Public Ownership in
Edinburgh I

The *Oil Paintings in Public Ownership* series of catalogues is an extraordinary work in progress. Published by The Public Catalogue Foundation, it is the result of the determined efforts of a small team of administrative staff, researchers and photographers spread across the United Kingdom.

Our national collection of oil paintings in public ownership is probably one of the finest anywhere in the world. It is held not just by our museums and galleries but is also to be found in hospitals, universities and other civic buildings throughout the United Kingdom. A large proportion of these paintings are not on display and many have never before been reproduced.

This series of books for the first time allows the public to see an entire photographic record of these works – a collection likely to number some 200,000 in total. In doing so, these volumes provide a unique insight into our nation's artistic and cultural history.

As Patron of The Public Catalogue Foundation, my visits to collections across the country have highlighted to me not only the desire of curators to publicise their paintings, but also the limited resources at their disposal. The Foundation's work goes a long way towards helping to create access to these collections, while at the same time giving the British public the opportunity to see and enjoy *all* the paintings that they own.

I wish The Public Catalogue Foundation every success in its continuing endeavours.

Camilla

Oil Paintings in Public Ownership in Edinburgh I

Master Patron:
Magnus Linklater (Scotland)

Coordinators: Dr Laura Walters and Anita Briggs
Photographer: Andrew Phillipson

The Public Catalogue Foundation

Patron HRH The Duchess of Cornwall

Contents

THE PAINTINGS

Edinburgh

Facing page: Nasmyth, Alexander, 1758–1840, *Edinburgh from the Calton Hill*, 1820, City of Edinburgh Council (p. 74)

Image opposite HRH The Duchess of Cornwall's statement: Nicholson, William, 1872–1949, *The Black Mirror* (detail), City of Edinburgh Council (p. 76)

Image opposite title page: Gear, William, 1915–1997, *Summer Fête* (detail), 1951, City of Edinburgh Council (p. 34)

Image opposite Founder's foreword: Byrne, John, b.1940, *Self Portrait*, City of Edinburgh Council (p. 13)

Foreword

One of the issues we have had to deal with over the past few months has been whether or not to continue with the printed catalogues, now that the Foundation's data is becoming universally available via Your Paintings, our online venture with the BBC. I felt strongly that we should continue, and that was agreed. There were many reasons for doing so, in particular the concern that virtual records, ones with no defined printed version, may not be enduring. At least not as enduring as a book. The printed volumes are lapidary and will record for posterity the national collection of oil paintings on a given date. The collections will of course change, but their catalogue is a definitive point of departure. In simple terms, as Sir Nicholas Serota said to me in support of continuing the printed version alongside Your Paintings: it is a different project.

I had not spotted another important reason. The American author, Jonathan Franzen, suggested, that digital books, by virtue of their impermanence, left open a potential door to Orwellian censorship. If books are electronic and not on paper, they can be changed or deleted by some Central Authority: "a situation not compatible with responsible self-government". One can easily dismiss that as paranoid and old-fashioned. But he has a point.

So I was rather encouraged when I noticed that, on no less than five occasions in her foreword to the University of Edinburgh's Fine Art Collection, Jacky MacBeath refers to works unfortunately not included in this catalogue. Their exclusion is because, whilst they form part of her university collection, they are not in oil, tempera or acrylic. I sympathise with her but, however regrettable, the Public Catalogue Foundation has had to limit its scope. This can and should be remedied in future years.

Her concern correctly reflects the fact that her record is incomplete. The problem, of course, is not just hers. The chief omission in the national record of our paintings is our collection of watercolours, size and whereabouts (in detail) unknown, which records so much not just of the history of this country, but of the world in general as seen by sailors, soldiers, colonial servants, missionaries and more, together with their spouses and over some 200 years. This record belongs to almost every nation on Earth and should be available for all of them to see. My hope is that a younger generation will soon do for this collection what the Foundation is doing for oils.

Some may be misled by the rather formal title of this catalogue to believe that this is a rather formal, hence dull, record of dull collections. It isn't. The University of Edinburgh's collection from The Torrie Collection through to its Modern Scottish Art Collection, the Montagu Douglas Scott Collection and the Talbot Rice Memorial Collection, is very rich indeed. Works owned by Historic Scotland on display in Edinburgh Castle and at Trinity House in Leith are every bit as good as those two important buildings deserve. And the City of Edinburgh Council, more generously treated by its donors than many of its counterparts throughout the Kingdom, has been the beneficiary of the institutional generosity of the Scottish Modern Arts Association and the Scottish Arts Council as well as of individuals, with quite extraordinary results.

Fred Hohler, Founder

Christie's is proud to be the sponsor of The Public Catalogue Foundation in its pursuit to improve public access to paintings held in public collections in the UK.

Christie's is a name and place that speaks of extraordinary art. Founded in 1766 by James Christie, the company is now the world's leading art business. Many of the finest works of art in UK public collections have safely passed through Christie's, as the company has had the privilege of handling the safe cultural passage of some of the greatest paintings and objects ever created. Christie's today remains a popular showcase for the unique and the beautiful.
In addition to acquisition through auction sales, Christie's regularly negotiates private sales to the nation, often in lieu of tax, and remains committed to leading the auction world in the area of Heritage sales.

CHRISTIE'S

The Public Catalogue Foundation: People Involved

Financial Supporters for Scotland

The Public Catalogue Foundation would like to express its profound appreciation to the following organisations and individuals who have supported the Scottish series and digitisation project.

Binks Trust
Marion Blythman
Janey Buchan
Rhona Callander
Creative Scotland
James Ferguson
Dunard Fund
Mrs Patricia Grayburn
    MBE DL
Edward and Anna
    Hocknell

The Hope Scott Trust
ICAP plc
The MacRobert Trust
Marc Fitch Fund
Allan and Carol
    Murray
Museums Galleries
    Scotland
NADFAS Scotland &
    Northern Ireland
    Area

Nancie Massey
    Charitable Trust
P .F. Charitable Trust
Scottish Government
Alexander Stewart
Swire Charitable Trust
Lord William Douglas
    Cullen of Whitekirk

Catalogue Scope and Organisation

Medium and Support

The principal focus of this series is oil paintings. However, tempera and acrylic are also included as well as mixed media, where oil is the predominant constituent. Paintings on all forms of support (e.g. canvas, panel, etc.) are included as long as the support is portable. The principal exclusions are miniatures, hatchments or other purely heraldic paintings and wall paintings *in situ*.

Public Ownership

Public ownership has been taken to mean any paintings that are directly owned by the public purse, made accessible to the public by means of public subsidy or generally perceived to be in public ownership. The term 'public' refers to both central government and local government. Paintings held by national museums, local authority museums, English Heritage and independent museums, where there is at least some form of public subsidy, are included. Paintings held in civic buildings such as local government offices, town halls, guildhalls, public libraries, universities, hospitals, crematoria, fire stations and police stations are also included.

Geographical Boundaries of Catalogues

The geographical boundary of each county is the 'ceremonial county' boundary. This county definition includes all unitary authorities. Counties that have a particularly large number of paintings are divided between two or more catalogues on a geographical basis.

Criteria for Inclusion

As long as paintings meet the requirements above, all paintings are included irrespective of their condition and perceived quality. However, painting reproductions can only be included with the agreement of the participating collections and, where appropriate, the relevant copyright owner. It is rare that a collection forbids the inclusion of its paintings. Where this is the case and it is possible to obtain a list of paintings, this list is given in the Paintings Without Reproductions section. Where copyright consent is refused, the paintings are also listed in the Paintings Without Reproductions section. All paintings in collections' stacks and stores are included, as well as those on display. Paintings which have been lent to other institutions, whether for short-term exhibition or long-term loan, are listed under the owner collection. In addition, paintings on long-term loan are also included under the borrowing institution when they are likely to remain there for at least another five years from the date of publication of this catalogue. Information relating to owners and borrowers is listed in the Further Information section.

Layout

Collections are grouped together under their home town. These locations are listed in alphabetical order. In some cases collections that are spread over a number of locations are included under a single owner collection. A number of collections, principally the larger ones, are preceded by curatorial forewords. Within each collection paintings are listed in order of artist surname. Where there is more than one painting by the same artist, the paintings are listed chronologically, according to their execution date.

The few paintings that are not accompanied by photographs are listed in the Paintings Without Reproductions section.

There is additional reference material in the Further Information section at the back of the catalogue. This gives the full names of artists, titles and media if it has not been possible to include these in full in the main section. It also provides acquisition credit lines and information about loans in and out, as well as copyright and photographic credits for each painting. Finally, there is an index of artists' surnames.

Key to Painting Information

Almost all paintings are reproduced in the catalogue. Where this is not the case they are listed in the Paintings Without Reproductions section. Where paintings are missing or have been stolen, the best possible photograph on record has been reproduced. In some cases this may be black and white. Paintings that have been stolen are highlighted with a red border. Some paintings are shown with conservation tissue attached to parts of the painting surface.

Adam, Patrick William 1854–1929
Interior, Rutland Lodge: Vista through Open Doors 1920
oil on canvas 67.3 × 45.7
LEEAG.PA.1925.0671.LACF ☀

Artist name This is shown with the surname first. Where the artist is listed on the Getty Union List of Artist Names (ULAN), ULAN's preferred presentation of the name is given. In a number of cases the name may not be a firm attribution and this is made clear. Where the artist name is not known, a school may be given instead. Where the school is not known, the painter name is listed as *unknown artist*. If the artist name is too long for the space, as much of the name is given as possible followed by (…). This indicates the full name is given at the rear of the catalogue in the Further Information section.

Painting title A painting title followed by *(?)* indicates that the title is in doubt. Where the alternative title to the painting is considered to be better known than the original, the alternative title is given in parentheses. Where the collection has not given a painting a title, the publisher does so instead and marks this with an asterisk. If the title is too long for the space, as much of the title is given as possible followed by *(…)* and the full title is given in the Further Information section.

Execution date In some cases the precise year of execution may not be known for certain. Instead an approximate date will be given or no date at all.

Artist dates Where known, the years of birth and death of the artist are given. In some cases one or both dates may not be known with certainty, and this is marked. No date indicates that even an approximate date is not known. Where only the period in which the artist was active is known, these dates are given and preceded with the word *active*.

Medium and support Where the precise material used in the support is known, this is given.

Dimensions All measurements refer to the unframed painting and are given in cm with up to one decimal point. In all cases the height is shown before the width. An (E) indicates where a painting has not been measured and its size has been calculated by sight only. If the painting is circular, the single dimension is the diameter. If the painting is oval, the dimensions are height and width.

Collection inventory number In the case of paintings owned by museums, this number will always be the accession number. In all other cases it will be a unique inventory number of the owner institution. (P) indicates that a painting is a private loan. Details can be found in the Further Information section. Accession numbers preceded by 'PCF' indicate that the collection did not have an accession number at the time of catalogue production and therefore the number given has been temporarily allocated by The Public Catalogue Foundation. The ☀ symbol indicates that the reproduction is based on a Bridgeman Art Library transparency (go to www.bridgemanart.com) or that Bridgeman administers the copyright for that artist.

Facing page: Rogers, Henry, b.1963, *An Initial Act of Creation* (detail), 1987, City of Edinburgh Council (p. 90)

THE PAINTINGS

City of Edinburgh Council

Riots, sieges and executions – Scotland's capital city, so often at the very heart of Scottish affairs, has had a turbulent and eventful history. Having received its original charter from King David I in the mid-twelfth century, at first Edinburgh was administered by burgesses (freemen) who enjoyed the right of being merchants or craftsmen.

As the town grew in size, a council was constituted to oversee the running of the city and, having gone through various incarnations, continues to do so. It is hardly surprising then that a large topographical and civic collection forms the backbone of the City's art collection. William Delacour's panoramic *View of Edinburgh* from 1759 is one the earliest large-scale paintings of the city, and depicts a view of the Old Town which had not changed significantly since medieval times.

Edinburgh was at the forefront of the Scottish Enlightenment, and no artist so successfully captured the city during this period as Alexander Nasmyth. His magnificent *The Port of Leith* from 1824 is one of the highlights of the Collection. Significant events such as royal visits are well documented, as is the rise of the Georgian New Town and the subsequent expansion of the City.

Throughout the ages, it has been customary practice that each Lord Provost (the Scottish equivalent of a Mayor) has their portrait painted upon demitting office. This collection of portraits is comprised of works by many of the major artists of their generations, including Allan Ramsay, Sir Henry Raeburn and, more recently, David Abercrombie Donaldson and Dame Elizabeth V. Blackadder.

In 1964, the City was given over 300 paintings by the Scottish Modern Arts Association. Founded in 1907, the SMAA was the first society established in Scotland for the purpose of creating a collection of modern art for the benefit of the nation. The Association received money from membership fees and the pictures were bought by committee. Among early acquisitions were Edward Atkinson Hornel's *Seashore Roses* and John Henry Lorimer's *The Flight of the Swallows*, and these paintings remain firm favourites with our visitors. Paintings by leading figures from the Glasgow School and the Scottish Colourists have come into the City's collection by way of this important gift. Sadly, by the late 1950s the Association had few members and little money, and no new purchases were made after 1960.

In 1961 an Edinburgh lady, Miss Jean F. Watson, at first gave, and then later bequeathed, sums of money with the wish that they should be used to create a collection of Scottish Art for the City. The fund is still in use today, and is the main source of money for new acquisitions. From the outset, the committee charged with administering the funds opted to purchase contemporary works of art by Scottish artists or artists based in Scotland. They also tried, where possible, to fill historic gaps in the City Collection. One of their very first purchases was by a young, rebellious artist not long out of art college, John Bellany. That painting, *The Obsession*, remains one of the key works in our Collection. Works by important contemporary artists such as Moyna Flannigan, Callum Innes, Peter Howson and Victoria Crowe have all been acquired with Bequest Funds.

In more recent times, the Art Collection has benefited greatly from a bequest through the Scottish Arts Council of over 100 works, and from being part of the National Collecting Scheme for Scotland. This latter scheme, made possible by the Scottish Arts Council with a major investment from the National Lottery and through partnership working with the Contemporary Art Society, has enabled us to acquire works by leading contemporary artists. Those now represented, although not all work in oils, include Toby Paterson, Christine Borland, Graham Fagen, Rosalind Nashashibi, Nathan Coley and Rose Frain.

The City's art collection now numbers over 4,500 items, including works on paper, sculpture and photographs as well as oil paintings. New additions are made by the Committee on the Jean F. Watson Bequest which meets on average twice a year. We are indebted to the Friends of the City Art Centre, to the National Fund for Acquisitions and the Art Fund, who have consistently awarded grants that have enabled us to make acquisitions which we would otherwise be unable to afford. We are delighted to be part of this marvellous project which we are confident will further enhance this significant collection of Scottish art.

David Patterson, Curator, Fine Art

Adam, Patrick William 1854–1929
A Ballroom 1915
oil on canvas 111 x 85
CAC1989/72

Adam, Patrick William 1854–1929
The Signet Library, Edinburgh
oil on canvas 75.5 x 94.6
CAC46/1964

Adams, William Dacres 1864–1951
The Cathedral of St Magnus, Kirkwall c.1912
oil on canvas 102.2 x 76.2
CAC1964/40

Adamson, Elizabeth A. b.1959
Gathering Flowers in the Rock Garden
oil on canvas 102.9 x 85.1
CAC1986/5

Aitchison, Craigie Ronald John 1926–2009
Silver Birch Trees at Tulliallan, Fife 1960
oil on canvas 34 x 24
CAC40/1998 🐝

Alexander, Robert L. 1840–1923
A Tangier Gateway 1887
oil on board 29.8 x 22.2
CAC24/1988

Alexander, Robert L. 1840–1923
Auld Freens 1909
oil on canvas 46.3 x 36.2
CAC30/1964

Alexander, Robert L. 1840–1923
Feeding the Horse
oil on canvas 86.3 x 103.2
CAC1978/3

Alexander, Vivien b.1940
Susan 1988/1989
oil on canvas 99.7 x 121.9
CAC9/1991

Alison, David 1882–1955
Sir Thomas Hunter, LLD, WS c.1919
oil on canvas 129.5 x 102.2
CAC1978/4

Alison, David 1882–1955
The Quiet Room c.1941
oil on canvas 76.8 x 64.7
CAC196/1964

Alison, David 1882–1955
*Sir James Spittal (1796–1842), Lord Provost of
Edinburgh (1833–1837)* (copy after John
Watson Gordon)
oil on canvas 238.8 x 153.7
CAC1978/5

Alison, David 1882–1955
The Interior
oil on canvas 91.4 x 88.9
CAC64/1964

Allan, David 1744–1796
Faith (triptych, left wing)
oil on canvas 140 x 60.5
HH118/1901

Allan, David 1744–1796
Hope (triptych, centre panel)
oil on canvas 140 x 60.5
HH119/1901

Allan, David 1744–1796
Charity (triptych, right wing)
oil on canvas 108 x 60.8
HH120/1901

Allan, William 1782–1850
*The Signing of the National Covenant in
Greyfriars Kirkyard, Edinburgh* c.1838
oil on canvas 81.5 x 130.2
CAC1991/58

Archer, James active c.1860–1870
A Dog Mourning Its Little Master 1866
oil on canvas 26 x 41.3
MC4124/1961

Armour, Mary Nicol Neill 1902–2000
The Wee Cumbrae from Corrie 1961
oil on panel 62.2 x 80.1
CAC1962/4 🐝

Arnott, Andrew 1963–1995
Self Portrait 1984
oil on canvas 87 x 72.4
CAC1985/36

J. R. B.
A Hallway
oil on board 21 x 20
CAC2003/1

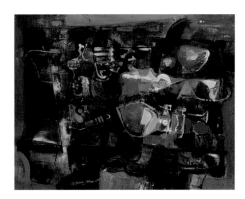

Baillie, William James b.1923
Child's Table 1961
oil on canvas 50.8 x 61
CAC8/1984

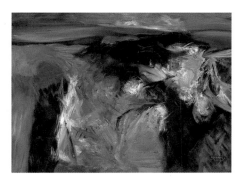

Baillie, William James b.1923
Cocos Landscape with Palms 1964
oil on canvas 76.2 x 101.6
CAC2/1975

Bain, Donald 1904–1979
The Pap of Glencoe 1966
oil on canvas 54.6 x 46.8
CAC12/1976

Ballantyne, John 1815–1897
John Kay, Senior Baillie (1855–1856)
oil on canvas 91.4 x 71.4
CAC1978/8

Balmer, Barbara b.1929
Shrouded Lunch 2
oil on canvas 120.7 x 151.1
CAC1987/12

Barker, Joanne b.1963
Study for 'The Battle of Britain Tapestry'
oil & collage on paper 15.4 x 33.6
CAC61/1992

Barns-Graham, Wilhelmina 1912–2004
Rocks, St Mary's, Scilly Isles 1953
oil on board 102.8 x 114.3
CAC1989/73

Barrie, Mardi 1930–2004
Farmland Autumn 1961
oil on canvas 84 x 111
CAC43/1998

Barrie, Mardi 1930–2004
Theatre (Château)
oil on canvas 91 x 91.5
CAC1983/7

Bear, George Telfer 1876–1973
Poppies
oil on canvas 61.5 x 51.5
CAC249/1964

Bear, George Telfer 1876–1973
Portrait with Still Life
oil on board 100.3 x 74.2
CAC3/1970

Beechey, William 1753–1839
Thomas Coutts (1735–1822)
oil on canvas 76.5 x 64.4
CAC1978/9

Behrens, Reinhard b.1951
Lost Valley II 1985
oil on canvas 168.9 x 134.6
CAC1985/14

Bell, John active c.1840–1860
Edinburgh from Craigleith Quarry
oil on canvas 139.8 x 193.1
CAC1978/10

Bellany, John b.1942
Self Portrait with a Razor Shell 1976
oil on canvas 187 x 152.5
CAC44/1998

Bellany, John b.1942
Bêche-de-mer 1984
oil on canvas 213.4 x 172.7
CAC1984/19

Bellany, John b.1942
Sweet Promise (triptych, left wing) c.1994
oil on canvas 203 x 91.5
CAC1995/5

Bellany, John b.1942
Sweet Promise (triptych, centre panel) c.1994
oil on canvas 203 x 178
CAC1995/5

Bellany, John b.1942
Sweet Promise (triptych, right wing) c.1994
oil on canvas 203 x 91.5
CAC1995/5 🐝

Bellany, John b.1942
The Obsession
oil on panel 212.1 x 242.6
CAC1968/7 🐝

Black, Dorothy b.1963
Gamine
oil on canvas 182.9 x 152.4
CAC1986/50

Black, Dorothy b.1963
Our Elsie
oil on canvas 168 x 137
CAC1989/25

Black, Dorothy b.1963
Scales 1988
charcoal & oil on paper 95.9 x 77.5
CAC1989/58

Blackadder, Elizabeth V. b.1931
Prayer Rug with Flowers 1966
oil on canvas 40.9 x 50.8
CAC1966/3

Blackadder, Elizabeth V. b.1931
Princes Street Gardens, Edinburgh c.1966
oil on canvas 71.2 x 91.4
CAC1966/2

Blackadder, Elizabeth V. b.1931
The Right Honourable Eric Milligan (b.1951),
Lord Provost of Edinburgh (1996–2003) 2007
oil on canvas 114 x 107
CAC2008/3

Blyth, Robert Henderson 1919–1970
Goalmouth
oil on board 121.9 x 106.3
CAC1965/1

Blyth, Robert Henderson 1919–1970
Hauling in the Anchor
oil on paper 15.2 x 11.5
CAC2/1990

Bone, Muirhead 1876–1953
The Old Racecourse, Ayr 1900
oil on canvas 50.8 x 86.2
CAC95/1964

Bonnar, William (attributed to) 1800–1855
Mother and Child
oil on wood 40 x 33
CAC1978/12

Borthwick, Alfred Edward 1871–1955
Marjorie c.1934
oil on canvas 112.4 x 68.2
CAC144/1964

Borthwick, Alfred Edward 1871–1955
Sir William J. Thomson (1881–1949), LLD,
Lord Provost of Edinburgh (1932–1935) 1937
oil on canvas 137.1 x 96.5
CAC1/1937

Borthwick, Alfred Edward 1871–1955
Betty
oil on canvas 108 x 85.5
CAC308/1964

Borthwick, Alfred Edward 1871–1955
Burnhouse
oil on canvas 76.2 x 101.6
CAC304/1964

Borthwick, Alfred Edward 1871–1955
Head of an Old Man
oil on board 50.8 x 40
CAC209/1964

Bowie, John Dick 1864–1941
Robert Miller, Lord Dean of Guild
(1890–1898)
oil on canvas 76.2 x 50.8
CAC1978/15

Bowie, John Dick 1864–1941
*Sir Andrew MacDonald (1836–1919), Lord
Provost of Edinburgh (1894–1897)*
oil on canvas 125.7 x 87.3
CAC1978/16

Brackett, Nancy A. b.1907
Mrs Dunlop and 'Smokey'
oil on board 35.6 x 45.7
CAC1978/19

Braes, Lex b.1956
Nelson Mandela (b.1918), at Nineteen 1986
oil on canvas 208.6 x 175.6
CAC1986/39

Braham, Philip b.1959
The Forest Edge, Augustowska, Poland 2001
oil on canvas 66 x 86
CAC2003/3

Brown, John b.1967
The Quiet Wood 1991
oil on canvas 151.5 x 244
CAC1991/23

Brown, John b.1967
International City
oil on canvas 160 x 70
CAC6/1995

Brown, Neil Dallas 1938–2003
Shroud and Barrier 1981
oil on board 214 x 161
CAC2006/5

Brown, William Marshall 1863–1936
Sardine Fishers, Concarneau, France
oil on canvas 51.2 x 61.5
CAC121/1964

Burns, Robert 1869–1941
*John Knox Preaching in St Giles Cathedral to a
Congregation Comprising Mary Queen of Scots
and Other Noble Personages*
oil on canvas 160.7 x 187.3
CAC1978/27

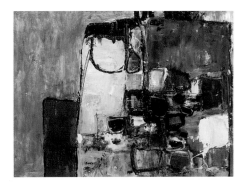

Burns, Robert 1869–1941
The Valley of the Shadow, Loch Coruisk
oil on canvas 105.4 x 161.3
CAC27/1964

Burns, William Alexander 1921–1972
Ebb Tide
oil on board 154.3 x 104.1
CAC1966/8

Burns, William Alexander 1921–1972
Seahouse 3
oil on paper 36.8 x 46.3
CAC1968/5

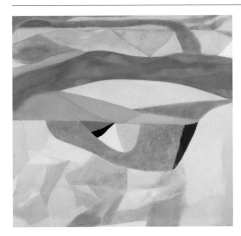

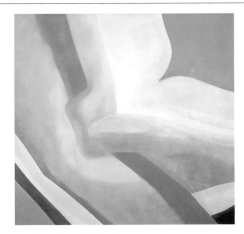

Busby, John Philip b.1928
Silent Landscape 1966
oil on canvas 99.1 x 100.4
CAC1967/17

Busby, John Philip b.1928
Sky Canticle for June 1972
acrylic on canvas 90.2 x 95.3
CAC49/1998

Busby, John Philip b.1928
Journey 1978
oil on canvas 90 x 100
CAC50/1998

Bushe, Robbie b.1964
Cat amongst the Glutton 1989
oil on canvas 152.4 x 114.3
CAC1989/65

Buttersworth, Thomas 1768–1842
The Arrival of George IV at Leith Harbour, 1822
oil on canvas 42 x 67
CAC1990/23

Byrne, John b.1940
Self Portrait c.1988
oil on canvas board 33.5 x 23.5
CAC1989/44 🐝

Facing page: Nasmyth, Alexander, 1758–1840, *The Port of Leith*, City of Edinburgh Council, 1824 (p. 74)

Cadell, Agnes Morrison 1873–1958
The Orange Hat
oil on canvas 145.5 x 66.3
CAC310/1964

Cadell, Francis Campbell Boileau
1883–1937
The Black Hat 1914
oil on canvas 107 x 84.5
CAC210/1964

Cadell, Francis Campbell Boileau
1883–1937
Iona
oil on panel 37.5 x 45.2
CAC283/1964

Cadell, Francis Campbell Boileau 1883–1937
Lady Lavery (1887–1935)
oil on canvas 127 x 101.6
CAC71/1964

Cadenhead, James 1858–1927
Lady with a Japanese Screen and Goldfish (The Artist's Mother) 1886
oil on canvas 91.4 x 185.4
CAC131/1964

Cadenhead, James 1858–1927
Deeside
oil on canvas 50.7 x 60.9
CAC325/1964

Cadenhead, James 1858–1927
Landscape
oil on canvas 48 x 60.7
CAC328/1964

Cairns, Joyce W. b.1947
War Games
oil on board 125 x 216.5
CAC1987/1

Callender, Robert 1932–2011
Dawn 1972
oil on canvas 177 x 177.5
CAC54/1998

Callow, John (imitator of) 1822–1878
French Fishing Boats
oil on canvas 61.6 x 91.5
CAC1978/274

Cameron, David Young 1865–1945
Criffel c.1908
oil on canvas 114.3 x 142.6
CAC9/1964

Cameron, David Young 1865–1945
A Garment of War
oil on canvas 121.9 x 167
CAC105/1964

Cameron, Hugh 1835–1918
A Summer Idyll 1865
oil on canvas 35.6 x 50.8
MC9540/1965

Cameron, Hugh 1835–1918
The Reaper 1868
oil on canvas 46.1 x 37.5
CAC69/1964

Cameron, Hugh 1835–1918
Children Boating 1896
oil on canvas 74.9 x 136.6
HH3133/1967

Cameron, Hugh 1835–1918
Going Visiting
oil on canvas 40 x 30
MC4379/1961

Cameron, Mary 1864–1921
An Edinburgh Halberdier 1894
oil on canvas 61.6 x 39.2
HH46/1899

Cameron, Mary 1864–1921
Les joueurs
oil on canvas 121.9 x 163.8
CAC153/1964

Campbell, Alexander S. b.1932
Cattle Trough
oil on board 39.7 x 78.2
CAC7/1966

Campbell, Steven 1953–2007
Gesturing Hiker with Furnace 1983
oil on board 190.5 x 121.9
CAC1990/75

Carlisle, Fionna b.1954
Cretan Landscape
oil on paper 163.8 x 182.9
CAC1987/2

Carmichael, Rodick 1931–2008
Hill Village II 1959
oil on board 83 x 80
CAC56/1998

Carmichael, Rodick 1931–2008
Burning Buddhist III c.1960–1966
oil on board 60.5 x 60.5
CAC57/1998

Carmichael, Stuart b.1960
Untitled
crayon & acrylic on paper 40.6 x 58.4
CAC1986/42

Carse, Alexander c.1770–1843
George IV Landing at Leith, 1822
oil on canvas 160.1 x 362
CAC1978/30

Carse, Alexander (attributed to)
c.1770–1843
The Barber's Shop
oil on canvas 43.5 x 54.1
CAC1978/32

Carse, William active 1818–1845
Tam o' Shanter
oil on panel 71.1 x 97.1
CAC2010/18

Chalmers, George c.1720–c.1791
*Archibald Macaulay, Lord Provost of
Edinburgh (1727–1729, 1737–1738 &
1748–1750)*
oil on canvas 128.3 x 102.2
CAC1978/34

Cheape, Malcolm b.1964
Construction
oil & collage on board 124.5 x 177.8
CAC1986/40

Cheyne, E. J. active 19th C
Portrait of an Unknown Gentleman
oil on canvas 73.6 x 61.6
CAC363/1964

Cheyne, Sally b.1964
Untitled
oil on canvas 48.3 x 40
CAC1987/25

Churchill, Martin b.1954
The Palace Continued 1979
oil on canvas 167.7 x 198.2
CAC1985/6

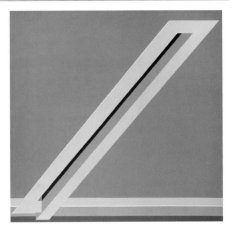

Cina, Colin b.1943
Running Grey 1960–1969
acrylic & emulsion on canvas 182 x 182.5
CAC62/1998

Clark, William 1731–1801
Hall of the Old Tolbooth, c.1795
oil on canvas 29.8 x 38.1
CAC1978/35

Clarkson, Kathleen b.1950
Jetty One
oil on canvas 138.1 x 137.1
CAC5/1972

Clausen, George 1852–1944
Still Life with Cucumber and Tomatoes
oil on canvas 36.2 x 41
CAC104/1964

Clays, Paul Jean 1819–1900
The Port of Leith
oil on canvas 106.7 x 165.1
CAC1984/21

Collingbourne, Stephen b.1943
Sunset Strip
oil & mixed media on board 49.7 x 38
CAC41/1989

Colombo, Russell b.1947
Reeker Pike c.1970
acrylic on canvas 177.8 x 167
CAC1990/71

Colquhoun, Robert 1914–1962
Circus Woman c.1949
oil on canvas 104.1 x 79.1
CAC5/1976 🐝

Colquhoun, Robert 1914–1962
Bitch and Pup 1958
oil on canvas 116.8 x 91.5
CAC1984/31 🐝

Condie, Robert Hardie 1898–1981
Winter Landscape
oil on canvas 51.9 x 76.2
CAC219/1964

Connard, Philip 1875–1958
Self Portrait with Still Life
oil on canvas 77.5 x 63.5
CAC130/1964

Connon, William John b.1929
Anticoli, Italy
oil on board 121.9 x 142.3
CAC1965/6

Convery, Francis b.1956
Model Resting (Night Class) 1994
oil on canvas 106.7 x 91.4
CAC1995/1

Cook, David b.1957
The Sound of the Drum Is Calling
c.1988–1989
oil on canvas 128 x 122
CAC64/1998

Cossaar, Jacobus Cornelis Wyand
1874–1966
Reredos, St Paul's Cathedral, London
(destroyed during the Second World War)
oil on canvas 106.7 x 78.8
CAC39/1964

Couling, Arthur Vivian 1890–1962
Yew Tree Farm, near Coniston, Cumbria
oil on panel 49.5 x 56.2
CAC190/1964

Coward, Charles R. b.1950
Landscape Number 3
oil on canvas 127.6 x 106
CAC6/1972

Cowie, James 1886–1956
Mists in the Valley
oil on canvas 46.1 x 55.6
CAC307/1964

Crawford, Edmund Thornton 1806–1885
A Dutch River Scene
oil on canvas 77.5 x 106.7
CAC1982/9

Crayk, Fred b.1952
Capital: Lovers 1984–1985
oil on canvas 141.6 x 134
CAC1986/46

Crayk, Fred b.1952
Small Inverleith Park
oil on board 20 x 32
CAC65/1998

Crowe, Victoria b.1945
Beech Tree, Winter 1973
oil on panel 120.5 x 90
CAC2009/13

Crowe, Victoria b.1945
Dr Winifred Rushforth (1885–1983)
1981–1982
oil on canvas 63.5 x 120.6
CAC1982/12

Crowe, Victoria b.1945
The Last Portrait of Jenny Armstrong
1986–1987
oil on board 122 x 91.5
CAC2007/14

Crowe, Victoria b.1945
*Tom Morgan, Lord Provost of Edinburgh
(1980–1984)* 1988
oil on board 106.7 x 91.5
CAC1988/16

Crowe, Victoria b.1945
Italian Reflections 1992–1993
oil on board 76.2 x 91.5
CAC2007/15

Crowe, Victoria b.1945
Dancer and Graffiti 2004
oil on linen 127 x 127
CAC2009/14

Crozier, William 1893–1930
*View from the Mound, Edinburgh, Looking
West* c.1929
oil on panel 55.2 x 46.3
CAC118/1964

Crozier, William 1930–2011
St James's Park
oil on canvas 106.7 x 114.5
CAC1989/70

Cumming, James 1922–1991
Charred Table with Lamp and Tins
oil on canvas 91.5 x 122.2
CAC1962/3

Cumming, James (attributed to) 1732–1793
William MacGregor, an Edinburgh Porter
oil on canvas 76.2 x 62.2
CAC4/1984

Facing page: Pietro della Vecchia, 1603–1678, *The Lovers*, The University of Edinburgh Fine Art Collection (p. 168)

Cumming, John Begg 1884–1968
Self Portrait
oil on canvas 36.2 x 26.1
CAC10/1976

Cursiter, Stanley 1887–1976
Synthesis of the Supper Room at an Arts Club Reception 1913
oil on canvas board 25.2 x 35.4
CAC1979/13

Cursiter, Stanley 1887–1976
Tea Room 1913
oil on canvas board 25.2 x 35.2
CAC1979/12

Cursiter, Stanley 1887–1976
A Glass of Milk 1923
oil on canvas 40.6 x 45.7
CAC207/1964

Cursiter, Stanley 1887–1976
The Fair-Isle Jumper 1923
oil on canvas 102.2 x 86.6
CAC250/1964

Cursiter, Stanley 1887–1976
Sir Louis Stewart Gumley (1872–1941), LLD, Lord Provost of Edinburgh (1935–1938) 1939
oil on canvas 128.2 x 101.5
CAC1978/40

Cursiter, Stanley 1887–1976
Sir John Ireland Falconer, LLD, WS, Lord Provost of Edinburgh (1944–1947) 1948
oil on canvas 127 x 101.8
CAC1978/41

Cursiter, Stanley 1887–1976
Sir John Garnett Banks, CBE, LLD, Lord Provost of Edinburgh (1954–1957) 1958
oil on canvas 127 x 104.2
CAC1978/42

Cursiter, Stanley 1887–1976
Pachmann at the Usher Hall, Edinburgh
oil on canvas 86.5 x 101.6
CAC1/1980

Davidson, Bessie 1879–1965
Interior
oil on panel 98.7 x 104.8
CAC160/1964

Davie, Alan b.1920
Scented Arrow 1961
oil on paper laid on canvas 43.2 x 54.6
CAC1986/10

Davie, Alan b.1920
Serpent's Breath 1966
oil on canvas 122 x 152.5
CAC1996/4

Delacour, William 1700–1767
View of Edinburgh 1759
oil on canvas 108.2 x 229.1
HH768/1922

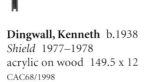

Dingwall, Kenneth b.1938
Shield 1977–1978
acrylic on wood 149.5 x 12
CAC68/1998

Dingwall, Kenneth b.1938
Calm Grey
acrylic on canvas 160 x 213
CAC1977/15

Dixon, Arthur Percy active 1884–1917
Bailie Waterson 1901
oil on canvas 111.7 x 142.2
CAC1978/46

Dobson, Cowan 1894–1980
*Sir Henry Steele (1879–1963), DL, Lord
Provost of Edinburgh (1938–1941)*
oil on canvas 128.2 x 101.6
CAC1978/48

Dobson, Cowan 1894–1980
*Sir William Lowrie Sleigh, DL, LLD, JP, Lord
Provost of Edinburgh (1923–1926)*
oil on canvas 223.5 x 132
CAC1978/47

Dobson, Henry Raeburn 1901–1985
Sir Herbert Archbold Brechin, KBE, DLitt,
Lord Provost of Edinburgh (1966–1969)
oil on canvas 127.1 x 101.6
CAC1978/49

Donald, George Malcolm b.1943
Stuffed Bird c.1972
oil & screenprint on canvas 124.4 x 132.1
CAC1972/3

Donald, George Malcolm b.1943
Blue Dragon Altar 1990
acrylic & mixed media on board 66.5 x 79
CAC2009/48

Donald, George Malcolm b.1943
Red Dragon Altar 1990
acrylic & mixed media collage on
board 102.5 x 130.1
CAC56/1990

Donaldson, David Abercrombie 1916–1996
Sir James Wilson Mackay (1912–1992), DLitt,
Lord Provost of Edinburgh (1969–1972)
oil on canvas 129.6 x 105.5
CAC1978/51

Donaldson, David Abercrombie 1916–1996
Sir John Greig Dunbar (b.1907), Lord Provost
of Edinburgh (1960–1963)
oil on canvas 125.7 x 106.8
CAC1978/50

Donaldson, David Abercrombie 1916–1996
The Pink Room, Young Girl
oil on panel 55.8 x 62.5
CAC264/1964

Donaldson, David Abercrombie 1916–1996
Two Glasgow Girls
oil on canvas 183 x 183
CAC1983/25

Dorrat, Gwen Debbie b.1964
Untitled
acrylic on canvas 58.4 x 74.9
CAC1986/43

Douglas, William Fettes 1822–1891
The Bibliophilist's Haunt (Creech's Bookshop)
1864
oil on canvas 66.3 x 86.7
CAC1982/11

Douglas, William Fettes 1822–1891
*The Village of the Water of Leith from a
Window in Rothesay Terrace* 1878
oil on canvas 119.3 x 82.5
CAC1980/5

Douthwaite, Pat 1939–2002
Woman with White Hair c.1970
oil on canvas 195 x 130.2
CAC70/1998

Douthwaite, Pat 1939–2002
Final Instructions before Take-Off 1976
oil on canvas 152.3 x 152.3
CAC3/1977

Douthwaite, Pat 1939–2002
Dr Helen Wright 1990
oil on canvas 144 x 107
CAC1993/12

Douthwaite, Pat 1939–2002
Suffolk Landscape
oil on board 120.6 x 151.7
CAC1986/52

Dow, Thomas Millie 1848–1919
Roses 1885
oil on canvas 30.5 x 46.1
CAC173/1964

Downie, Kate b.1958
Leith Docks, Perimeter Road, Edinburgh 1985
ink, watercolour & acrylic on paper 50 x 70
CAC1990/24

Downie, Kate b.1958
The Coal Yard 1988
acrylic & coal dust on canvas 170 x 177.5
CAC1989/23

Drummond, James 1816–1877
Sabbath Evening
oil on canvas 71.2 x 91.5
CAC7/1976

Drummond, James 1816–1877
Tam o' Shanter
oil on canvas 33 x 49.5
CAC1978/53

Drummond, Les 1920–1997
The Bull that Dreamed of Immortality 1992
acrylic on canvas 38.1 x 61
CAC2002/7

Duguid, Henry Gibson 1805–1860
*Castlehill, Edinburgh, As It Was before
Alterations, c.1849*
oil on panel 25 x 32.5
HH1152/1948

Duncan, John 1866–1945
Hymn to the Rose 1907
oil on canvas 122.2 x 122
CAC5/1964

Duncan, John 1866–1945
Tristan and Isolde 1912
tempera on canvas 76.6 x 76.6
CAC41/1964

Duncan, John 1866–1945
Aoife
oil on panel 59.7 x 45.1
CAC352/1964

Duncan, John 1866–1945
Jehanne d'Arc et sa garde Ecossaise
oil on canvas 107.1 x 138.4
CAC1978/54

Duncan, John 1866–1945
The Challenge
oil on canvas 49.5 x 59.7
CAC171/1964

Duncan, John 1866–1945
The Children of Lir
tempera on canvas 153.1 x 153.7
CAC292/1964

Duncan, John 1866–1945
The Taking of Excalibur
oil on canvas 63.5 x 91.8
CAC229/1964

Durward, Graham b.1966
Blood Goes on Being Red 1984
oil on canvas 182.9 x 167.6
CAC1986/7

Duthie, Philip G. b.1957
Trembling Veil II c.1991–1992
oil on canvas 140 x 159.5
CAC73/1998

Eardley, Joan Kathleen Harding 1921–1963
Farmhouse Stove c.1950
oil on canvas 95 x 73
CAC74/1998

Eardley, Joan Kathleen Harding 1921–1963
Seascape c.1950
oil on board 88.2 x 118.1
CAC1985/13

Eardley, Joan Kathleen Harding 1921–1963
Summer Grasses and Barley on the Clifftop
c.1962
oil on board 110.2 x 137.8
CAC1962/5

Eardley, Joan Kathleen Harding 1921–1963
July Fields
oil on canvas 52.7 x 61
CAC317/1964

Edgar, James R. c.1819–1876
*Sir John Melville (1802–1860), WS, Lord
Provost of Edinburgh (1845–1859)*
oil on panel 41.9 x 36.2
CAC1978/55

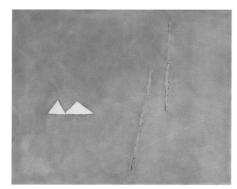

Egan, Felim b.1952
Land-Score 1988
acrylic & mixed media on canvas 160 x 198
CAC68/1992

Emmott, Constance active early 20th C
From Swanston Bungalow, 1913
oil on panel 35.5 x 45.4
CAC1978/56

Evans, David Pugh b.1942
Cheap Rooms 1980
oil on canvas 152.3 x 162.5
CAC75/1998

Evans, David Pugh b.1942
Late Steaming
acrylic on board 74.3 x 99
CAC20/1983

Evans, David Pugh b.1942
The Bridge
oil on canvas 94 x 129.5
CAC1972/4

Ewart, David Shanks 1901–1965
Sir Ian A. Johnston-Gilbert (1892–1974), CBE,
LLD, Lord Provost of Edinburgh (1957–1960)
oil on canvas 110.5 x 86.3
CAC1978/57

Ewbank, John Wilson c.1799–1847
The Entry of George IV into Edinburgh from
the Calton Hill, 1822
oil on canvas 150.5 x 240
CAC1978/58

Ewbank, John Wilson c.1799–1847
The Military Review on the Occasion of George
IV's Visit to Edinburgh
oil on canvas 134.6 x 195.5
HH2009/1960

Faed, James the younger 1857–1920
At Cramond, Early Spring 1885
oil on canvas 27 x 36.5
CAC1996/7

Faed, Thomas 1826–1900
Study for 'Sir Walter Scott and His Literary Friends at Abbotsford'
oil on panel 27.3 x 35.9
HH3131/1967

Fairclough, Wilfred 1907–1996
Olivelli's
oil on board 50.8 x 37.2
CAC301/1964

Fairgrieve, James H. b.1944
Cosimo Portulano 1968
oil on paper 19.3 x 13.3
CAC1969/3

Fairgrieve, James H. b.1944
Winter Feed 1982
acrylic on canvas 122 x 152.5
CAC76/1998

Fairgrieve, James H. b.1944
Bari, Sea Dog
oil on paper 20.7 x 13
CAC1969/2

Fergusson, John Duncan 1874–1961
The Blue Hat, Closerie des Lilas 1909
oil on canvas 76.2 x 76.2
CAC1962/2

Fergusson, John Duncan 1874–1961
The Blue Lamp 1912
oil on panel 66 x 57.2
CAC115/1964

Fergusson, John Duncan 1874–1961
Villa Gotte Garden c.1920
oil on canvas 37.5 x 37.1
CAC1983/18

Fergusson, John Duncan 1874–1961
Study for 'Les Tilleuls, Bécheron, France' c.1927
oil on board 27 x 19.5
CAC1998/16

Fergusson, John Duncan 1874–1961
Les Tilleuls, Bécheron 1932
oil on canvas 63.6 x 50.7
CAC1978/2

Flannigan, Moyna b.1963
Monuments 1990
oil on canvas 152 x 117.3
CAC77/1998

Flannigan, Moyna b.1963
Happy Valley (I) 1999
oil on linen 200 x 135
CAC2002/12

Fleming, Ian 1906–1994
Kirn Pier, Winter 1960
oil on canvas 71.1 x 91.9
CAC318/1964

Fleming, Ian 1906–1994
Early Morning, Winter 1967
oil on board 79.5 x 63.5
CAC78/1998

Fleming, John B. 1792–1845
Robert Andrew Macfie (1811–1893)
oil on canvas 92.7 x 78
HH2014/1960

Flockhart, Helen b.1963
Maire
oil on canvas 76.2 x 61
CAC1992/2

Foggie, David Simpson 1878–1948
Dreams
oil on canvas 92 x 71.4
CAC120/1964

Foggie, David Simpson 1878–1948
Joanne
oil on canvas 47.1 x 36.2
CAC1978/63

Facing page: Halliday, Dorothy, 1923–2001, *MacTavish*, City of Edinburgh Council (p. 42)

Ford, John A. active 1880–1923
*The Right Honourable Ronald Craufurd
Munro Ferguson (1860–1934), LLD, MP
(1884–1885 & 1886–1914)* 1912
oil on canvas 114.3 x 88.9
CAC1978/65

Ford, John A. active 1880–1923
*Malcolm Smith (1856–1935), Provost of Leith
(1908–1917), MP (1921–1922)* 1915
oil on canvas 127.1 x 99.2
CAC1978/64

Ford, John A. active 1880–1923
*John A. Lindsay (1865–1942), CBE, Provost of
Leith (1917–1920)* 1921
oil on canvas 124.5 x 97
CAC1978/66

Forster, David b.1962
*'For the thorns and bushes laid hold of them as
it were with hands, and there they were stuck
fast and died miserably'* 2003
acrylic on paper 56 x 75
CAC2005/17

Forster, David b.1962
*'And yet in the midst of the sky there was still a
bit of blue'* 2005
acrylic on gesso on board 30 x 45
CAC2005/18

Foulis, James 1770–1842
*James Gillespie of Spylaw (1726–1797),
Founder of Gillespie's Hospital*
oil on canvas 213.3 x 149.8
CAC1978/72

Fraser, Alexander 1827–1899
Barncluith Well, South Lanarkshire
oil on canvas 31.5 x 37.5
MC4378/1961

Fraser, Alexander 1827–1899
Cadzow Forest, South Lanarkshire
oil on canvas 37.8 x 50.6
CAC276/1964

Fraser, Alexander b.1940
Boat Underfoot 1974
oil on canvas 81 x 81
CAC80/1998

Fraser, Alexander b.1940
More Room 1987
acrylic on canvas 244 x 275.5
CAC81/1998

Frazer, William Miller 1864–1961
Landscape
oil on canvas 78.8 x 62.3
CAC1978/74

Frazer, William Miller 1864–1961
On the Nene, Northamptonshire
oil on canvas 71.2 x 94.7
CAC18/1969

Fulton, David 1848–1930
Kyles of Bute
oil on canvas 76.1 x 127
CAC1985/42

Gage, Edward 1925–2000
Fishermen, Falconera, Greece 1965
oil on canvas 78.1 x 102.2
CAC1965/10

Gage, Edward 1925–2000
Lluch Alcari, Deia, Mallorca, Spain 1965
oil on canvas 101.6 x 126.4
CAC1965/9

Gallagher, Mary b.1953
Flowers from Aberdeen
acrylic on paper 57.2 x 57.2
CAC1984/23

Gallagher, Mary b.1953
Sunflowers
oil on canvas 144.8 x 144.8
CAC1984/22

Galt, Alexander Milligan 1913–2000
Vera c.1964
oil on canvas 48.7 x 40.3
CAC235/1964

Gauld, David 1865–1936
Spring Morning
oil on canvas 70.5 x 90.2
CAC108/1964

Gavin, Charles b.1944
Los perros cazadores (de Balboa) 1986
oil on canvas 172.7 x 233.7
CAC1986/51

Gear, William 1915–1997
Summer Fête 1951
oil on canvas 101.6 x 71.1
CAC1985/21

Geddes, Andrew (attributed to) 1783–1844
Daft Jamie (James Wilson, 1810–1828), One of the Victims of Burke and Hare
oil on canvas 78.2 x 64
HH1313/1952

Geikie, Walter 1795–1837
Edinburgh from the South 1832
oil on canvas 46.5 x 79.5
CAC8/1982

Geikie, Walter 1795–1837
A Hallow Fair Scene
oil on panel 35.5 x 42.2
CAC1978/77

Geikie, Walter 1795–1837
Fisherfolk at Their Boats
oil on panel 27.3 x 36.8
CAC1978/78

Geikie, Walter 1795–1837
Woodland Scene
oil on board 22 x 19.5
CAC1978/79

Gibb, Peter James b.1951
Wave
oil on canvas 91.6 x 70.7
CAC15/1974

Gibb, Robert II 1845–1932
William Law (1799–1878), Lord Provost of Edinburgh (1869–1872)
oil on canvas 76.5 x 64.1
CAC1978/80

Gibbons, Carole b.1935
Figure in a Landscape c.1968
oil on board 122 x 79.5
CAC83/1998

Gibbons, Carole b.1935
Waiting Figure in a Landscape
oil on board 95.5 x 104.5
CAC82/1998

Gibroy, C.
Ye Auld Smithy, Roseburn, Edinburgh 1881
oil on canvas 36.2 x 46.2
HH2899/1966

Gibson, Patrick 1782–1829
View of Edinburgh from the Calton Hill
oil on canvas 50.8 x 73.7
HH48/1899

Gillespie, Joan b.1954
Riviera Afternoon
oil on canvas 61 x 71.1
CAC1993/13

Gillies, William George 1898–1973
Emma 1931
oil on canvas 72 x 63
CAC1995L2/14 (P)

Gillies, William George 1898–1973
Sisters Emma and Janet 1932
oil on canvas 91 x 75
CAC1995L2/12 (P)

Gillies, William George 1898–1973
Woods at Humbie, East Lothian 1936
oil on canvas 89 x 100
CAC1995L2/10 (P)

Gillies, William George 1898–1973
The Green Dish 1950
oil on canvas 76.2 x 107.9
CAC261/1964

Gillies, William George 1898–1973
Interior, Temple Cottage 1951
oil on canvas 123 x 176
CAC1995L2/13 (P)

Gillies, William George 1898–1973
Studio Table 1951
oil on canvas 132 x 200
CAC1995L2/15 (P)

Gillies, William George 1898–1973
Arniston Woods, Midlothian
oil on canvas 75 x 88
CAC1995L2/3 (P)

Gillies, William George 1898–1973
Back Gardens, Temple
oil on canvas 63.5 x 115.5
CAC13/1967

Gillies, William George 1898–1973
Landscape, 1932
oil on canvas 61.3 x 75.6
CAC1983/26

Gillies, William George 1898–1973
Moorfoot
oil on board 29.2 x 35.6
CAC20/1988

Gillies, William George 1898–1973
River Tyne near Haddington, East Lothian
oil on board 78 x 90
CAC1995L2/11 (P)

Gillies, William George 1898–1973
Shadowed Interior
oil on panel 108.2 x 98.1
CAC1970/4

Gillies, William George 1898–1973
Studio Table
oil on canvas 115 x 85
CAC1995L2/1 (P)

Gillies, William George 1898–1973
Temple, Dusk
oil on canvas 87.1 x 101.1
CAC1968/1

Gillies, William George 1898–1973
Woods at Arniston, Midlothian
oil on board 68 x 57.7
CAC90/1992

Gillies, William George 1898–1973
Woods at Temple
oil on board 43 x 59.5
CAC1995L2/9 (P)

Glass, John 1820–1885
Companions
oil on board 16.5 x 26
HH1458/1953

Glass, John 1820–1885
High School Yards, Edinburgh
oil on canvas 116.8 x 78.7
HH1455/1953

Glass, John 1820–1885
Interior of a Highland Cottage
oil on board 27 x 41
HH1444/1953

Glen, George b.1965
Beyond the Rock
oil on canvas 128.9 x 152.4
CAC1988/33

Glen, Graham active 1895–1925
Meditation
oil on canvas 76.3 x 63.5
CAC8/1964

Gloag, Isobel Lilian 1865–1917
A Bunch of Flowers
oil on canvas 77.4 x 64.4
CAC47/1964

Gordon, Carola Rosemary Helen b.1940
The Old Town, Edinburgh
oil on canvas 69.5 x 90
CAC2009/41

Gordon, John Watson 1788–1864
Mrs Campbell 1819
oil on canvas 91 x 70
CAC8/1994

Gordon, John Watson 1788–1864
*Adam Black (1784–1874), Lord Provost of
Edinburgh (1843–1848)* 1847
oil on canvas 238.7 x 147.3
CAC1978/83

Gordon, John Watson 1788–1864
Sir Walter Scott (1771–1832), at Abbotsford
oil on canvas 100.3 x 76.2
CAC1978/450

Gordon, John Watson 1788–1864
*Sir William Johnston of Kirkhill (1802–1888),
Lord Provost of Edinburgh (1848–1851)*
oil on canvas 241.3 x 151.1
CAC21/1976

Goudie, Alexander 1933–2004
*Jack Kane (1911–1999), Dr (h.c.), Lord Provost
of Edinburgh (1972–1975)* 1977
oil on canvas 112.3 x 117
CAC1978/3

Graham, Thomas Alexander Ferguson
1840–1906
Boats in a Harbour
oil on canvas 42.6 x 55.9
CAC275/1964

Graham-Gilbert, John 1794–1866
*Charles Lawson of Borthwick Hall (d.1874),
Lord Provost of Edinburgh (1862–1865)*
oil on canvas 238.8 x 147.3
CAC1978/86

Facing page: Barns-Graham, Wilhelmina, 1912–2004, *Rocks, St Mary's, Scilly Isles*, City of Edinburgh Council (p. 7)

Graham-Gilbert, John (attributed to)
1794–1866
Portrait of a Lady
oil on canvas 76.2 x 64.1
CAC1978/87

Grant, Francis 1803–1878
Sir Walter Scott (1771–1832), in His Study
oil on canvas 76.2 x 62.2
HH3130/1967

Grant, Thomas F. active 1868–1879
The Drongs, Shetlands 1874
oil on canvas 66.1 x 106.6
HH2010/1960

Grant, Thomas F. active 1868–1879
View from Craigmillar, Edinburgh
oil on canvas 68 x 121
HH2008/1960

Gray, Euan b.1973
Enchanted Days
oil on board 169 x 122
CAC1996/5

Gray, George active c.1874–1909
Sunset, Highland Landscape with Cattle
oil on canvas 61.5 x 92.1
CAC1978/88

Gray, George active c.1874–1909
The Tweed at Abbotsford, Melrose
oil on canvas 77 x 126.1
CAC1978/89

Green, Alfred H. b.c.1822
A Newhaven Fishwife
oil on board 37 x 30.8
HH3425/1969

Green, Alfred H. b.c.1822
Mending the Nets, Newhaven, East Sussex
oil on board 31.3 x 47.3
CAC1994/1

Grieve, Alec 1864–1933
Will o' the Wisp
oil on canvas 182.9 x 78.8
CAC134/1964

Gunn, Herbert James 1893–1964
James Pryde (1866–1941)
oil on canvas 127.7 x 102
CAC101/1964

Gunn, Herbert James 1893–1964
*Sir Thomas B. Whitson (1869–1948), DL,
LLD, Lord Provost of Edinburgh (1929–1932)*
oil on canvas 127 x 101.6
CAC1978/94

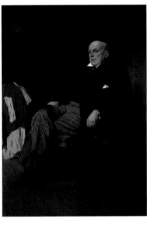

Gunn, Herbert James 1893–1964
*Sir William Young Darling (1885–1962), Lord
Provost of Edinburgh (1941–1944)*
oil on canvas 198.2 x 137.2
CAC1978/93

Guthrie, James 1859–1930
*Archibald Stodart Walker (1869–1934), MA,
MB, OBE*
oil on canvas 111.1 x 77.5
CAC49/1964

Guthrie, James 1859–1930
*Study of 'Sir John James Burnet (1857–1938),
RSA'*
oil on canvas 51.2 x 36.8
CAC277/1964

Hadden, Robert active 1876–1889
View of Portobello from the West 1889
oil on board 35.5 x 57.8
CAC1983/28

Hähnisch, Anton 1817–1897
Miss Sarah Lumsden Smith
oil on canvas 64 x 63.8
HH2708/1964

Haig, George Douglas 1918–2009
Leaderfoot, Scottish Borders 1963
oil on canvas 71.1 x 91.4
CAC1963/2

Haig, George Douglas 1918–2009
Campo San Vio, Venice
oil on canvas 71 x 91
CAC35/1997

Haig, George Douglas 1918–2009
Gateheugh
oil on canvas 96.5 x 130.1
CAC286/1964

Halkerston, Charles 1829–1899
*Princes Street from the Mound,
Edinburgh* 1843
oil on panel 28 x 47.3
CAC7/1982

Hall, George Wright 1895–1974
Studio Interior with Figure
oil on canvas 76.2 x 94.6
CAC1/1975

Hall, James W. 1797–1854
'Show Jamie', 1842
oil on panel 29.9 x 24.8
HH750/1920

Halliday, Dorothy 1923–2001
Double Portrait 1964
oil on canvas 75 x 63
CAC2002/11

Halliday, Dorothy 1923–2001
MacTavish
oil on canvas 100 x 75
CAC2002/10

Hamilton, James Whitelaw 1860–1932
A West Highland Loch
oil on canvas 76.8 x 97.7
CAC306/1964

Hamilton, James Whitelaw 1860–1932
At Mayford, Surrey
oil on paper 26.1 x 35.3
CAC1978/96

Hamilton, James Whitelaw 1860–1932
*Landscape, Kirkcudbright, Dumfries and
Galloway*
oil on canvas 76.8 x 99.1
CAC36/1964

Hansen, Lys b.1936
Stance 1983
acrylic & collage on canvas 41.9 x 38.1
CAC1985/17

Hardie, Charles Martin 1858–1916
Robert Burns (1759–1796)
oil on canvas 76.8 x 30.5
CAC1978/98

Hardie, Gwen b.1962
Coupling 1984
acrylic on canvas 200 x 200
CAC1990/29

Harvey, George (after) 1806–1876
Robert Macfie (1746–1827)
oil on canvas 93.3 x 76.1
HH2011/1960

Hawkins, James b.1954
The Shore of the Loch
oil on canvas 185.5 x 244
CAC1997/3

Henderson, Joseph 1832–1908
The Storm, Ballantrae, South Ayrshire
oil on canvas 116.8 x 194.3
CAC25/1964

Henderson, Keith 1883–1982
Scottish Landscape
oil on canvas 60.3 x 90.2
CAC262/1964

Hendriksen, Harry b.1937
Two Cravens
oil on board 91 x 114
CAC1/1983

Henry, George 1858–1943
Poppies
oil on canvas 61 x 50.8
CAC267/1964

Henry, George 1858–1943
The Chalk Pit
oil on canvas 106.7 x 127.1
CAC214/1964

Herdman, Robert Duddingstone 1863–1922
Borrowed Plumes
oil on canvas 69 x 55
CAC2009/97

Herdman, Robert Inerarity 1829–1888
Sir James Falshaw (1810–1889), Bt, Lord Provost of Edinburgh (1874–1877) 1877
oil on canvas 238.8 x 152.4
HH496/1909

Herdman, William Gawin 1805–1882
View of the Mound, Edinburgh 1854
oil on canvas 57.1 x 89.5
CAC1986/45

Herdman, William Gawin 1805–1882
View of the Lawnmarket, Edinburgh
oil on canvas 87 x 144.7
HH1928/1960

Highmore, Joseph (attributed to)
1692–1780
Andrew Bell (1726–1809)
oil on canvas 79 x 63.5
CAC1/1926

Hill, David Octavius 1802–1870
In Memoriam: The Calton
oil on panel 14.9 x 20
HH2500/1964

Hill, David Octavius 1802–1870
Old Edinburgh, Showing the Castle from Greyfriars Churchyard
oil on canvas 86.4 x 119.3
HH558/1909

Hislop, Joseph 1884–1977
Landscape*
oil on board 47 x 73
CAC17/1992

Hislop, Margaret 1894–1972
Girl in Green
oil on board 60.7 x 45.7
CAC1965/13

Hock-Aun-Teh b.1950
Summer in Beijing, China
acrylic on paper 154 x 152.5
CAC1990/27

Hodder, Charles D. 1835–1926
An Old Piper
oil on canvas 76.9 x 63.5
HH898/1934

Hodges, J. Sidney Willis 1829–1900
*John Coutts (1699–1750), Lord Provost of
Edinburgh (1743–1744)* (after Allan Ramsay)
oil on canvas 76.2 x 64.8
CAC1978/105

Hogg, Alistair b.1966
Where is Your Superhero Now?
oil & wax on board 182.9 x 243.9
CAC1989/63

Hole, William Brassey 1846–1917
After Flodden 1887–1889
oil on canvas 190.8 x 146
CAC1978/115

Hole, William Brassey 1846–1917
*The Coronation of King James II at Holyrood,
1437* 1902
oil on canvas 252.8 x 235
CAC1978/110

Hole, William Brassey 1846–1917
*The Signing of the National Covenant in
Greyfriars Churchyard, 1638* 1903
oil on canvas 254.1 x 218.4
CAC1978/113

Hole, William Brassey 1846–1917
*The State Entry of Queen Mary into
Edinburgh, 1561* 1904
oil on canvas 252.8 x 182.8
CAC1978/107

Hole, William Brassey 1846–1917
*The Presentation of a Charter to the Burgesses
of Edinburgh by King Robert the Bruce at
Cardross, 1329* 1906
oil on canvas 248 x 168.9
CAC1978/111

Hole, William Brassey 1846–1917
*Queen Mary Brought Captive to Edinburgh
from Carberry Hill, 1567* 1910
oil on canvas 134.6 x 182.8
CAC1978/106

Hole, William Brassey 1846–1917
*Queen Mary's First Farewell to Scotland,
1548* 1910
oil on canvas 134.6 x 182.9
CAC1978/108

Hole, William Brassey 1846–1917
News of Flodden
oil on canvas 255.3 x 167.7
CAC1978/109

Hole, William Brassey 1846–1917
*News of the Accession of James VI to the
Throne of England, 1603*
oil on canvas 134.6 x 161.3
CAC1978/114

Hole, William Brassey 1846–1917
*Prince Charles Edward Stuart in Edinburgh,
1745*
oil on canvas 127.5 x 160
CAC1978/112

Holmes, Charles John 1868–1936
The Head of Wensleydale, Yorkshire
oil on canvas 48.3 x 81.3
CAC68/1964

Home, Bruce James 1830–1912
Brodie's Close, Edinburgh
oil on board 48 x 35.1
CAC1978/126

Honder, J. L. active 1905
General Douglas Haig (1861–1928) 1905
oil on canvas 80.3 x 66
CAC1978/159

Hone, Nathaniel II 1831–1917
The Derelict
oil on canvas 86.3 x 121.9
CAC24/1964

Hood, Angus b.1962
Nobody Worried
acrylic & collage on canvas 215.3 x 154.9
CAC1985/34

Hope, Robert 1869–1936
The Presentation by King James III and Queen Margaret of the Banner Known as the Blue Blanket to the Craftsmen in the (...) 1912
oil on canvas 162.6 x 188
CAC1978/160

Hope, Robert 1869–1936
Swanston Farm, Edinburgh 1913
oil on board 27 x 40
CAC28/1988

Hope, Robert 1869–1936
An Old Herd
oil on board 41 x 30.8
CAC149/1964

Hope, Robert 1869–1936
Edinburgh from Craiglockhart
oil on canvas 64.7 x 76.9
CAC1978/162

Hope, Robert 1869–1936
Edinburgh from the Arboretum
oil on canvas 63.5 x 76.2
CAC1978/161

Hope, Robert 1869–1936
No.8 Howard Place, Edinburgh, 1914
oil on panel 35.2 x 24.1
CAC1978/165

Hope, Robert 1869–1936
No.17 Heriot Row, Edinburgh
oil on panel 35.5 x 24.1
CAC1978/163

Hope, Robert 1869–1936
*Swanston and Caerketton in Winter,
Edinburgh*
oil on panel 25.3 x 34.2
CAC1978/164

Hope, Robert 1869–1936
Swanston Cottage, Edinburgh
oil on panel 20 x 25.5
PCF14

Hope, Robert 1869–1936
The Blue Veil
oil on canvas 71.8 x 61.3
CAC157/1964

Hope, Robert 1869–1936
The Remnant Stall
oil on canvas 89.2 x 108
CAC158/1964

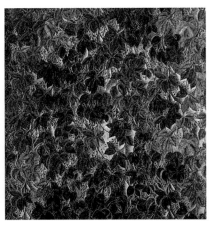

Hopkins, Louise b.1965
Relief (739) (diptych, left wing) 2005
oil on patterned furnishing fabric 153 x 145
CAC2007/2a

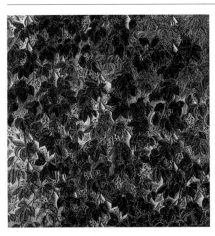

Hopkins, Louise b.1965
Relief (739) (diptych, right wing) 2005
oil on patterned furnishing fabric 153 x 145
CAC2007/2b

Horne, R. J. Maule
Kilchurn Castle, Argyllshire
oil on canvas 25 x 35
HH2829/1965

Hornel, Edward Atkinson 1864–1933
In the Orchard 1898
oil on canvas 116.8 x 102.3
CAC252/1964

Facing page: Martin, David, 1736/1737–1798, *Robert Trotter (c.1750–1807)*, 1782, The University of Edinburgh Fine
Art Collection (p.160)

Hornel, Edward Atkinson 1864–1933
Seashore Roses c.1907
oil on canvas 122.8 x 154.3
CAC2/1964

Horsburgh, John A. 1835–1924
*James Pringle (1822–1886), Provost of Leith
(1881–1886)* 1887
oil on canvas 161.3 x 99.2
CAC1978/167

Horsburgh, John A. 1835–1924
*Thomas Hutchison (1796–1852), Provost of
Leith (1845–1848)* 1887
oil on canvas 149.8 x 90.2
CAC1978/166

Horsburgh, John A. 1835–1924
*William Lindsay (1819–1884), Provost of Leith
(1860–1866)*
oil on canvas 241.3 x 165.2
CAC1978/168

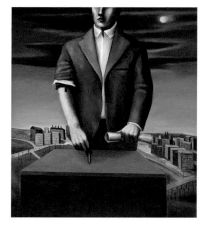

Hosie, David b.1962
New Town 1986
oil on canvas 122 x 107
CAC85/1998

Houston, George 1869–1947
Early Morning
oil on canvas 71.5 x 91.5
CAC139/1964

Houston, John 1930–2008
Beach and Night Sky 1968
acrylic on canvas 111.7 x 127
CAC1978/169

Houston, John 1930–2008
Winter Sea, North Berwick, East Lothian 1982
oil on canvas 71.1 x 71.1
CAC1983/9

Houston, John 1930–2008
Elizabeth with Yellow Lily 1982–1983
oil on canvas 127.2 x 101.3
CAC1983/8

Houston, John 1930–2008
Summer Sea 1987–1988
oil on canvas 152.4 x 182.9
CAC1988/35

Howard, Ian b.1952
The Priest, the Beast and the Rest (triptych, left wing)
acrylic gel & collage on paper 121.9 x 101.6
CAC1985/25

Howard, Ian b.1952
The Priest, the Beast and the Rest (triptych, centre panel)
acrylic gel & collage on paper 121.9 x 101.6
CAC1985/25

Howard, Ian b.1952
The Priest, the Beast and the Rest (triptych, right wing)
acrylic gel & collage on paper 121.9 x 101.6
CAC1985/25

Howe, James 1780–1836
All Hallows Fair on the Boroughmuir, Edinburgh
oil on canvas 91.4 x 144.1
CAC1978/170

Howe, James 1780–1836
The Horse Fair in the Grassmarket, Edinburgh
oil on canvas 91.5 x 114.3
CAC6/1980

Howson, Peter b.1958
Study for 'Backstreet Crucifixion' 2006
oil on gessoed panel 20 x 21
CAC2007/3

Howson, Peter b.1958
Regimental Bath
oil on canvas 185 x 138
CAC1990/54

Hughes, Ian b.1958
Consumed by Fire 1988
oil on canvas 183 x 167.7
CAC1993/6

Hughes, Ian b.1958
Self Portrait (1)
oil on photograph on board 183.1 x 122.5
CAC7/1993

Hughes, Ian b.1958
Self Portrait (2)
oil on photograph on board 183.1 x 122.5
CAC8/1993

Hughes, Ian b.1958
Self Portrait (3)
oil on photograph on board 183.1 x 122.5
CAC9/1993

Hughes, Ian b.1958
Self Portrait (4)
oil on photograph on board 183.1 x 122.5
CAC10/1993

Hunter, George Leslie 1877–1931
Pathway, Loch Lomond
oil on canvas 61.7 x 74.3
CAC200/1964

Hutchison, George active 1957
Old Canonmills as It Was in c.1875
oil on canvas 51.2 x 59.8
HH1735/1957

Hutchison, Robert Gemmell 1855–1936
A Christmas Morning
oil on canvas 75 x 63
PCF3 (P)

Hutchison, Robert Gemmell 1855–1936
Sleep
oil on canvas 38.5 x 36
CAC1983/5

Hutchison, Robert Gemmell 1855–1936
The New Sabot
oil on panel 14.6 x 10.8
CAC305/1964

Hutchison, William Oliphant 1889–1970
Sir Andrew Murray (1903–1977/1978), OBE,
LLD, Lord Provost of Edinburgh (1947–
1951) 1952
oil on canvas 127 x 104.2
CAC1978/175

Hutchison, William Oliphant 1889–1970
Sir James Miller (1905–1977), LLD, Lord
Provost of Edinburgh (1951–1954) 1956
oil on canvas 115.6 x 101.6
CAC1978/176

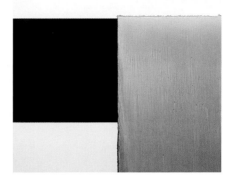

Innes, Callum b.1962
Exposed Painting, Black/Red Oxide 2000
oil on linen 96 x 91.5
CAC2000/12

Irvine, Olivia b.1960
Figures in an Interior c.1985
oil on canvas 219.7 x 171.4
CAC1985/35

Irvine, Olivia b.1960
Rain 1989
oil on canvas 152.5 x 152.5
CAC1990/64

Isbister, Arlene b.1966
From Red (Sister) 1990
wax & acrylic on canvas 151.5 x 228.5
CAC1990/61

Jacob, Julius I (attributed to) 1811–1882
Baroness Burdett Coutts (1814–1906)
oil on canvas 90.2 x 71.2
CAC1978/178

Jenkins, Arthur Henry 1871–1940
The Scent of the Rose 1904
oil on canvas 46 x 28.1
MC20027/1978

Johansen, John Christian 1876–1964
Sir Douglas Haig (1861–1928), FM, in His
Study 1919
oil on canvas 76.2 x 76.2
HH609/1964

Johnstone, Dorothy 1892–1980
Study for 'Rest Time in the Life Class'
oil on canvas 48.6 x 41
CAC7(A)/1980

Johnstone, Dorothy 1892–1980
Study for 'Rest Time in the Life Class'
oil on canvas 56 x 41.8
CAC7(C)/1980

Johnstone, Dorothy 1892–1980
Rest Time in the Life Class 1923
oil on canvas 121.5 x 106.2
CAC1980/3

Johnstone, John 1937–2001
Dream
oil on canvas 120.6 x 120.6
CAC1965/8

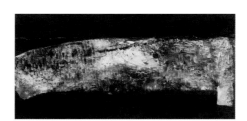

Johnstone, William 1897–1981
Untitled c.1966
oil on canvas 92 x 191
CAC93/1998

Johnstone, William 1897–1981
Hugh MacDiarmid (1892–1978) (Christopher M. Grieve) 1975
oil on canvas 45.7 x 35.6
CAC1985/27

Johnstone, William 1897–1981
Sanctuary
oil on board 122.5 x 121.9
CAC1988/1

Johnstone, William 1897–1981
Wotan
oil on canvas 167.6 x 198.1
CAC1988/2

Kay, Archibald 1860–1935
Winter Sunshine
oil on canvas 75.9 x 101.7
CAC62/1964

Kay, James 1858–1942
Harbour and Figures 1895
oil on canvas 46.1 x 69.2
CAC1979/7

Kay, John (style of) 1742–1826
The Parliament Close and Public Characters of Edinburgh, 50 Years Since
oil on panel 59 x 91.1
HH1174/1948

Keith, Alexander active 1808–1874
Portrait of a Gentleman (possibly Dr Hill)
oil on canvas 61.3 x 50.8
CAC1978/183

Kenyon-Wade, Corinna b.1961
Assembly Rooms, Edinburgh 1985
oil on card 63.5 x 57.6
CAC1985/38

Kerr, Henry Wright 1857–1936
Thomas Aitken (1832–1912), Provost of Leith (1887–1893) 1893
oil on canvas 153.7 x 91.5
CAC1978/184

Knott, Tavernor 1816–1890
Bailie Robert Cranston (1815–1892)
oil on canvas 127.2 x 101.9
CAC1978/188

Knox, Jack b.1936
Square and Constellation 1963
oil on canvas 109.3 x 85.1
CAC1963/5

Knox, Jack b.1936
Chair with Hat, Île de Ré
oil on canvas 158.8 x 184.8
CAC15/1988

Knox, Jack b.1936
Flower Piece
oil on board 76.2 x 68.5
CAC16/1993

Kondracki, Henry b.1953
The Red Park
oil on canvas 218.5 x 198.5
CAC1997/2

Lamb, Henry 1883–1960
The Elliott Family 1935
oil on canvas 144 x 159
CAC2009/45

Lamb, Henry 1883–1960
Oil Sketch of Lord Elliott
oil on canvas board 60 x 49.5
CAC2009/46

Lauder, Robert Scott 1803–1869
John Lauder of Silvermills (1768–1838)
oil on canvas 92.7 x 72.7
CAC31/1992

Lauder, Robert Scott (school of) 1803–1869
William Macfie of Clermiston (1822–1895)
oil on canvas 76 x 63.5
HH2017/1960

Lavery, John 1856–1941
*Miss Esther Joanna Marie McLaren (d.1950)
and Mrs Katherine Oliver, née McLaren
(c.1870–1966)*
oil on canvas 220 x 169
CAC1981/2

Lavery, John 1856–1941
View of Edinburgh from the Castle
oil on canvas 63.5 x 75.5
CAC1994/19

Lawrie, Hamish 1919–1987
Scalpay Croft, Harris 1974
oil on panel 40.6 x 50.8
CAC6/1974

Lawson, Thomas b.1951
Untitled 1990
acrylic on canvas 122 x 122
CAC2010/20

Facing page: Strang, William, 1859–1921, *Dreams*, 1915, City of Edinburgh Council (p. 96)

Le Conte, John 1816–1887
Cardinal Beaton's House, Cowgate, Edinburgh
1883
oil on panel 54.5 x 35.9
HH777/1922

Leggett, Alexander 1828–1884
Sale of Bait: The Arrival of the Mussel Boats,
Newhaven
oil on canvas 49 x 83.5
CAC2007/6

Leishman, Robert 1916–1989
Fountains 1948
oil on board 75 x 56
CAC100/1998

Leyde, Otto Theodor 1835–1897
Sir Thomas Jamieson Boyd, Master of the
Edinburgh Merchant Company (1869–1871),
Lord Provost of Edinburgh (1877–1882) 1873
oil on canvas 238.6 x 144.8
CAC1978/203

Lintott, Henry John 1877–1965
Sir Alexander Stevenson (1860–1936), LLD,
DL, Lord Provost of Edinburgh (1926–1929)
1931
oil on canvas 229.8 x 132.7
CAC1978/204

Lintott, Henry John 1877–1965
Modo Crepuscolare
tempera on canvas 110.6 x 136.6
CAC181/1964

Lintott, Henry John 1877–1965
Near Surrey
oil on canvas 62.3 x 101.1
CAC1965/12

Lintott, Henry John 1877–1965
Portrait of a Lady
oil on canvas 78.8 x 68.6
CAC57/1964

Lizars, William Home 1788–1859
The Old Town Guard
oil on panel 34.3 x 43.5
CAC1978/207

Lizars, William Home (attributed to)
1788–1859
The Edinburgh Old Town Guard
oil on canvas 38.7 x 55.9
CAC1978/208

Lorimer, John Henry 1856–1936
The Flight of the Swallows 1906
oil on canvas 115 x 89.6
CAC7/1964

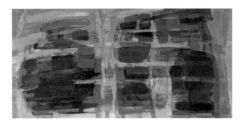

Low, Bet 1924–2007
Merge and Emerge 1961
oil on canvas 60 x 121
CAC101/1998

Lucas, Edwin George 1911–1990
Pentland Hills from Kingsknowe, Winter 1947
oil on canvas 74.5 x 62
CAC14/2003

Lucas, Edwin George 1911–1990
Caley Station, Edinburgh, 1942
oil on canvas 99 x 73.7
CAC67/1990

MacArthur, Lindsay Grandison
c.1866–1945
Coasting, Ceylon
oil on canvas 63.5 x 76.5
CAC233/1964

MacArthur, Lindsay Grandison
c.1866–1945
Dawn over Galilee
oil on canvas 76.2 x 101.6
CAC232/1964

Macbeth, Norman 1821–1888
Mrs Adam Primrose 1871
oil on canvas 76.8 x 63.5
HH2149/1961

Macbeth, Norman 1821–1888
William Forrest (1805–1889), ARA
oil on canvas 76.5 x 63.8
HH2836/1965

Macbride, William 1856–1913
The Sheepfold
oil on canvas 45.7 x 36.2
CAC56/1964

MacBryde, Robert 1913–1966
Woman at Fireplace, No.1
oil on canvas 89.8 x 57.1
CAC1988/3

Macdonald, Arthur active 1895–1940
The Bell Rock Lighthouse
oil on panel 29.8 x 45.7
CAC1978/362

MacEwan, Geoffrey b.1943
Lanark Market
oil on canvas 63 x 79
CAC32/1998

MacGeorge, William Stewart 1861–1931
Kirkcudbright
oil on canvas 107.3 x 153.7
CAC29/1964

Macgillivray, James Pittendrigh 1856–1938
The Tea Table 1885
oil on canvas 38.2 x 46.3
CAC202/1964

MacGoun, Hannah Clarke Preston
1864–1913
Cupid
oil on canvas 38.7 x 34.3
CAC76/1964

MacGoun, Hannah Clarke Preston
1864–1913
St Andrew's Fisherfolk
oil on canvas 17.7 x 25.1
CAC77/1964

MacGregor, William York 1855–1923
The Quarry (sketch) 1896
oil on panel 38.8 x 41.9
CAC268/1964

MacGregor, William York 1855–1923
Melrose
oil on canvas 81.9 x 81.2
CAC82/1964

Mackenzie, Andrew b.1969
Ribmarkings
oil on board 46.2 x 54.4
CAC1992/18

Mackenzie, William Murray
active 1880–1908
Joppa Saltpans 1887
oil on canvas 41.3 x 61.1
CAC22/1976

Mackie, Charles Hodge 1862–1920
'There were three maidens pu'd a flower (by the bonnie banks o' Fordie)' c.1897
oil on canvas 62 x 91
CAC20/1982

Mackie, Charles Hodge 1862–1920
Study for 'La piazzetta, Venice'
oil on canvas 23.2 x 27.3
CAC326/1964

Mackie, Charles Hodge 1862–1920
La piazzetta, Venice 1902
oil on canvas 100.7 x 125.7
CAC32/1964

Mackie, Charles Hodge 1862–1920
La musica veneziana c.1909
oil on canvas 53.3 x 101.6
CAC20/1964

Mackie, Charles Hodge 1862–1920
Artis ancilla 1911
oil on canvas 152.7 x 189.2
CAC53/1964

Mackie, Charles Hodge 1862–1920
In the Borghese Gardens
oil on canvas 61 x 53.3
CAC225/1964

Mackie, Charles Hodge 1862–1920
Margaret Cumming
oil on canvas 38.5 x 30.2
CAC9/1976

Mackie, Charles Hodge 1862–1920
St Monans, Fife
oil on canvas 34.3 x 43.8
CAC322/1964

Mackie, Peter Robert Macleod 1867–1959
Flowers of Springtime
oil on canvas 33.7 x 45.1
CAC208/1964

Maclagan, Philip Douglas 1901–1972
San Gimignano, Italy, 1925
oil on canvas 43.3 x 63.8
CAC6(A)/1981

Maclagan, Philip Douglas 1901–1972
Still Life, Peony and Primrose
oil on canvas 40 x 31
CAC6(B)/1981

MacLaren, John Stewart 1860–c.1929
James Crichton (1808–1889) 1890
oil on canvas 76.2 x 58.4
CAC1978/218

Maclaurin, Robert b.1961
In Eastern Territory 1988
oil on canvas 152.4 x 152.4
CAC1988/38

Maclaurin, Robert b.1961
Theatrical Scene
oil on canvas on board 60.3 x 53.3
CAC1984/15

MacNee, Daniel 1806–1882
Burns and 'Highland Mary'
oil on panel 28.6 x 23.5
CAC1978/220

MacNicol, Bessie 1869–1904
Baby Crawford 1902
oil on canvas 61.7 x 50.8
CAC13/1964

MacNicol, Bessie 1869–1904
Portrait of a Lady (The Green Hat)
oil on canvas 51.4 x 36.6
CAC178/1964

MacTaggart, William 1903–1981
Some Yellow Flowers c.1954
oil on canvas 73 x 53.5
CAC103/1998

MacTaggart, William 1903–1981
Storm Cloud 1966
oil on canvas 71.2 x 91.5
CAC1/1966

MacTaggart, William 1903–1981
A Glimpse of Stockholm
oil on panel 51.4 x 61.2
CAC251/1964

MacTaggart, William 1903–1981
Autumn Leaves
oil on board 81.2 x 100.3
CAC6/1975

MacTaggart, William 1903–1981
Still Life with an Oval Table
oil on canvas 102.5 x 128
CAC1982/2

MacTaggart, William 1903–1981
Telemark, Norway, Revisited
oil on canvas 86.4 x 111.8
CAC6/1966

MacWhirter, John 1839–1911
Edinburgh from Corstorphine
oil on panel 50.2 x 74.9
CAC1978/221

Main, Kirkland b.1942
Shelter 1977
tempera on gesso 42 x 42
CAC104/1998

Malcolm, Ellen 1923–2002
Flower Piece c.1965
oil on canvas 71.2 x 81.3
CAC1965/7

Malietoa, Savea 1914–1994
Robert Louis Stevenson (1850–1894), in Bed
oil on panel 53.3 x 63.5
HH3356/1969

Malietoa, Savea 1914–1994
Samoan Taupou Officiating at the Keva Ceremony
oil on board 49.5 x 39
HH3357/1969

Mann, Harrington 1864–1936
Annabel
oil on canvas 76.3 x 63.5
CAC54/1964

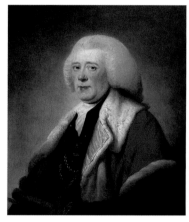

Martin, David 1736/1737–1798
Gilbert Laurie (1729–1809), Lord Provost of Edinburgh (1766–1768 & 1772–1774)
oil on canvas 76.2 x 63.5
CAC2002/3

Massys, Quinten (imitator of) 1466–1530
The Philosopher
oil on panel 78.7 x 63.5
HH710/1914

Maxwell, John 1905–1962
Man with Flowers 1942
oil on canvas 76.5 x 63.5
CAC1995L1/25 (P)

Maxwell, John 1905–1962
The Trellis 1951
oil on canvas 114.3 x 152.4
CAC1995L1/19 (P)

Maxwell, John 1905–1962
Birds against the Sun 1952
oil on canvas 50.8 x 76.2
CAC1995L1/2 (P)

Maxwell, John 1905–1962
Figure and a Bird with a Jug of Flowers 1952
oil on canvas 71.1 x 53.3
CAC1995L1/21 (P)

Maxwell, John 1905–1962
The Window 1956
oil on canvas 76.2 x 62.2
CAC1995L1/16 (P)

Maxwell, John 1905–1962
Flowers and Frost Flowers 1959
oil on canvas 67.3 x 54.6
CAC316/1964

Maxwell, John 1905–1962
Garden at Night (Moth) 1960
oil on canvas 50.8 x 91.5
CAC1995L1/12 (P)

Maxwell, John 1905–1962
Harvest Moon 1960
oil on canvas 76.2 x 101.6
CAC1995L1/23 (P)

McArtney, Sylvia active 1976
Waiting for the Tide
oil on canvas 48.3 x 45.8
CAC15/1976

McCall, Charles James 1907–1989
At the Dressing Table 1978
oil on board 50.8 x 40.7
CAC1978/12

McCall, Charles James 1907–1989
London Street in Snow
oil on panel 61 x 45.7
CAC244/1964

McCance, William 1894–1970
Kimono Study 1919
oil on canvas 111.7 x 76.2
CAC1998/23

McCarthy, Robin b.1957
It's all Upside Down 1988
acrylic on canvas 159 x 122
CAC1989/51

McCheyne, Alistair 1918–1981
The Seaside Photographer 1952
oil on board 82 x 100
CAC21/1982

McClure, David 1926–1998
Joyce a Firenze 1956
gouache, ink & oil on card 49.5 x 40.6
CAC1989/61

McClure, David 1926–1998
Boat at Gourdon, France 1966
oil on canvas 63.5 x 76.2
CAC1966/4

McClure, David 1926–1998
The Mirror II 1966
oil on canvas 76.2 x 86.4
CAC1966/12

McClure, David 1926–1998
Girl Pinning up Her Hair 1970
oil on board 14.3 x 19
CAC5/1990

McClure, David 1926–1998
Bananas and Pansies II
oil on board 27 x 38.5
CAC106/1998

McCulloch, Ian b.1935
Palm Sunday: Uitenhage 1985
oil on canvas 259 x 259.5
CAC1986/6

Facing page: Ward, Edward Matthew, 1816–1879, *The Last Sleep of Argyll before His Execution, 1685*, 1857, Historic
Scotland, Edinburgh (p. 125)

McDougall, Lily Martha Maud 1875–1958
Roses against a Striped Background
oil on canvas 45.6 x 60.9
CAC299/1964

McFadyen, Jock b.1950
Watney Market, London
oil on canvas 213.3 x 152.4
CAC57/1988

McGlashan, Archibald A. 1888–1980
Still Life
oil on canvas 63.6 x 74.9
CAC1962/7

McGlashan, Archibald A. 1888–1980
The Sleeping Child
oil on canvas 31.7 x 48.9
CAC111/1964

McGowan, Gerald b.1949
Cafeteria 2004
oil on canvas 29 x 29
CAC2005/10

McGregor, Robert 1847–1922
Gathering Stones
oil on canvas 68.7 x 127.1
CAC61/1964

McIntyre, Peter 1910–1995
Dunedin
oil on canvas 91.5 x 149.8
CAC1978/212

McKay, William Darling 1844–1924
Summer at Kilspindie
oil on canvas 80.1 x 113.1
CAC50/1964

McLachlan, Thomas Hope 1845–1897
The Wind on the Hill 1890
oil on canvas 97.8 x 74.2
CAC48/1964

McLaren, Peter b.1964
Cyclist
oil on board 152.4 x 182.9
CAC1986/18

McLaren, Peter b.1964
Lovers in a Car
oil on board 91.4 x 121.9
CAC77/1989

McLaurin, Duncan 1848–1921
Home from the Plough
oil on canvas 47.1 x 68.6
CAC35/1964

McLaurin, Duncan 1848–1921
Moorland and Mist
oil on canvas 58.4 x 96.5
CAC311/1964

McLean, Bruce b.1944
Ladder Head
acrylic on canvas 219.7 x 149.9
CAC38/1992

McLean, Bruce b.1944
Untitled
acrylic on paper 51.5 x 38.5
CAC2008/2

McLean, John b.1939
Whaup
acrylic on canvas 173 x 204
CAC1995/2

McNab, Janice b.1964
Chairs 3 2002
oil on panel 122.5 x 178
CAC2008/8

McNairn, Caroline 1955–2010
In the Making 1987
oil on canvas 182.9 x 182.9
CAC1987/21

McNairn, John 1910–2009
Crail, Fife
oil on board 52 x 89
CAC22/1994

McNairn, John 1910–2009
Garden at Broomhill
oil on board 96 x 122
CAC23/1994

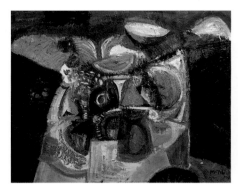

McNeish, Alexander 1932–2000
Beach Still Life 1958
oil on canvas 63 x 78
CAC108/1998

McNeish, Alexander 1932–2000
The Table 1958
oil on board 55 x 99
CAC17/1982

McNeish, Alexander 1932–2000
Red Rift 1964
oil on panel 19.9 x 24.8
CAC1964/344

McNeish, Alexander 1932–2000
Small Dreaming Stone 1964
oil on panel 24.2 x 34
CAC1964/345

McTaggart, William 1835–1910
Flotsam and Jetsam 1883
oil on canvas 66.3 x 91.2
CAC271/1964

McTaggart, William 1835–1910
Running for Shelter 1887
oil on canvas 100.3 x 137.2
CAC266/1964

McTaggart, William 1835–1910
Noontide, Jovie's Neuk 1894
oil on canvas 88.9 x 97.8
CAC211/1964

McTaggart, William 1835–1910
The Preaching of St Columba
oil on canvas 159.4 x 221.2
CAC206/1964

McTaggart, William (attributed to)
1835–1910
Portrait of a Boy
oil on canvas 52.2 x 41.9
CAC161/1964

McVeigh, Michael b.1957
The City Art Centre
oil on canvas on board 172 x 217
CAC1991/1

Mellis, Margaret 1914–2009
Sea 1991
assemblage & oil on wood 90 x 90
CAC1998/12

Melville, Arthur 1855–1904
Homeward 1880
oil on canvas 64.5 x 96.8
CAC1977/5

Melville, Arthur 1855–1904
A Scene in Tunis 1899
oil on panel 25.1 x 35.6
CAC319/1964

Michie, David Alan Redpath b.1928
Public Beach 1965
oil on canvas 63.5 x 91.5
CAC1965/3

Michie, David Alan Redpath b.1928
Accordion, Saxophone and Drum
oil on board 19 x 19
CAC2009/44

Michie, David Alan Redpath b.1928
Dark Garden with a Yellow Border
oil on canvas 91.5 x 127
CAC1989/50

Miller, John 1911–1975
Still Life with Chrysanthemums
oil on paper 39.3 x 50.8
CAC1967/16

Miller, Josephine 1890–1975
The House on the Canal
oil on canvas 63.6 x 76.3
CAC150/1964

Miller, Robert b.1910
Tea in the Garden 1968
oil on canvas 76.2 x 50.8
CAC1985/39

Milne, John Maclauchlan 1885–1957
Achmelvich
oil on canvas 71.5 x 92
CAC154/1964

Milne, Maggie b.1957
The Diggers' Triptych (left wing)
oil on canvas 122 x 76.5
CAC1989/27

Milne, Maggie b.1957
The Diggers Triptych (centre panel)
oil on canvas 122 x 152
CAC1989/27

Milne, Maggie b.1957
The Diggers' Triptych (right wing)
oil on canvas 122 x 76.5
CAC1989/27

Mitchell, John Campbell 1865–1922
Landscape, the Plains of Lora 1909
oil on canvas 124.4 x 155
CAC248/1964

Mitchell, John Campbell 1865–1922
Edinburgh from Corstorphine Hill
oil on canvas 24.5 x 34.6
CAC25/1988

Moodie, Donald 1892–1963
A Frosty Morning
oil on canvas 73.7 x 91.5
CAC1964/378

Mooney, John b.1948
Operation without an Aesthetic
acrylic on canvas 181 x 242
CAC1990/70

Mooney, John b.1948
Phoenis I
acrylic on canvas 40 x 51
CAC115/1998

Morris, Oliver active 1866–1895
*John Traill (1835–1897), Master of Greyfriars
Bobby* 1895
oil on panel 20 x 12.1
HH2201(f)/1962

Morrison, James b.1932
Grasses and Trees on Craigs Road 1983
oil on board 43.2 x 88.9
CAC1985/18

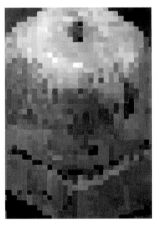

Morrison, Neil
Apple 1972
acrylic on canvas 105.5 x 75
CAC1/1972

Morrocco, Alberto 1917–1998
The Pub 1954
oil on panel 76.2 x 61
CAC290(a)/1964

Morrocco, Alberto 1917–1998
Still Life with Clay Pipe 1985
oil on canvas 61 x 73.7
CAC1985/19

Morrocco, Alberto 1917–1998
Calle de Coseolano Rosas
oil on panel 60.4 x 75.5
CAC290/1964

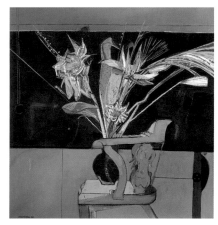

Morrocco, Leon Francesco b.1942
Dried Corn 1966
oil on canvas 127.5 x 122
CAC5/1966 ※

Mosman, William c.1700–1771
James Stuart, Lord Provost of Edinburgh (1764–1766 & 1768–1770)
oil on canvas 85 x 71.1
CAC3/1930

Munro, David active 1846–1872
John Macfie (1783–1852)
oil on canvas 125.7 x 99.3
HH2012/1960

Murray, David 1849–1933
Woodland Landscape 1903
oil on canvas 123.2 x 184.2
CAC1978/226

Murray, David 1849–1933
The Half Moon
oil on canvas 122.6 x 184.2
CAC55/1964

Murray, Graeme James b.1963
East of Eden 1986
oil on canvas 228.6 x 183
CAC1986/21

Narzynski, Juliusz b.1934
A Play for Nothing 1966
oil on canvas 119.4 x 148.6
CAC1967/3

Nasmyth, Alexander 1758–1840
Edinburgh from the Calton Hill 1820
oil on canvas 53.3 x 81.9
CAC1978/228

Nasmyth, Alexander 1758–1840
The Port of Leith 1824
oil on canvas 111.8 x 149.8
CAC1978/227

Facing page: Raeburn, Henry, 1756–1823, *John Robison (1739–1805)*, c.1798, The University of Edinburgh Fine Art Collection (p.169)

Nasmyth, Alexander (after) 1758–1840
Robert Burns (1759–1796)
oil on canvas 32.4 x 26.7
CAC1978/229

Nasmyth, Alexander (attributed to)
1758–1840
The Old Tolbooth of Edinburgh during Demolition
oil on panel 27.9 x 40
HH2081/1960

Nasmyth, Patrick 1787–1831
Edinburgh from the Water of Leith
oil on canvas 116.8 x 167.7
CAC1978/230

Nerli, Girolamo Pieri 1853–1926
Robert Louis Stevenson (1850–1894), Vailima, Samoa 1893
oil on canvas 57.1 x 44.4
CAC1978/238

Nerli, Girolamo Pieri 1853–1926
A Friend of the Stevenson Household, 1892
oil on canvas 55.9 x 41.9
CAC1978/236

Newbery, Francis Henry 1855–1946
Daydreams c.1920
oil on canvas 82.4 x 51.2
CAC127/1964

Nicholson, William 1872–1949
The Black Mirror
oil on canvas 191.8 x 143.5
CAC70/1964

Nicolson, John 1843–1934
Andrew Lamb's House, Leith
oil on canvas 40.7 x 50.8
CAC39/1988

Nisbet, Pollok Sinclair 1848–1922
John Knox's House, High Street, Edinburgh, 1885
oil on canvas 91.1 x 71.1
HH827/1928

Nisbet, Robert Buchan 1857–1942
The Bend of the River
oil on panel 19 x 20
CAC17/1964

Nixon, Jacqui Miller b.1964
Frequently Confused
oil, acrylic & collage on board 116.8 x 83.2
CAC1987/24

Noble, Robert 1857–1917
A Misty Morning
oil on canvas 127.2 x 97.9
CAC38/1964

Noble, Robert 1857–1917
Dovecot, East Linton, East Lothian
oil on board 22.2 x 29.8
CAC23/1988

Noble, Robert 1857–1917
Plainstane's Close, Edinburgh, 1878
oil on canvas 62 x 47
CAC1978/241

Norie, Robert active 1840–1850
Martello Tower, Leith, Low Water 1843
oil on canvas 86 x 124.5
CAC2003/9

O'Connor, Marcel b.1958
Two Flags on Purple 1991
oil, wax & dammar resin on board 27 x 50
CAC1994/2

Ogilvie, Elizabeth b.1946
Sea Journals (triptych, left wing) 1988
ink, acrylic & graphite on hand-made
paper 64.7 x 125.7
CAC1988/52

Ogilvie, Elizabeth b.1946
Sea Journals (triptych, centre panel) 1988
ink, acrylic & graphite on hand-made
paper 64.7 x 186.7
CAC1988/52

Ogilvie, Elizabeth b.1946
Sea Journals (triptych, right wing) 1988
ink, acrylic & graphite on hand-made
paper 64.7 x 125.7
CAC1988/52

Onwin, Glen b.1947
Subterranean Fire 1984
oil, earth & wax on canvas on board
213 x 191
CAC2007/17

Onwin, Glen b.1947
Subterranean Water 1984
oil, earth & wax on canvas on board
213 x 191
CAC1989/52

Oppenheimer, Charles 1875–1961
A Late Snowfall, Galloway
oil on canvas 71.2 x 92.7
CAC155/1964

Orchardson, William Quiller 1832–1910
In the Picture Gallery
oil on canvas 72.4 x 54.6
CAC274/1964

Owens, H.
Trawler 'GW34' 1926
oil on panel 40 x 54.5
CAC2010/19

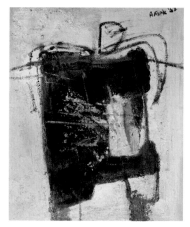

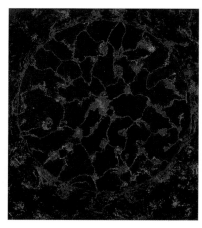

Park, Alistair 1930–1984
Yachting Lake 1957
oil on canvas 57 x 93
CAC123/1998

Park, Alistair 1930–1984
Blue Little Man 1962
oil on canvas 74.5 x 61.5
CAC121/1998

Park, Stuart 1862–1933
Pink and Yellow Roses 1889
oil on canvas 61.1 x 91.1
CAC1979/11

Paterson, James 1854–1932
Edinburgh's Playground 1905
oil on canvas 77 x 128
CAC3/1964

Paterson, James 1854–1932
Sunset, Arthur's Seat, Edinburgh 1931
oil on canvas 63.5 x 76
CAC1994/14

Paterson, Toby b.1974
Citrus Fruit Market 2005
acrylic on perspex 120 x 185
CAC2006/17

Paton, Joseph Noel 1821–1901
At Bay
oil on board 53 x 64.8
CAC281/1964

Patrick, James McIntosh 1907–1998
Stobo Kirk, Peeblesshire 1936
oil on canvas 50.8 x 61
CAC205/1964

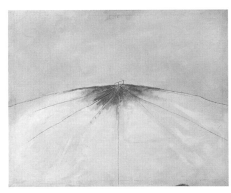

Patterson, Iain b.1946
For Enver 1969
acrylic on canvas 53.3 x 64
CAC128/1998

Patterson, Iain b.1946
Bindings and Patches 1976
acrylic on canvas on blockboard 70.5 x 53
CAC127/1998

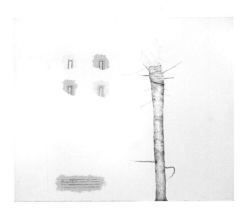

Patterson, Iain b.1946
New Buds 2 1978
acrylic on canvas 101 x 122
CAC125/1998

Patterson, Iain b.1946
New Buds 8 1979
acrylic on canvas 122 x 153
CAC126/1998

Patterson, Iain b.1946
Some Other Spring (panel 1 of 12)
acrylic on canvas board 9.5 x 14
CAC1980/7

Patterson, Iain b.1946
Some Other Spring (panel 2 of 12)
acrylic on canvas board 9.5 x 14
CAC1980/7

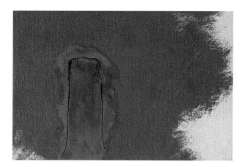

Patterson, Iain b.1946
Some Other Spring (panel 3 of 12)
acrylic on canvas board 9.5 x 14
CAC1980/7

Patterson, Iain b.1946
Some Other Spring (panel 4 of 12)
acrylic on canvas board 9.5 x 14
CAC1980/7

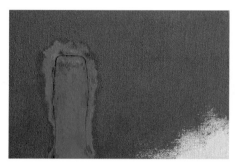

Patterson, Iain b.1946
Some Other Spring (panel 5 of 12)
acrylic on canvas board 9.5 x 14
CAC1980/7

Patterson, Iain b.1946
Some Other Spring (panel 6 of 12)
acrylic on canvas board 9.5 x 14
CAC1980/7

Patterson, Iain b.1946
Some Other Spring (panel 7 of 12)
acrylic on canvas board 9.5 x 14
CAC1980/7

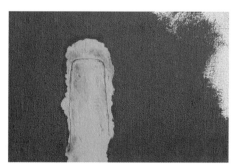

Patterson, Iain b.1946
Some Other Spring (panel 8 of 12)
acrylic on canvas board 9.5 x 14
CAC1980/7

Patterson, Iain b.1946
Some Other Spring (panel 9 of 12)
acrylic on canvas board 9.5 x 14
CAC1980/7

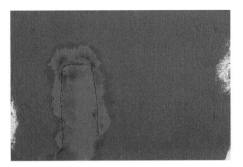

Patterson, Iain b.1946
Some Other Spring (panel 10 of 12)
acrylic on canvas board 9.5 x 14
CAC1980/7

Patterson, Iain b.1946
Some Other Spring (panel 11 of 12)
acrylic on canvas board 9.5 x 14
CAC1980/7

Patterson, Iain b.1946
Some Other Spring (panel 12 of 12)
acrylic on canvas board 9.5 x 14
CAC1980/7

Patterson, Janet b.1941
Brisbane Garden with Possum 1988
oil on paper 49 x 65
CAC1989/43

Peploe, Denis Frederic Neal 1914–1993
An Italian Peasant
oil on board 71.1 x 50.8
CAC240/1964

Peploe, Samuel John 1871–1935
A Rocky Shore, Iona
oil on canvas 40.7 x 50.5
CAC198/1964

Peploe, Samuel John 1871–1935
Still Life
oil on panel 26.7 x 34.8
CAC4/1964

Peploe, Samuel John 1871–1935
Still Life with Melon and Grapes
oil on canvas 39.4 x 45.7
CAC288/1964

Peploe, Samuel John 1871–1935
Still Life with Pears and Grapes
oil on canvas 31.7 x 45.7
CAC199/1964

Perigal, Arthur the younger 1816–1884
Edinburgh from the South
oil on canvas 14 x 35.7
HH3564/1971

Perrett, E. D. active 19th C
The Tomb of Tusitala
oil on panel 30.5 x 40
CAC1978/244

Pettie, John 1839–1893
Portrait of a Boy with a Cat
oil on canvas 114.3 x 65.3
CAC1978/245

Philipson, Robin 1916–1992
Burning in a Wasteland
oil on canvas 91.5 x 203
CAC1964/357

Philipson, Robin 1916–1992
Summer Morning
oil on canvas 77 x 110
CAC2006/15

Philipson, Robin 1916–1992
Zebra
oil on canvas 91.5 x 122
CAC1983/6

Phillips, Stanley active 20th C
West Princes Street Gardens, Edinburgh, from the East
oil on board 44.5 x 58.4
HH2228/1962

Philpot, Glyn Warren 1884–1937
Sir Thomas Hutchison, Lord Provost of Edinburgh (1921–1923)
oil on canvas 229.8 x 122.5
CAC1978/246

Pirie, George 1863–1946
Cock, Hen and Chickens
oil on canvas 80 x 107.3
CAC176/1964

Pissarro, Lucien 1863–1944
Blackpool Valley, 1913
oil on canvas 54.6 x 65.4
CAC99/1964

Pollock, Fred b.1937
Blush 1974
acrylic on cotton duck 152 x 222
CAC129/1998

Pope, Perpetua b.1916
Still Life with Ivy
oil on canvas 51.4 x 72.2
CAC303/1964

Potter, Alan b.1949
The Inquisitor 1984
acrylic on canvas 111.7 x 78.7
CAC1985/20

Pow, Tom 1909–1996
Eyemouth, Berwickshire
oil on board 39 x 50
CAC1997/15

Pow, Tom 1909–1996
Fallen Angels
oil on canvas 64 x 76
CAC1997/14

Prehn, Eric Thornton 1894–1985
Brave New World 1943
tempera on board 41.2 x 34.3
CAC16_1986

Prehn, Eric Thornton 1894–1985
Greyfriars Churchyard
oil on board 36.2 x 26
CAC12/1986

Prehn, Eric Thornton 1894–1985
Head of Loch Long
oil on card 20.4 x 26.7
CAC15/1986

Prehn, Eric Thornton 1894–1985
Russian Snow Scene
oil on canvas on board 24.1 x 31.1
CAC13/1986

Prehn, Eric Thornton 1894–1985
Scottish Landscape with Mountains and Loch
oil on card on board 14 x 20.9
CAC14/1986

Pringle, John Quinton 1864–1925
Muslin Street, Bridgeton, Glasgow
oil on canvas 35.9 x 41.2
CAC96/1964

Pringle, John Quinton 1864–1925
The Loom
oil on canvas 30.7 x 37.5
CAC156/1964

Provan, Donald b.1964
Window View at Sighthill, Edinburgh
oil on board 122 x 152.4
CAC1990/55

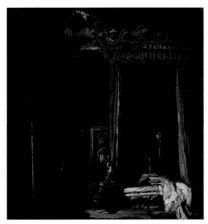

Pryde, James 1866–1941
The Red Bed
oil on canvas 68 x 62.9
CAC103/1964

Rae, Barbara b.1943
West Highland Landscape
oil & mixed media on canvas 152.4 x 182.9
CAC1988/53

Raeburn, Henry 1756–1823
Robert Scott Moncrieff
oil on canvas 74.5 x 62
CAC2010/23/L (P)

Raeburn, Henry (studio of) 1756–1823
*Sir James Hunter Blair (1741–1787), Lord
Provost of Edinburgh (1784–1786)*
oil on canvas 90.2 x 68.6
CAC1978/249

Facing page: Mooney, John, b.1948, *Cornucopia*, The University of Edinburgh Fine Art Collection (p.162)

Ramsay, Allan 1713–1784
Thomas Shairp of Houston (1724–1781) 1750
oil on canvas 76.2 x 63.5
CAC1993/2

Ramsay, Allan 1713–1784
John Coutts (1699–1751), Lord Provost of Edinburgh (1742–1743)
oil on canvas 76.8 x 64.8
HH1313(a)/1952

Ramsay, Allan 1713–1784
Katherine Hall of Dunglass (d.1745)
oil on canvas 127 x 104.1
CAC1997/11

Ramsay, Allan b.1959
Lord Provost Dr John McKay & City Officer Charles Allan
oil on canvas 204.5 x 190.5
CAC28/1991

Ranken, William Bruce Ellis 1881–1941
The Saloon, Moor Park, Hertfordshire
oil on panel 97.2 x 69.8
CAC100/1964

Ranken, William Bruce Ellis 1881–1941
The Tapestry Panel
oil on panel 78.8 x 56.5
CAC324/1964

Ranken, William Bruce Ellis 1881–1941
The Throne Room, Royal Palace, Madrid
oil on board 105.7 x 74.9
CAC228/1964

Redfern, June b.1951
On the Edge of the World
oil on canvas 231.1 x 308.6
CAC1985/28

Redpath, Anne 1895–1965
Causewayside, Edinburgh c.1950
oil on board 48.3 x 58.4
CAC1977/7

Redpath, Anne 1895–1965
Black and White Checks
oil on canvas 77.5 x 83.8
CAC280/1964 🐝

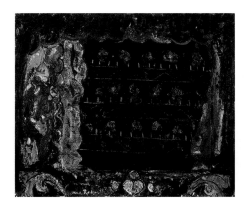

Redpath, Anne 1895–1965
Shooting Booth, Brittany, France
oil on board 68.9 x 81.3
CAC1966/11 🐝

Reed, William Thomas 1845–1881
Leith Races
oil on canvas 90 x 154
CAC1983/17

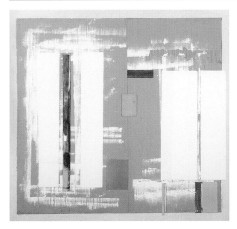

Reeves, Philip b.1931
New Year
acrylic & mixed media on board 151 x 154
CAC2003/11

Reid, Archibald David 1844–1908
Landscape with Cattle
oil on canvas 31.8 x 53.3
CAC116/1964

Reid, George 1841–1913
Dunnotar Castle, Aberdeenshire 1864
oil on canvas 43.2 x 62.2
CAC327/1964

Reid, George 1841–1913
*Duncan McLaren (1800–1886), Lord Provost of
Edinburgh (1851–1854)*
oil on canvas 238.8 x 146.1
CAC1978/250

Reid, George Ogilvy 1851–1928
*The Granting of a Royal Charter by King
James III to the Provost, Bailies and
Councillors of the Burgh of Edinburgh in (...)*
oil on canvas 162.6 x 184.8
CAC1978/251

Renton, Joan b.1935
Olive Trees, Castagne to Carducci, Italy
oil on canvas 122 x 122
CAC1992/69

Reynolds, Joshua 1723–1792
Charles Smith (1688–1768), Merchant and Banker
oil on canvas 76.2 x 63.5
CAC1997/1

Rhodes, Carol b.1959
Town 2005
oil on board 60 x 53.5
CAC2006/16

Ritchie, Alexander Hay 1822–1895
The Execution of Deacon Brodie and George Smith 1838
oil on panel 25.7 x 33.7
CAC1978/254

Roberts, David 1796–1864
Donaldson's College, Edinburgh
oil on canvas 128 x 190.5
CAC2006/20(L) (P)

Roberts, David 1796–1864
The Toll House, Edinburgh
oil on panel 25.5 x 35.5
CAC1987/26

Roberts, Derek b.1947
Indigo Trail 1976
oil on canvas 93.5 x 107.5
CAC136/1998

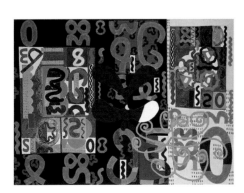

Roberts, Derek b.1947
Painting on Green and Black
oil & charcoal on linen 141 x 188
CAC1993/11

Robertson, Eric Harald Macbeth 1887–1941
Love's Invading c.1919
oil on canvas 170.2 x 137.2
CAC1982/3

Robertson, Eric Harald Macbeth 1887–1941
Shellburst
oil on canvas 71.2 x 83.8
CAC11/1976

Robertson, Iain b.1955
Jig 1994
oil on canvas 199.5 x 78.5
CAC2009/32

Robertson, James Downie 1931–2010
Sand and Cliff 1966
oil on canvas 76.2 x 50.8
CAC1966/10

Robertson, John Ewart 1820–1879
Robert Andrew Macfie (1811–1893) 1851
oil on canvas 92.7 x 69.8
HH2015/1960

Roche, Alexander Ignatius 1861–1921
Landscape c.1897
oil on canvas 94 x 114.2
CAC11/1964

Roche, Alexander Ignatius 1861–1921
Pittenweem, Fife
oil on canvas 76.2 x 102.9
CAC12/1964

Roche, Alexander Ignatius 1861–1921
Self Portrait
oil on canvas 61 x 52.1
CAC60/1964

Roche, Alexander Ignatius 1861–1921
Sir Robert Cranston (1843–1923), KCVO, VD,
Lord Provost of Edinburgh (1903–1906)
oil on canvas 218.4 x 146.1
CAC1978/257

Roche, Alexander Ignatius 1861–1921
Tell Me, Shepherds
oil on canvas 135.6 x 168.3
CAC152/1964

Roche, Alexander Ignatius 1861–1921
The Prison Gate, Mogador, Morocco
oil on canvas 33.7 x 26.7
CAC26/1964

Rogers, Henry b.1963
An Initial Act of Creation 1987
oil on canvas 198.2 x 213.4
CAC1987/15

Ross, John H.
Waverley Station, Edinburgh 1848
oil on board 17 x 49.5
CAC2007/7

Rossi, Mario b.1958
Whirlwind
oil on paper on canvas 233.7 x 173.4
CAC9/1986

Russell, Kathleen b.1940
St Abbs, Berwickshire, Storm
oil on canvas 101.6 x 152.3
CAC1978/259

Russell, Walter Westley 1867–1949
Camilla
oil on canvas 101.6 x 76.3
CAC43/1964

Russell, Walter Westley 1867–1949
Joseph Crawhall (1861–1913)
oil on canvas 76.5 x 63.4
CAC97/1964

Sandeman, Margot 1922–2009
Hawthorn (Mayflower) 1988
oil on canvas 76.2 x 50.8
CAC1989/48

Sanderson, Robert 1848–1908
Drill Parade, Edinburgh Castle, 1886
oil on panel 80.1 x 152.4
CAC1978/260

Schueler, Jon 1916–1992
Summer Day: Sleat
oil on canvas 175 x 192
CAC1994/15

Schunemann, L. (attributed to)
active c.1666–1674
Sir Alexander Gilmour (1658–1731), Bt of
Craigmillar
oil on canvas 82.5 x 67.9
CAC1978/287

Scott, David (attributed to) 1806–1849
Samuel Gilmour
oil on canvas 92.3 x 71.2
HH1634/1956

Scougall, David (attributed to)
c.1610–c.1680
Sir James Steuart of Coltness (1608–1681),
Lord Provost of Edinburgh (1648–1650 & (...)
oil on canvas 127.8 x 103.3
CAC1978/1231

Seaton, William active 19th C
A Man Playing a Penny Whistle
oil on board 17.5 x 13.6
CAC1978/261

Sekalski, Józef 1904–1972
Lobster Pots c.1952
oil on canvas 63.5 x 76.2
CAC1990/76

Shanks, Duncan b.1937
Muddy Pool
acrylic on paper 148 x 116.2
CAC1988/36

Shanks, William Somerville 1864–1951
Demarco, M. de Munkácsy's Private Model
oil on canvas 25.1 x 35.6
CAC245/1964

Shields, Douglas Gordon 1888–1943
Glassford Walker c.1940
oil on canvas 86.3 x 66
CAC1978/262

Shields, Douglas Gordon 1888–1943
Florence Chalmers (d.1993)
oil on canvas 60 x 49.5
CAC17/1993

Shipway, Alan b.1956
Last Month
acrylic on canvas 162.5 x 126
CAC2009/31

Sims, Charles 1873–1928
Mrs MacWhirter
oil on canvas 53.3 x 43.1
CAC98/1964

Sims, Charles (attributed to) 1873–1928
Study of a Female Figure
oil on canvas 50.8 x 25.1
CAC376/1964

Sims, Charles (attributed to) 1873–1928
Study of a Female Nude
oil & conte on board 33 x 36.8
CAC375/1964

Sims, Charles (attributed to) 1873–1928
Study of Children Bathing
oil on panel 21.6 x 20.2
CAC356/1964

Sivell, Robert 1888–1958
Eve
oil on panel 61 x 38.2
CAC312/1964

Smeall, William active 1824–1830
At Currie, Old Bridge and Old Inn
oil on panel 18.7 x 29.3
HH1463/1953

Smeall, William active 1824–1830
The Entrance Gate of Trinity College Church, Edinburgh, 1830
oil on panel 23.1 x 29.7
HH1461/1953

Smeall, William active 1824–1830
The Lodge, Trinity College Church, Edinburgh, 1824
oil on panel 28.9 x 23
HH1441/1953

Facing page: Behrens, Reinhard, b.1951, *Lost Valley II*, City of Edinburgh Council (p. 8)

Smeall, William (attributed to)
active 1824–1830
A Harbour Scene
oil on board 24 x 31
HH1460/1953

Smeall, William (attributed to)
active 1824–1830
Bakehouse Close, Canongate, Edinburgh
oil on board 33 x 20
HH1446/1953

Smeall, William (attributed to)
active 1824–1830
Cross Causeway and Buccleuch Church, Edinburgh
oil on board 28.6 x 21.4
HH1449/1953

Smeall, William (attributed to)
active 1824–1830
Old Edinburgh Close
oil on canvas 29.5 x 22
HH1447/1953

Smeall, William (attributed to)
active 1824–1830
Part of Audley House and the Priory of the Holy Trinity, Aldgate, London
oil on canvas 15.5 x 23.8
HH1445/1953

Smeall, William (attributed to)
active 1824–1830
Shoemaker Close, Edinburgh
oil on panel 32 x 22.2
HH1448/1953

Smeall, William (attributed to)
active 1824–1830
Study of Boats on Sand
oil on board 18 x 26.8
HH1464/1953

Smeall, William (attributed to)
active 1824–1830
Unidentified Old Inn
oil on board 21.5 x 30.4
HH1465/1953

Smith, Colvin 1795–1875
George Thomson
oil on canvas 79 x 64.1
CAC1978/270

Smith, George 1870–1934
Carting Timber
oil on canvas 122.3 x 198.2
CAC197/1964

Smith, Ian McKenzie b.1935
Tidemark
oil on canvas 86.5 x 98
CAC146/1998

Smith, Jane Stewart 1839–1925
Dunbar Close, Edinburgh, 1868
oil on board 30.8 x 23.1
CAC1978/179

Smith, Jane Stewart 1839–1925
*View of the High Street, Looking East, from the
Lawnmarket, Edinburgh*
oil on canvas 36 x 54.2
CAC1978/272

Smith, John Guthrie Spence 1880–1951
*John Knox's House, High Street,
Edinburgh* 1929
oil on board 76.2 x 63.5
CAC1984/6

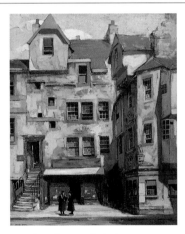

Smith, John Guthrie Spence 1880–1951
Mowbray House, High Street, Edinburgh 1930
oil on panel 75.2 x 61
CAC212/1964

Smith, Marian b.1951
Still Life
oil on canvas 109.2 x 121.9
CAC1/1973

Souter, John Bulloch 1890–1972
Sorting Garlic
oil on canvas 54 x 69.2
CAC124/1964

Standen, Peter b.1936
View of Princes Street, Edinburgh 1979
oil on canvas 101.6 x 147.3
CAC1988/37

Stevenson, Fanny Vandergrift Osbourne
1840–1914
The Bridge at Grez, Forest of Fontainebleau,
France
oil on canvas 34.4 x 55.2
CAC1978/92

Stevenson, Robert active c.1880–1910
Robert Louis Stevenson (1850–1894) (after
Girolamo Pieri Nerli) c.1900
oil on canvas 60.9 x 35.5
HH3142/1967

Stevenson, Robert active 1961
Swanston Village before Reconstruction, 2
November 1961
oil on board 35.8 x 47.7
HH2159/1961

Stevenson, Robert Macaulay 1854–1952
Wooded Landscape c.1910
oil on canvas 41.3 x 55.8
CAC329/1964

Strang, William 1859–1921
Dreams 1915
oil on canvas 76.2 x 61.2
CAC59/1964

Stronach, Ancell 1901–1981
The Other Wise Man 1927
oil on canvas 127.6 x 102.9
CAC112/1964

Stuart, Robert Easton active 1887–1940
Maule's Corner after Rain, Edinburgh 1925
oil on canvas 71.1 x 92
CAC201/1964

Sturrock, Alick Riddell 1885–1953
A Solway Farm
oil on canvas 76.2 x 91.4
CAC138/1964

Sturrock, Alick Riddell 1885–1953
The Silo
oil on panel 31.1 x 39.9
CAC289/1964

Sutherland, Alan b.1931
Sir Duncan M. Weatherstone (1898–1972),
MC, TD, LLD, DLitt, Lord Provost of
Edinburgh (1963–1966) 1968
oil on canvas 125.7 x 104.2
CAC1978/280

Sutherland, David Macbeth 1883–1973
The Demolition of the Crown Hotel,
Edinburgh 1925
oil on canvas 81.3 x 66.3
CAC1/1982

Sutherland, David Macbeth 1883–1973
Winter Landscape, West Cults, Aberdeen 1940
oil on panel 71.2 x 91.4
CAC189/1964

Sutherland, David Macbeth 1883–1973
Concarneau, Brittany, France 1964
oil on board 76.2 x 101.6
CAC1965/2

Sutherland, David Macbeth 1883–1973
Plockton from Duncraig 1967
oil on board 36.7 x 43.9
CAC1968/35

Sutherland, George active 19th C
The International Forestry Exhibition,
Edinburgh, 1884
oil on canvas 135.9 x 242.2
HH1289/1951

Telford, Zoë b.1964
Marshland, Rising Mountain 1987
oil on canvas 135.9 x 170.2
CAC1987/14

Thomas, Margaret b.1916
Castle Nocturne
oil on canvas 64.1 x 78.7
HH2151/1961

Thomas, Margaret b.1916
Christmas
oil & charcoal on wax paper 91.5 x 70.5
MC4370/1961

Thoms, Colin 1912–1997
Strutting Bird 1994
oil on canvas 96.5 x 155
CAC1998/24

Thoms, Colin 1912–1997
Haddington, East Lothian
oil on panel 50.8 x 38.1
CAC257/1964

Thomson, Adam Bruce 1885–1976
Cedars
oil on board 45.7 x 55.9
CAC1985/3

Thomson, Adam Bruce 1885–1976
From My Bedroom Window
oil on canvas 50.8 x 61
CAC119/1964

Thomson, Adam Bruce 1885–1976
*North Bridge and Salisbury Crags, Edinburgh,
from the North West*
oil on canvas 109.2 x 137.1
CAC1978/283

Thomson, Adam Bruce 1885–1976
Palm, Pampas Grass and Duncraig
oil on board 71.2 x 91.5
CAC1967/5

Thomson, Adam Bruce 1885–1976
Willow Trees, Cattle and River
oil on board 35.6 x 45.7
CAC21/1988

Thomson, Jennifer b.1969
Newhaven Harbour 1993
oil on board 55.9 x 81.3
CAC1993/14

Thomson, Jennifer b.1969
The Fisherman's Choice, Newhaven 1993
oil on board 51.3 x 43.2
CAC1993/15

Thomson, John 1778–1840
Abbotsford, Melrose, 1828
oil on canvas 73.6 x 94
HH2463/1963

Thomson, John 1778–1840
Craigmillar Castle from the South East,
Edinburgh, 1821
oil on panel 35.9 x 48.2
HH2464/1963

Thomson, John 1778–1840
Edinburgh from Inverleith
oil on canvas 26 x 47
CAC9(a)/1984

Thomson, John 1778–1840
View of Edinburgh from Craiglockhart
oil on panel 36.2 x 46.3
HH1926/1960

Thomson, John 1778–1840
View of Edinburgh from Duddingston
oil on canvas 61 x 92
HH1927/1960

Thomson, John (attributed to) 1778–1840
General View of Edinburgh from the Vicinity
of Craiglockhart
oil on canvas 94 x 138.5
HH1929/1960

Torrance, James 1859–1916
Still Life, Harness
oil on canvas 50.8 x 76.8
CAC67/1964

Torrance, James 1859–1916
The Question
oil on canvas 47 x 36.2
CAC66/1964

Torrance, James 1859–1916
The Smile
oil on canvas 73.7 x 66.1
CAC65/1964

Trojanowska, Anna
Red House by a Canal 1953
oil on canvas 49.5 x 50.5
CAC1967/4

Turner, William active 1767–1831
The Gold Cup, Musselburgh, East Lothian
1822
oil on canvas 66 x 116
CAC1996/3

Turner, William active 1767–1831
*The Arrival of the Mail Coach at the 'Black
Bull', Edinburgh*
oil on canvas 63 x 81.5
CAC1991/18

Turner, William 1789–1862
*The Procession of King George IV Entering
Princes Street, Edinburgh, August, 1822*
oil on canvas 85.1 x 117.4
HH694/1913

unknown artist 18th C
Agrippina Mourning the Ashes of Germanicus
oil on panel 93.7 x 44.9
CAC1978/294(a)

unknown artist 18th C
Europa and the Bull
oil on panel 37.2 x 45.2
CAC1978/294(b)

unknown artist 18th C
Jove Driving across the Heavens
oil on panel 37 x 45.5
CAC1978/294(c)

unknown artist 18th C
The Death of Socrates
oil on panel 37.2 x 45.5
CAC1978/294(d)

unknown artist 18th C
*A Putto Driving a Chariot Led by Two
Cheetahs*
oil on panel 37.3 x 45.3
CAC1978/294(e)

unknown artist 18th C
A River Landscape with Ruins
oil on panel 40 x 135
CAC1978/293

unknown artist 18th C
Landscape with a Hunting Scene
oil on oak panel 19 x 87.9
HH1495/1953

unknown artist 18th C
A Harbour Scene
oil on oak panel 21.9 x 95.8
HH1496/1953

unknown artist 18th C
Pastoral Landscape with a Ruin
oil on oak panel 23.5 x 95.4
HH1497/1953

unknown artist 18th C
Portrait of a Gentleman (possibly Sir George
Warrender, c.1658–1721, Bt, Lord Provost of
Edinburgh, 1713–1715)
oil on canvas 123.8 x 95.2
CAC1978/187

unknown artist 18th C
Portrait of an Unknown Architect (possibly J.
McVey)
oil on canvas 91 x 72.1
HH1938/1953

unknown artist 18th C
*Portrait of an Unknown Lady in Early
Seventeenth-Century Dress*
oil on panel 50.9 x 38
HH302/1895

unknown artist 18th C
*Sir Charles Gilmour (1701–1750), Bt of
Craigmillar*
oil on canvas 76.2 x 63.5
CAC1978/288

unknown artist 18th C
*The Right Honourable David Steuart, Lord
Provost of Edinburgh (1780–1781)*
oil on canvas 91.5 x 71
HH1314/1952

unknown artist 18th C
Thomas Ruddiman (1714–1747)
oil on canvas 76.5 x 64
HH2387/1962

unknown artist
'The Comet', Smack 1809
oil on canvas 82.5 x 123.2
CAC27/1991

unknown artist
Portrait of an Unknown Lady c.1840
oil on canvas 92.1 x 77.2
CAC1978/314

unknown artist
Portrait of an Unknown Gentleman with a Dog c.1850
oil on canvas 127 x 101.6
CAC1978/315

unknown artist
Portrait of an Unknown Gentleman c.1870
oil on canvas 76.6 x 63.5
CAC1978/317

unknown artist
Portrait of an Unknown Gentleman c.1880
oil on canvas 239 x 147.3
CAC1978/320

unknown artist
Portrait of an Unknown Gentleman c.1880
oil on canvas 90.5 x 75
CAC1978/321

unknown artist
Two Children Holding a Finch and a Bird's Nest c.1880
oil on canvas 147.5 x 117
CAC1978/319

unknown artist 19th C
A Mother and Child in a Bower
oil on panel 41.9 x 36.8
CAC1978/333

Facing page: Lorimer, John Henry, 1856–1936, *The Flight of the Swallows*, 1906, City of Edinburgh Council (p. 59)

unknown artist 19th C
A Putto Sailing
oil on panel 48.2 x 62.9
CAC1978/335

unknown artist 19th C
A Putto Crowning Another with a Garland of Roses
oil on panel 47.9 x 60.3
CAC1978/334

unknown artist 19th C
A View of the Old Town from the North
oil on panel 34.9 x 121.3
HH1204/1949

unknown artist 19th C
Adam White of Fens (1760–1843), First Provost of Leith, (1833–1839)
oil on canvas 120.7 x 88.9
CAC1978/309

unknown artist 19th C
Andrew Wemyss (1806–1858), Councillor, Treasurer, Lord Dean of Guild and Benefactor of Trinity Hospital
oil on canvas 91.4 x 71.4
CAC1978/308

unknown artist 19th C
Ann Taylor Ferguson (1832–1910)
oil on canvas 37 x 32
HH3362/1969

unknown artist 19th C
Bakehouse Close, Canongate, Edinburgh
oil on panel 20.1 x 18.6
HH908(a)/1934

unknown artist 19th C
Condemned Covenanters on Their Way to Execution in the West Bow, Edinburgh
oil on panel 43.2 x 30.8
HH383/1904

unknown artist 19th C
Edinburgh from the South
oil on panel 41.3 x 56.5
CAC1978/338

unknown artist 19th C
Edinburgh's City Officers, c.1830
oil on panel 53.3 x 42.5
HH1222/1949

unknown artist 19th C
Elizabeth Dick Ferguson
oil on board 45 x 37
HH3360/1969

unknown artist 19th C
George Meikle Kemp (1795–1844)
oil on canvas 38.5 x 31.5
CAC1978/301

unknown artist 19th C
George Meikle Kemp (1795–1844) with the Model for the Scott Monument, Edinburgh
oil on canvas 68.8 x 68.8
HH1638/1953

unknown artist 19th C
Helen Ferguson (1828–1849)
oil on board 41 x 30.8
HH3361/1969

unknown artist 19th C
Jacob Liebe (b.1779)
oil on canvas 76.8 x 64.1
CAC55/1986

unknown artist 19th C
James Waldie (1831–1915), JP 1902
oil on canvas 75 x 64
HH2120/61

unknown artist 19th C
John Allan
oil on canvas 64 x 53.8
HH1456/1953

unknown artist 19th C
John Macfie (1820–1875)
oil on canvas 77.4 x 64.7
HH2016/1960

unknown artist 19th C
Low Calton, Edinburgh
oil on paper on panel 18 x 27
CAC1978/340

unknown artist 19th C
Mrs James Waldie, née Margaret Patterson of Coldingham (c.1803–1884)
oil on canvas 75 x 62
HH2121/1961

unknown artist 19th C
Nine Views of the Old Town of Edinburgh: Main Point, West Port (panel 1 of 9)
oil on canvas 21 x 28
HH1936(a)/1960

unknown artist 19th C
Nine Views of the Old Town of Edinburgh: Foot of Leith Wynd (panel 2 of 9)
oil on canvas 21 x 28
HH1936(b)/1960

unknown artist 19th C
Nine Views of the Old Town of Edinburgh: Canongate (panel 3 of 9)
oil on canvas 21 x 28
HH1936(c)/1960

unknown artist 19th C
Nine Views of the Old Town of Edinburgh: Grassmarket (panel 4 of 9)
oil on canvas 21 x 28
HH1936(d)/1960

unknown artist 19th C
Nine Views of the Old Town of Edinburgh: Cowgate Port (panel 5 of 9)
oil on canvas 21 x 28
HH1936(e)/1960

unknown artist 19th C
Nine Views of the Old Town of Edinburgh: Foot of West Port (panel 6 of 9)
oil on canvas 21 x 28
HH1936(f)/1960

unknown artist 19th C
Nine Views of the Old Town of Edinburgh: In Pleasance (panel 7 of 9)
oil on canvas 21 x 28
HH1936(g)/1960

unknown artist 19th C
Nine Views of the Old Town of Edinburgh:
Foot of Candlemakers Row (panel 8 of 9)
oil on canvas 21 x 28
HH1936(h)/1960

unknown artist 19th C
Nine Views of the Old Town of Edinburgh:
Calton (panel 9 of 9)
oil on canvas 21 x 28
HH1936(i)/1960

unknown artist 19th C
Portrait of a Boy
oil on board 43.3 x 35.8
HH2115/1961

unknown artist 19th C
Portrait of an Unknown Gentleman Holding a
Letter
oil on canvas 92 x 77
CAC1978/316

unknown artist 19th C
Portrait of an Unknown Gentleman with a
Child and a Dog
oil on canvas 67.4 x 54.1
CAC1978/328

unknown artist 19th C
Portrait of an Unknown Girl
oil on canvas 36 x 30.8
CAC1978/324

unknown artist 19th C
Robert Burns (1759–1796)
oil on canvas 121.9 x 97.8
HH1924/1960

unknown artist 19th C
Sir William Arbuthnot (1776–1829), Bt, Lord
Provost of Edinburgh (1815–1817 & 1821–
1823)
oil on canvas 92 x 71.8
CAC1978/296

unknown artist 19th C
The Edinburgh Town Guard
oil on board 12.7 x 10.8
HH715/1915

unknown artist 19th C
The Entrance to Sir Thomas Dick Lauder's, the
Grange, Edinburgh
oil on canvas 31 x 41
CAC1978/345

unknown artist 19th C
The Hall, Abbotsford, Melrose
oil on canvas 62.8 x 52
CAC1978/361

unknown artist 19th C
The Netherbow Port, Edinburgh
oil on canvas 30.7 x 23
HH1595/1955

unknown artist 19th C
The Old Grassmarket from the North,
Edinburgh, c.1850
oil on canvas 44.4 x 60.9
HH400/1905

unknown artist 19th C
Part of Trinity College and Hospital,
Edinburgh (demolished, 1845–1848)
oil on panel 63.2 x 76.2
CAC1978/404a

unknown artist 19th C
Part of Trinity College Hospital, Edinburgh
(demolished, 1845–1848)
oil on panel 62.5 x 76.2
CAC1978/404b

unknown artist 19th C
Trinity College Church, Edinburgh, from the
South West (demolished, 1845–1848)
oil on canvas 30.5 x 45.7
HH2082/1960

unknown artist 19th C
Unidentified Old Town Close, Edinburgh
oil on canvas 45.9 x 30.8
CAC1978/358

unknown artist 19th C
William Nelson (1816–1887)
oil on canvas 76.2 x 65.3
CAC1/1942

unknown artist 19th C
*William Oliphant and His Wife Mary with
Their Children: William, Mary, Margaret,
John, Elizabeth, Ebenezer, David and (...)*
oil on canvas 91.4 x 114.3
HH2405/1963

unknown artist 20th C
Advocate's Close, Edinburgh
oil on canvas 40.5 x 20
HH1597/1955

unknown artist 20th C
Reid's Close, Edinburgh
oil on canvas 40.5 x 20
HH1598/1955

unknown artist 20th C
Bailie Waterson
oil on paper 31 x 38.2
CAC1978/368

unknown artist 20th C
James Waldie (1831–1915), JP
oil on canvas 61 x 53.2
HH2122/1961

unknown artist 20th C
*The Edinburgh City Keys: Robert Paton, City
Chamberlain (1895–1925)*
oil on canvas 146.1 x 94
CAC28/1987

unknown artist
A Dog (possibly 'Greyfriars Bobby')
oil on canvas 37.5 x 45
HH3345/1969

unknown artist
Ancient Chapel, Kirkgate, Edinburgh
oil on board 29.5 x 20
CAC2009/104

unknown artist
Christ
oil on canvas 86 x 74
CAC2010/21

unknown artist
Johnston Terrace and Castle Wynd, Edinburgh
oil on panel 43.5 x 43.7
CAC1978/348

unknown artist
Portrait of an Old Man with a Staff
oil on canvas 61 x 51
CAC2010/22

unknown artist
Richard Mackie (1851–1923), Provost of Leith (1899–1908)
oil on canvas 147.3 x 88.9
CAC1978/303

unknown artist
The Trawler 'Anworth'
oil on board 15.2 x 40.8
CAC8/1997

Urie, Joseph b.1947
Beauty and the Beast, No.5
oil on canvas 153 x 154
CAC1989/60

Vos, Hubert 1855–1935
Alexander Brand (1836–1931), Provost of Portobello 1892
oil on canvas 106.6 x 86.3
CAC2003/10

Walker, Andrew b.1959
Women on Wheels
oil on canvas 160 x 191.8
CAC1985/40

Walker, Ethel b.1941
Stockbridge, Edinburgh 1986
oil on board 111.7 x 94
CAC1986/48

Walker, George active 1792–1797
Edinburgh from the South East, 1797
oil on canvas 57.8 x 92
HH1092/1947

Facing page: Herdman, William Gawin, 1805–1882, *View of the Mound, Edinburgh*, City of Edinburgh Council (p. 44)

Watson, William Stewart 1800–1870
Holyrood Dairy, Edinburgh, c.1840 1886
oil on canvas 40.6 x 55.9
HH379/1903

Watt, George Fiddes 1873–1960
*William Slater Brown, Lord Provost
(1909–1912)* 1907
oil on canvas 132.1 x 94
CAC1988/10

Watt, George Fiddes 1873–1960
Alison Cunningham (1822–1913) 1908
oil on canvas 68.5 x 54.6
CAC1978/381

Watt, George Fiddes 1873–1960
*Sir Robert Kirk Inches, Lord Provost
(1912–1916)* 1916
oil on canvas 110 x 93
CAC6/1996

Watt, George Fiddes 1873–1960
*Sir John Lorne Macleod (1873–1946), CBE,
LLD, Lord Provost (1916–1919)*
oil on canvas 227.3 x 138.4
CAC1978/383

Wehrschmidt, Daniel Albert 1861–1932
*Anthony J. O. Maxtone Graham (1900–1971),
16th Laird of Culloquhey and 9th Laird of
Redgorton* 1904
oil on canvas 147 x 91
CAC1978/385

Wells, T.
'Show Jamie', a Canongate Character 1842
oil on board 18 x 13
CAC2009/110

Wells, William Page Atkinson 1872–1923
A Lancashire Village, 1908
oil on canvas 102.2 x 127
CAC22/1964

Williams, Andrew b.1954
Deposition II 1982
acrylic, mixed media & papier collé on
paper 152 x 152
CAC158/1998

Williams, Andrew b.1954
Study for 'Body Builders, Venice Beach, California, USA'
oil on paper 59.3 x 41.9
CAC1986/17/1

Williams, Andrew b.1954
Body Builders, Venice Beach, California, USA
oil on canvas 230 x 200.7
CAC1986/17

Wilson, Andrew 1780–1848
Edinburgh, before the Mound Was Completed
oil on board 13 x 20.5
CAC2009/42

Wilson, William active 1798–1836
Douglas Cross, Braes of Yarrow
oil on canvas 94 x 128.2
CAC1978/387

Wingate, James Lawton 1846–1924
Veiled Moonlight c.1902
oil on canvas 44.4 x 48.9
CAC21/1964

Wingate, James Lawton 1846–1924
Autumnal Sunset
oil on canvas 40.7 x 61
CAC270/1964

Wingate, James Lawton 1846–1924
Harvest in Arran
oil on canvas 37 x 51.2
CAC253/1964

Wiszniewski, Adrian b.1958
Self Portrait 1985
oil on panel 79 x 58
CAC1994/4

Young, Andrew 1855–1925
A Select Tea Party
oil on panel 29.9 x 23.5
CAC29/1987

Young, Edward Drummond 1877–1946
Corner of the Fife Coast
oil on board 20 x 25
CAC17/1998

Young, Edward Drummond 1877–1946
Satsuma Vase
oil on canvas 52.1 x 41.3
CAC44/1964

Young, William Drummond 1855–1924
*John Bennet (1820–1902), Provost of Leith
(1893–1899)* 1899
oil on canvas 127.5 x 105
CAC1978/391

Zhijun, Suo
Duddingston, Edinburgh 2001
acrylic on paper 72 x 123
CAC2001/1

Zhijun, Suo
Old Town of Edinburgh from Salisbury Crags
2001
acrylic on paper 78 x 122.5
CAC2001/2

Żyw, Aleksander 1905–1995
Red Figures 1952
oil on canvas 90.8 x 72
CAC161/1998

Żyw, Aleksander 1905–1995
Olivier (Olive Trees) c.1964–1965
oil & charcoal on canvas 161 x 116.5
CAC162/1998

Historic Scotland, Edinburgh

Historic Scotland is the Scottish Government agency which safeguards the nation's historic environment and promotes its understanding and enjoyment. It looks after 345 places to visit throughout Scotland, including castles, abbeys and other historical buildings and archaeological sites. Within Edinburgh there are two venues in which Historic Scotland displays some of its fine art collection: Edinburgh Castle in the heart of the city and Trinity House in Leith.

Historic Scotland's paintings at Edinburgh Castle reflect the site's significance in Scottish history, and cover varying subject matter from royal portraits to topographical illustrations and historical scenes. Among the most significant are four portraits of James VI of Scotland, including a rare early portrait attributed to the Flemish artist Adrian Vanson. This hangs in the royal apartments where the King was born in 1566. Other notable historical subjects include *The Last Sleep of Argyll before His Execution, 1685* by Edward Matthew Ward (1816–1879), recalling the night before the execution of Archibald, 9th Earl of Argyll at Edinburgh Castle, and *The Fight for the Standard* by Richard Ansdell (1815–1885), which depicts Ensign Charles Ewart of the Royal North British Dragoons (Scots Greys) capturing the Standard of the 45th Regiment of the Line at Waterloo. Historic Scotland's paintings are displayed at different locations throughout the Castle. A twentieth-century work by James N. Madison, *The Highland Charge of Drummossie Moor*, hanging in the café, features a detailed realisation of the Battle of Culloden, 16th April 1746. Within the *Prisons of War* exhibition, the eighteenth-century painting *View of Edinburgh Castle*, by an unknown artist, provides a detailed historical record of the Castle.

For centuries, Trinity House has served as the headquarters of the Incorporation of Masters and Mariners of Leith, a charity supporting the welfare and interests of local seafarers. The building, rebuilt in 1816 on much earlier foundations, houses an extensive collection that reflects the work of the Incorporation and the rich history of seafaring associated with the Port of Leith. Along with oil paintings and other artworks are nautical instruments, charts, ship models, furniture and an eclectic range of objects brought back from voyages around the world. The paintings in the collection include portraits, maritime and local topographical subjects.

The portraits largely feature the former masters and honorary members of the charity. These include four works by the celebrated Edinburgh portraitist Sir Henry Raeburn (1756–1823), including the full-length portrait of *Admiral Adam Duncan (1731–1804), 1st Viscount Duncan of Camperdown*, who was made an honorary member after his famous victory at Camperdown in 1797.

The most prominent maritime painting in the collection is *Vasco da Gama Encountering the Spirit of the Storm* by David Scott, RSA (1806–1849). This canvas dominates the north end of the Convening Room. It depicts the Portuguese explorer and his crew rounding the Cape of Good Hope in 1497. Other paintings feature important ships associated with Leith and seascapes of Newcastle by Bernard Benedict Hemy (1845–1913), and Liverpool by Clarkson Stanfield (1793–1867).

The local topographical paintings provide a valuable record of how the Port of Leith developed from the early eighteenth century to the late nineteenth century. Most notable of these is the Flemish School work *A View of Leith with Galleon* (c.1710), showing key landmarks, including the Signal Tower, King's Wark and the Timber Bush. The nineteenth-century paintings capture Leith as a busy commercial port at the time when steamboats were replacing traditional sailing vessels.

Hugh Morrison, Collections Registrar

Anglo/Chinese School
The Barque 'Loch Broom' of Glasgow c.1885
oil on canvas 43.7 x 57.5
TRH013

Ansdell, Richard 1815–1885
The Fight for the Standard
oil on canvas 395.5 x 302
EDIN077 (P)

Belle, Alexis-Simon (attributed to)
1674–1734
James VIII (1688–1766), 'The Old Pretender'
before 1719
oil on canvas 92 x 81
EDIN078

Blair, John 1850–1934
Edward Brown (d.1802) (after Daniel Orme) after 1797
oil on canvas 181.2 x 143.7
TRH039

British (Scottish) School
The Ship 'Loch Carron' of Glasgow c.1880
oil & silk collage on wood 60 x 105
TRH022

British (Scottish) School mid-19th C
Thomas Sutherland, Teacher of Mathematics at Trinity House
oil on canvas 75 x 62.5
TRH042

British (Scottish) School
Mrs Colina Mary Grant
oil on canvas 89.5 x 72
TRH034

British (Scottish) School
The Clipper 'Nonsuch' Making for Sea
oil on canvas 45 x 72.5
TRH017

Bury, W.
A View of Portobello, Edinburgh
oil on canvas 60 x 117.5
TRH019

Critz, John de the elder (after)
1551/1552–1642
James VI and I (1566–1625)
oil on oak panel 55 x 41
EDIN010

Cromarty, Alexander 1838–1926
The Barque 'Bencleuch' 1917
oil on canvas 60 x 90
TRH014

Cruikshanks, Francis (attributed to)
active 1855–1880
*Mr Robert Thomson, Elected Member of
Trinity House, 1873*
oil on canvas 126 x 100.5
TRH027

Cruikshanks, Francis (attributed to)
active 1855–1880
*Mr Thomas Robertson, Secretary to the
Corporation (1847–1865)*
oil on canvas 110 x 85
TRH030

David, Antonio (after) active from 1684
*Princess Maria Clementina Sobieska
(1702–1735)* 1717–1735
oil on canvas 83.5 x 70.5
EDIN008

Fairslough, R. B.
The HMS 'Bounty' 1933
oil on board 22.5 x 30
TRH475

Flemish School
A View of Leith with a Galleon c.1710
oil on canvas 50 x 91.2
TRH023

Ford, John A. active 1880–1923
Charles Kinghorn Mackintosh, Treasurer to the Corporation (1912–1917) 1919
oil on canvas 199 x 108
TRH029

Gordon, John Watson 1788–1864
John Smith, Master of Trinity House (1833–1856) 1850
oil on canvas 125 x 100
TRH037

Gordon, John Watson (circle of) 1788–1864
Captain Walter Smith, Master Member of Trinity House 19th C
oil on canvas 90 x 69.5
TRH431

Granges, David des 1611–after 1670
Charles II (1630–1685) (after Adriaen Hanneman)
oil on canvas 70 x 58
EDIN007 (P)

Hardie, Charles Martin 1858–1916
Mr Abraham Howling, Master of Trinity House (1901–1902) 1902
oil on canvas 125.5 x 100.5
TRH031

Hemy, Bernard Benedict 1845–1913
A Tug Towing a Sailing Boat 1891
oil on canvas 50 x 75
TRH004

Hemy, Bernard Benedict 1845–1913
An Estuary Scene 1891
oil on canvas 50 x 75
TRH003

Hill, David Octavius 1802–1870
A View of Leith 1828
oil on board 27.5 x 37
TRH007

Jamesone, George (attributed to)
c.1586–1644
John Erskine (c.1585–1654), 3rd Earl of Mar,
Lord High Treasurer
oil on canvas 70 x 60
PPD211 (P)

Kneller, Godfrey (studio of) 1646–1723
John Erskine (1675–1732), 6th Earl of Mar
oil on canvas 125 x 99
PPD213 (P)

Lely, Peter (after) 1618–1680
Charles II (1630–1685)
oil on canvas 203 x 134.5
EDIN035

Madison, James N.
The Highland Charge of Drummossie Moor
(The Battle of Culloden, 16 April 1746) 1979
oil on canvas 121 x 183
NHS342 (P)

McLean, J. W.
The SS 'Venus'
oil on canvas 60 x 90
TRH015

Miller, William c.1740–c.1810
Mr Robert Innes, Treasurer of Trinity House
(1734–1773) 1773
oil on canvas 123 x 101
TRH044

Mitchell, A.
A View of the Port of Leith with Arthur's Seat
in the Distance 1880
oil on canvas 50 x 75
TRH002

Mitchell, A.
The Port of Leith
oil on canvas 50 x 75
TRH001

Monro, Hugh 1873–1928
James VI (1566–1625) (after Cornelis Janssens
van Ceulen) 1928
oil on panel 65 x 50
EDIN004

Facing page: Robertson, Eric Harald Macbeth, 1887–1941, *Shellburst*, City of Edinburgh Council (p. 88)

Mytens, Daniel I (after) c.1590–before 1648
Mary, Queen of Scots (1542–1587) 17th C
oil on panel 70.5 x 54
TRH032

Percival, Harold 1868–1914
The Ship 'Zuleika' of Leith 1897
oil on canvas 45 x 65
TRH016

Raeburn, Henry 1756–1823
Admiral Adam Duncan (1731–1804), 1st Viscount Duncan of Camperdown 1798
oil on canvas 227.5 x 157.5
TRH038

Raeburn, Henry 1756–1823
Mr George Smith, Master of Trinity House (1796–1805) 1807
oil on canvas 74 x 62
TRH028

Raeburn, Henry 1756–1823
Mr John Hay, Master of Trinity House (1808–1820) 1820
oil on canvas 74 x 61.5
TRH043

Raeburn, Henry 1756–1823
Peter Wood (1749–1846), Whaleship Owner
oil on canvas 126 x 98.5
TRH045

Ritchie, Thomas L. active 1837–1865
Mr Walter Paton, Master of Trinity House (1856–1868) 1862
oil on canvas 125 x 100
TRH040

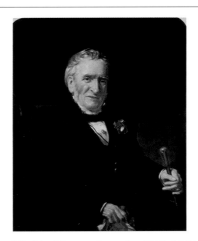

Ritchie, Thomas L. active 1837–1865
Captain Archibald Ritchie, Master Member of Trinity House 1865
oil on canvas 100 x 75
TRH035

Robertson, Charles Kay d.1939
Mr Francis Riddell 1892
oil on canvas 141 x 100.5
TRH033

Robertson, Nora
Captain William M. Reid, Master of Trinity House (1960–1964) 1972
oil on canvas 14.8 x 13.7
TRH1049

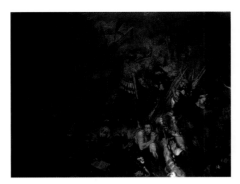

Scott, David 1806–1849
Vasco da Gama Encountering the Spirit of the Storm 1842
oil on canvas 406.4 x 533.4
TRH434

Somer, Paulus van I (after) 1576–1621
James VI (1566–1625)
oil on canvas 243.8 x 121.9
PPD209 (P)

Stanfield, Clarkson 1793–1867
A Busy Shipping Lane off Liverpool
oil on canvas 90 x 150
TRH006

Sutherland, David Macbeth 1883–1973
Captain Cromarty 1924
oil on canvas 75 x 62.5
TRH036

unknown artist 17th C
John Erskine (d.1572), 1st Earl of Mar, Regent of Scotland (copy after an earlier painting)
oil on canvas 140 x 104.5
PPD212 (P)

unknown artist
View of Edinburgh Castle c.1746
oil on canvas 103.5 x 92.5
EDIN017

unknown artist 18th C
Louisa Maria von Stolberg-Golden (1753–1824), Countess of Albany (copy after an earlier painting by an unknown artist)
oil on canvas 79 x 68
EDIN009

unknown artist
View of Newhaven from Forth c.1850
oil on canvas 57.5 x 120
TRH005

unknown artist
The 'Warrior' 1860
oil on canvas 37.5 x 50.5
TRH489

unknown artist 19th C
The Lighthouse Tender SS 'Pharos'
oil on canvas 50 x 75
TRH021

unknown artist
James VI (1566–1625)
oil on panel 44 x 34
EDIN043

unknown artist
Mary, Queen of Scots (1542–1587)
oil on canvas 85.5 x 73.2
EDIN030

unknown artist
'North Carr' Light Vessel
oil on canvas 27.2 x 37.5
TRH481

unknown artist
Prince Henry Stuart, Cardinal York (1724–1807) (copy after an earlier painting by an unknown artist)
oil on canvas 37.3 x 31.5
EDIN012

unknown artist
The 'Ben Ledi'
oil on canvas 54.5 x 70
TRH490

unknown artist
The Miller's Wharf, London
oil on canvas 35 x 42.5
TRH018

unknown artist
Twin Funnel Paddle Steamer
oil on canvas 42 x 59
TRH535

Vanson, Adrian (attributed to)
d. before 1610
James VI (1566–1625) 1585
oil on panel 83 x 62
EDIN038

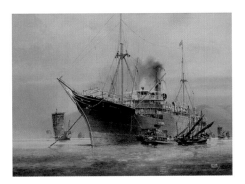

Verity, Colin b.1924
The 'Benavon'
oil on canvas 54 x 69
TRH491

Ward, Edward Matthew 1816–1879
*The Last Sleep of Argyll before His Execution,
1685* 1857
oil on canvas 142 x 167.5
EDIN046

Wright, John Michael (attributed to)
1617–1694
*Lady Anne Bruce, Daughter of the 2nd Earl of
Elgin, Robert Bruce (...)* 1665–1670s
oil on canvas 122 x 97
PPD001 (P)

Wright, John Michael (attributed to)
1617–1694
James VII and II (1633–1701)
oil on canvas 117 x 102
PPD002 (P)

Young, Edward Drummond 1877–1946
*Captain William Wright, Master of Trinity
House (1939–1947)* 1945
oil on canvas 75 x 62.5
TRH041

Young, Edward Drummond 1877–1946
*Captain Robert Meikle, JP, Master of Trinity
House (1927–1937)*
oil on canvas 72 x 61.5
TRH430

The University of Edinburgh Fine Art Collection

The University of Edinburgh holds approximately 1,400 works of art in its collections, which are focused on Dutch and Flemish art of the seventeenth and eighteenth centuries, Scottish portraits, and contemporary Scottish art. A large percentage of works in the Collection can be seen on display throughout the University, enhancing public, private and student spaces, and select works are used in exhibitions at the Talbot Rice Gallery, the University's art gallery. Many of the most important portraits and modern works are on view in public spaces spread across the University, from Old College at the heart of Edinburgh, to the Chancellor's Building.

The Torrie Collection is perhaps the most well known of the University's collections. Sir James Erskine, 3rd Baronet of Torrie was born in 1772 at Torrie House in Fife. He was a successful professional soldier as well as a collector and an amateur artist. He served with Wellington in the Napoleonic Wars and was personal secretary to King George III between 1802 and 1804. He bequeathed the collection of works kept in his London house to the University in 1824, and it eventually came to the University on the death of his brother, John Drummond Erskine, in 1836. The collection consists of Dutch and Flemish landscape painting, Italian painting and sculpture, and a number of Renaissance bronzes. Outstanding works include Jacob van Ruisdael's, *The Banks of a River*, currently on loan to the National Gallery of Scotland, Jan Steen's *The Doctor's Visit*, and David Teniers II's *Peasants Playing Bowls*. Of the sculpture collection, the two outstanding works are the Écorché Horse, attributed to Giambologna (considered by some as the centrepiece of the collection), and the group of Cain and Abel by Adriaen de Vries.

The Portrait and Bust Collection includes 400 portraits assembled over the 400 years of the University's history, and is second only in scope and quality in Scotland to the Scottish National Portrait Gallery. Most of the portraits in the Collection represent historical figures connected to the University, augmented by recent commissions such as the bust of the Chancellor, HRH the Duke of Edinburgh, and the portrait of renowned physicist Professor Peter Higgs by Ken Currie. Painters represented include David Scougall, John Watson Gordon, Alberto Morrocco, Stanley Cursiter and Sir Henry Raeburn, whose works are showcased in a room in the Old College. Of particular note is the portrait of *Robert Trotter (c.1750–1807)* by David Martin, and the portrait of *John Knox (c.1510–1572)* by an unknown artist, said to be the first representation of his features. Sculptors include William Brodie, John Steell and Francis Chantry.

Originally works assembled to furnish offices, the University's Modern Scottish Art Collection holds a significant number of important works by renowned artists. This section includes the Talbot Rice Memorial Collection, the Scottish Arts Council Bequest, the Chancellor's Building Picture Collection and the larger part of the Hope Scott Bequest. Artists represented include Joan Kathleen Harding Eardley, Anne Redpath, James Cowie, Elizabeth V. Blackadder, George Leslie Hunter, Francis Campbell Boileau Cadell, Samuel John Peploe, William MacTaggart, David McClure, John McLean, Talbert McLean and Ann Oram as well as works not executed in oil, acrylic and tempera, and so not included in this catalogue, by artists such as Willie Rodger, David Michie, John Houston, Alastair Mack, Paul Furneaux, David Foggie and

Barbara Rae. Artists John Bellany, Elizabeth V. Blackadder, Alan Davie and, not included in this catalogue, Jake Harvey, have made important gifts of their own work. A bequest given through the Scottish Arts Council consists of eight works including paintings by Penelope Beaton, Ivor Davies, Talbert McLean, Kenneth Dingwall, John Mooney and, outside the scope of this catalogue, William Wilson.

Hope Montague Douglas Scott was a member of the Younger family of Scottish brewers and the wife of the grandson of the 5th Duke of Buccleuch. Following her death in 1989, her collection of paintings was bequeathed to the University of Edinburgh. The smaller part of this collection consists of five small works by artists of international repute: Max Ernst, Kees van Dongen, Maurice Utrillo, Pablo Picasso and Pierre Bonnard, although these last two are not executed in oil, acrylic and tempera and so fall outside the scope of this catalogue. The larger part of the Hope Scott Bequest consists mainly of a group of works by William Johnstone, the innovative Scottish abstract painter whose work has been influential to the current generation of artists in Scotland. Twenty oil paintings including *Red Spring* as well as works by other artists were included in the bequest along with a large group of drawings and prints. The Hope Scott Bequest also includes other works representative of twentieth-century Scottish painting and includes oils by Joan Kathleen Harding Eardley, Samuel John Peploe and David Abercrombie Donaldson as well as works on paper by William George Gillies, Francis Campbell Boileau Cadell and Alan Davie.

Friends and former pupils of David Talbot Rice (1903–1972), CBE, Watson Gordon Professor of Fine Arts at the University of Edinburgh (1934–1972), commemorated him by giving to the University works of art either from their own collections, or, in the case of practising artists, examples of their own work. This idea was conceived by the late Dr Harold Fletcher, who remembered that, on an occasion when he bought a picture by John Houston, Professor Rice said he wished he could have bought it for the University. Dr Fletcher donated this picture, which unfortunately falls outside the scope of this catalogue, and many friends and former pupils have followed suit. Altogether, some 20 oils and watercolours have so far been donated by friends, colleagues and former students.

This Collection has Full Accreditation status with the Museums, Libraries and Archives Council. Conservation and other work is supported by grants from Museums Galleries Scotland, and the collections continue to grow. The current focus is on commissioning or acquiring works which contribute to the dispersed nature of the Collection, or for new building projects, enriching the cultural environment of the campus and enhancing the University's role in teaching, research and service.

The Chancellor's Building Picture Collection was formed in 2003 by the Art Committee of the Faculty of Medicine to decorate the public and private rooms of the Chancellor's Building, the University's new medical school, opened in 2002. In 2007, a collection of Palozzi prints, works and sculptures was acquired for the new Informatics Forum. Alec Finlay's *Interleaved* (mesostic circle poem), 2008, is a text-based permanent installation at the entrance of the University's newly renovated Main Library, fittingly composed from a quotation by Clement Litill, its founder.

Jacky MacBeath, Museums Development Manager

Aikman, John active c.1712–1731
William Carstares (1649–1715) c.1712
oil on canvas 127 x 101.5
EU0003

Aikman, William 1682–1731
Landscape with a River
oil on canvas 50 x 75
EU0539

Alison, David 1882–1955
Adam Cleghorn Welch (1864–1943)
before 1935
oil on canvas 101 x 76
EU0418 (P)

Alison, David 1882–1955
James Walker (1864–1922)
oil on canvas 111.7 x 86.3
EU0047

Alison, David 1882–1955
Robert William Johnstone (1879–1969)
oil on canvas 101 x 75
EU0437

Alison, David 1882–1955
Sir John Rankine (1846–1922)
oil on canvas 101 x 76
EU0099

Allan, David (attributed to) 1744–1796
Professor Francis Home (1719–1813)
oil on canvas 71 x 55
EU0445

Allan, William 1782–1850
Fair Maid of Perth
oil on panel 47.5 x 71.5
Corson P.2687

Anderson, J. Alasdair active 1972
Blair Atholl, Perthshire and Kinross
oil on canvas 34 x 24
EU0227

Facing page: Thomson, Adam Bruce, 1885–1976, *North Bridge and Salisbury Crags, Edinburgh, from the North West,*
City of Edinburgh Council (p. 98)

Asper, Hans Kaspar (after)
1592–before 1655
Johannes Œcolampadius (1482–1531)
c.1650–c.1696
oil on panel 56 x 37
EU0206

Asper, Hans Kaspar (after)
1592–before 1655
Ulrich Zwingli (1484–1531) 17th C
oil on panel 60.3 x 38.1
EU0209

Backhuysen, Ludolf I 1630–1708
A Squall: A Lugger Running into Harbour
oil on canvas 43.5 x 58.8
EU0701

Baillie, William James b.1923
Table with Violins 1961
oil on canvas 71 x 91
EU0868

Baillie, William James b.1923
Harbour Still Life
acrylic on canvas 50 x 70 (E)
EU1027

Baldi, Lazzaro c.1623–1703
Battle Piece (after Giulio Romano)
oil on canvas 64 x 48
EU0714

Barclay, John MacLaren 1811–1886
Anthony Hall (model for golden boy on the
dome of Old College)
oil on canvas 84 x 42.5
EU0281

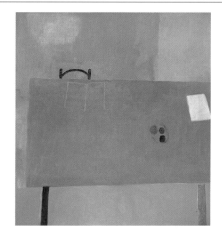

Barrett, John Macdonald
Untitled
oil on canvas 182 x 166.5
PCF18

Barrie, Mardi 1931–2004
Harbour Evening
oil on canvas 39.5 x 49.5
EU0491

Barrie, Mardi 1931–2004
Harbour Wall
oil on canvas 74.5 x 100
EU0759

Barrie, Mardi 1931–2004
Off Shore
oil on canvas 90 x 69.5
EU0758

Barrie, Mardi 1931–2004
Scunthorpe, North Lincolnshire, II
oil on board 40 x 44.5
EU0471

Beaton, Penelope 1886–1963
Fruit
oil on canvas 62 x 74
EU0860

Bellany, John b.1942
Lovers by the Sea
oil on canvas 152 x 152
EU0762

Bellucci, Giovanni Battista (attributed to) 1684–1760
Portrait of an Unknown Man (possibly Robert Moubray) c.1740–1760
oil on canvas 74 x 61
EU0248

Berchem, Nicolaes 1620–1683
A Herdsman Driving Cattle down a Lane
oil on panel 24 x 31
EU0703

Berchem, Nicolaes 1620–1683
Cattle in a Stream, with a Herd Boy Resting
oil on panel 31 x 25
EU0702

Beveridge, M.
Welders
oil on canvas 125 x 230 (E)
EU1006

Blackadder, Elizabeth V. b.1931
Figures at Night 1966
oil & pastel on board 24 x 33.5
EU0328

Blackadder, Elizabeth V. b.1931
Ochre House 1966
oil on canvas 69 x 89.5
EU0765

Blackadder, Elizabeth V. b.1931
Sir David Smith (b.1930) 1994
oil on canvas 119 x 110.5
EU0044

Blackadder, Elizabeth V. b.1931
Staffin, Skye
oil on canvas 108 x 158
EU0544

Blackadder, Elizabeth V. b.1931
Walltown, Northumberland (Roman Wall)
oil on canvas 85.5 x 111
EU0763

Bond, Marj b.1939
*White House in a Warm Perthshire
Valley* 1980
oil on panel 75 x 75
EU0873

Bond, Marj b.1939
Three Figures in a Landscape
oil on panel 37 x 37
EU0872

Bond, Marj b.1939
Undulating Perthshire
oil on board 50 x 50
EU0871

Bonnar, Wiliam 1800–1855
Interior Scene, Woman with a Knife 1835
oil on canvas 69 x 87
PCF9

Borthwick, Alfred Edward 1871–1955
Andrew Seth Pringle-Pattison (1856–1931)
1925
oil on canvas 147 x 109
EU0062

Borthwick, Alfred Edward 1871–1955
Sir Francis Albert Ely Crew (1886–1973)
(sketch)
oil on canvas 90 x 70
EU0460

Borthwick, Alfred Edward 1871–1955
Sir Francis Albert Ely Crew (1886–1973) 1956
oil on canvas 106 x 76
EU0531

Borthwick, Alfred Edward 1871–1955
A Rocky Landscape
oil on canvas 101.5 x 124.5
EU0304

Borthwick, Alfred Edward 1871–1955
*Sir Alexander Gray (1882–1968), CBE, MA,
LLD*
oil on canvas 75 x 62.5
EU0232

Both, Andries Dirksz. (attributed to)
1611/1612–1641
A Rocky Landscape with Figures, Sunset
oil on panel 47 x 58
EU0704

Both, Jan c.1618–1652
Landscape with Figures
oil on panel 106 x 101.5
EU0705

Both, Jan c.1618–1652
Landscape with Mounted Figures
oil on panel 40.5 x 54
EU0706

Bough, Samuel 1822–1878
Harbour Scene
oil on canvas 20 x 27.5
EU0609

Bourne, Peter b.1931
The Old Gable 1986
oil on board 59 x 61
PCF19

British School 19th C
Landscape
oil on canvas 60 x 90
EU0316

Bronckhorst, Arnold (after) c.1566–1586
George Buchanan (1506–1582)
oil on canvas 71 x 56
EU0002

Bronckhorst, Arnold (after) c.1566–1586
George Buchanan (1506–1582)
oil on panel 45.7 x 27.9
EU0214

Brown, John Caldwell b.1945
Hugh MacDiarmid (1892–1978) 1968
oil on canvas 80 x 75
EU0489

Burns, William Alexander 1921–1972
Seakirk 1
oil on hardboard 76 x 101.5
EU0466

Cadell, Francis Campbell Boileau
1883–1937
Mountain Landscape
oil on canvas 35.5 x 44.5
EU0619

Calderwood, William Leadbetter
1865–1950
Charles Saroléa (1870–1953) 1924
oil on canvas 139.7 x 88.9
EU0290

Calvert, Edward 1799–1883
Alexander Monro 'Secundus' (1733–1817)
oil on canvas 46.5 x 36.5
EU0456

Cameron, Hugh 1835–1918
Dumbiedykes and Jeanie Dean's
oil on canvas 29 x 44.5
PCF14

Cameron, Mary 1864–1921
Alexander Inglis McCallum (1845–1921)
oil on canvas 127 x 101.5
EU0936

Carlisle, Fionna b.1954
Professor Sir Kenneth Murray and Lady Noreen Murray (b.1935) 2009
oil on canvas 111 x 109
EU1279

Carrick, Anne b.1919
Evening Sky over Rum 1960
oil on canvas 49 x 59
EU0543

Carse, Alexander c.1770–1843
Covenanters in a Glen c.1800
oil on canvas 69 x 89.5
EU0608

Caw, James Lewis 1864–1950
Sir John Leslie (1766–1832) (copy after David Wilkie)
oil on panel 47.5 x 34.5
EU0949

Christie, James Elder 1847–1914
Mary Dick (1791–1883)
oil on canvas 127 x 101
EU0929

Cockburn, Tim b.1955
Law Faculty
oil on canvas 106 x 106
PCF2

Cockburn, Tim b.1955
Sir Thomas Broun Smith (1915–1988)
oil on canvas 74.5 x 61.5
EU0098

Collet, Ruth 1909–2001
A Conversation
oil on canvas 39.5 x 29
EU0271

Convery, Francis b.1956
Holy Isle
oil on canvas 91.5 x 106
EU0882

Courtois, Jacques 1621–1676
A Battle Scene
oil on panel 34 x 57
EU0707

Courtois, Jacques 1621–1676
Skirmish
oil on panel 34.5 x 57.5
EU0708

Cowie, James 1886–1956
Hugh Watt (1879–1968)
oil on canvas 100.5 x 90
EU0417

Cowie, James 1886–1956
The Blue Shirt
oil on canvas 66 x 55.5
EU0776

Crabb, William 1811–1876
Sir William Fraser (1816–1898) 1869
oil on canvas 60.5 x 50.5
EU0053

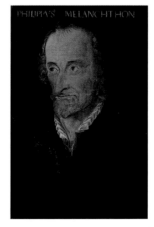

Cranach, Lucas the elder (after) 1472–1553
Philip Melanchthon (1497–1560)
oil on panel 57.7 x 39.3
EU0205

Crawford, Edmund Thornton 1806–1885
Watermill
oil on canvas 29.5 x 39.5
EU0607

Crome, William Henry 1806–1873
Wooded Landscape 1845
oil on canvas 55 x 80 (E)
EU0559

Crowe, Victoria b.1945
John McIntyre (1916–2005) 1986
oil on canvas 108 x 76.5
EU0419

Crowe, Victoria b.1945
Dr Ann Matheson 2009
oil on canvas 76 x 71
EU1284

Crozier, William 1893–1930
Via Piero della Francesca, Sansepolcro, Italy
1929
oil on canvas 59.5 x 45
EU0600

Cruikshank, Robert Isaac 1789–1856
William Patrick of Roughwood (1770–1861)
(after Colvin Smith)
oil on canvas 141 x 111
EU0295

Cuming, William 1769–1852
Sir John Macpherson (c.1745–1821) (after
Joshua Reynolds) after 1781
oil on canvas 76 x 63.5
EU0028

Cuming, William 1769–1852
Sir William Fettes (1750–1836) (after Henry
Raeburn)
oil on canvas 91 x 71
EU0048

Cumming, James 1922–1991
Peat and Paraffin
oil on canvas 132 x 102
EU0562

Cumming, James 1922–1991
The Invalid
oil on board 29.5 x 46.5
EU0219

Currie, Ken b.1960
Peter Higgs (b.1929) 2008
oil on canvas 197 x 274
EU1249

Cursiter, Stanley 1887–1976
Dr Orlando Charnock Bradley (1871–1937)
1936
oil on canvas 127 x 101
EU0917

Cursiter, Stanley 1887–1976
Dr Orlando Charnock Bradley (1871–1937)
1936
oil on canvas 45 x 36
EU0918

Cursiter, Stanley 1887–1976
Sir Donald Pollock (1868–1962) 1941
oil on canvas 127 x 101
EU0092

Cursiter, Stanley 1887–1976
Sir Thomas Henry Holland (1868–1947) 1944
oil on canvas 127 x 109
EU0097

Cursiter, Stanley 1887–1976
Sir Thomas Henry Holland (1868–1947) 1944
oil on canvas 89.5 x 69.5
EU0538

Cursiter, Stanley 1887–1976
William Curtis (1876–1961) 1949
oil on canvas 100 x 82.5
EU0407

Cursiter, Stanley 1887–1976
Sir Donald Pollock (1868–1962) 1952
oil on canvas 93 x 127
EU0536

Cursiter, Stanley 1887–1976
Dr John Gillies (1870–1952)
oil on canvas 125 x 100
EU0980

Facing page: Home, Bruce James, 1830–1912, *Brodie's Close, Edinburgh*, City of Edinburgh Council (p. 46)

Cursiter, Stanley 1887–1976
Sir Donald Pollock (1868–1962) (copy of an
earlier painting)
oil on canvas 124 x 99
EU0957

Davie, Alan b.1920
The Golden Palace 1999
oil on board 30 x 37.5
EU0782

Davie, Alan b.1920
Kaleidoscope for a Parrot
oil on canvas 190 x 300 (E)
EU0773

Davies, Ivor b.1935
White Landscape with Sky Forms
acrylic on canvas 152 x 152
EU0861

Delacour, William 1700–1767
Landscape* (triptych, left wing)
oil on plaster 100 x 70 (E)
EU0892

Delacour, William 1700–1767
Landscape* (triptych, centre panel)
oil on plaster 85 x 100 (E)
EU0893

Delacour, William 1700–1767
Landscape* (triptych, right wing)
oil on plaster 100 x 70 (E)
EU0894

Dingwall, Kenneth b.1938
Between Dark and Dark
oil on canvas 160 x 213.5
EU0778

Dingwall, Kenneth b.1938
Calm Grey
acrylic on canvas 160 x 213
EU0862

Dobson, Cowan 1894–1980
*Sir Leybourne Stanley Patrick Davidson
(1894–1981)* 1941
oil on canvas 49.5 x 39.5
EU0433

Domenichino (after) 1581–1641
The Martyrdom of Saint Andrew
oil on canvas 33.5 x 43.5
EU0709

Donald, George Malcolm b.1943
Gladys Davis (b.c.1940) 2006
oil on canvas 100 x 75
EU1042

Donaldson, David Abercrombie 1916–1996
Nude (Birth of Venus) 1963
oil on panel 18.5 x 18.5
EU0177

Dongen, Kees van 1877–1968
A Vase of Flowers 1920
oil on canvas 26 x 21.5
EU0102

Dughet, Gaspard 1615–1675
Land Storm
oil on canvas 53 x 79.5
EU0728

Dujardin, Karel 1626–1678
Halt at an Italian Winehouse Door
1675–1678
oil on canvas 81 x 89.6
EU0719

Dujardin, Karel (style of) 1626–1678
Farrier's Shop
oil on canvas 36.5 x 42
EU0720

Duncan, John 1866–1945
Unicorns 1933
tempera on canvas 87.5 x 166
EU0779

Dunn, John active 1768–1841
William Dick (1793–1866)
oil on canvas 128 x 101.5
EU0932

Dutch School (attributed to)
Portrait of an Unknown Man with a Jewelled, Plumed Hat 1650–1700 (?)
oil on canvas 56 x 44.5
EU0270

Dyce, William 1806–1864
John Small (1828–1886) and His Son
oil on canvas 76 x 63.5
EU0487

Dyce, William 1806–1864
Nicholson Bain (c.1787–1840)
oil on canvas 74.5 x 62
EU0490

Dyck, Anthony van (style of) 1599–1641
Alexander Henderson (c.1583–1646) 17th C
oil on panel 59.6 x 51.4
EU0213

Eardley, Joan Kathleen Harding 1921–1963
Back Street Bookie 1952
oil on canvas 107.5 x 59.5
EU0780

Eardley, Joan Kathleen Harding 1921–1963
Bagged Potatoes
oil on board 42 x 16
EU0178

Eardley, Joan Kathleen Harding 1921–1963
January Flow Tide
oil on board 88 x 156
EU0070

Ernst, Max 1891–1976
Antediluvian Landscape
oil on board 15 x 20.5
EU0103

Ewart, David Shanks 1901–1965
Sir John Fraser (1885–1947) 1948
oil on canvas 110 x 86
EU0040

Feledi, Tivadar 1852–1896
Man on a Horse
oil on board 32 x 24
EU1033

Fenwick, Thomas active 1835–1850
Late Autumn Landscape c.1850
oil on panel 24 x 29
EU0610

Ferguson, William active 1835–1850
A Beach in Coll
oil on board 24 x 34
EU0783

Ferguson, William active 1835–1850
Near Drem, East Lothian
oil on board 24.5 x 34
EU0784

Firth, Helen active late 20th C
Kettle
oil on canvas 100.5 x 49
EU0884

Fleming, John B. 1792–1845
The Clyde
oil on canvas 133 x 207
EU0612

Forbes, Phillippa
Major Christopher Henry John Deighton (b.1898)
oil on canvas 91 x 71
EU0532

Fraser, Alexander 1827–1899
Harvest Scene
oil on panel 20 x 31
EU0622

Gear, William 1915–1997
Untitled 1959
acrylic & watercolour on paper 23.5 x 31
EU0975

Gear, William 1915–1997
October Landscape
oil on canvas 72 x 54
EU0859

Geddes, Andrew (attributed to) 1783–1844
Professor James Home (1758–1842)
oil on canvas 76 x 53
EU0447

Geddes, Andrew (style of) 1783–1844
Ann Duncan (d.1851), Later Mrs James Home
oil on canvas 76 x 52
EU0443

Geddes, Andrew (style of) 1783–1844
George Husband Baird (1761–1840)
oil on canvas 127 x 101.5
EU0018

German School (attributed to)
Martin Bucer (1491–1551) c.1650–1689
oil on panel 48.2 x 34.2
EU0203

German School (attributed to)
Theodore Beza (1519–1605) c.1650–1689
oil on panel 60.9 x 44.4
EU0208

German School (attributed to)
John Calvin (1509–1564) c.1650–c.1696
oil on panel 60 x 40 (E)
EU0210

Ghisolfi, Giovanni c.1623–1683
Architectural Composition
oil on canvas 117 x 96
EU0712

Ghisolfi, Giovanni c.1623–1683
Ruins and Figures
oil on canvas 116.5 x 96.5
EU0713

Gillespie
The Lady of Avenil Leaving
oil on canvas 18.5 x 16
Corson P.2574

Gillies, William George 1898–1973
St Monans, East Neuk of Fife (Sketch) 1932
oil on canvas 39 x 55
EU0087

Gillies, William George 1898–1973
Landscape with a House and a Field 1961
oil on canvas 80 x 99
EU0226

Gordon, Cora Josephine 1879–1950
Italian Landscape
oil on canvas 38 x 46
EU0300

Gordon, John Watson 1788–1864
Reverend Alexander Brunton (1772–1854)
1846
oil on canvas 203 x 142
EU0020

Gordon, John Watson 1788–1864
John Inglis (1810–1891) 1854
oil on canvas 236 x 144.5
EU0019

Gordon, John Watson 1788–1864
HRH Edward, Prince of Wales (1841–1910)
1859
oil on canvas 75 x 48
EU0052

Gordon, John Watson 1788–1864
Sir James Young Simpson (1811–1870) c.1860
oil on canvas 127 x 101
EU0441

Gordon, John Watson 1788–1864
Alexander Monro 'Tertius' (1773–1859)
oil on canvas 90 x 70
EU0438

Gordon, John Watson 1788–1864
Andrew Duncan (1744–1828)
oil on canvas 127 x 101
EU0434

Gordon, John Watson 1788–1864
George Dunbar (1774–1851)
oil on canvas 127 x 101.5
EU0056

Gordon, John Watson 1788–1864
John Lee (1779–1859)
oil on canvas 133.5 x 109
EU0007

Gordon, John Watson 1788–1864
John Lee (1779–1859)
oil on canvas 238 x 149
EU0023

Gordon, John Watson 1788–1864
Sir David Baxter of Kilmaron (1793–1872)
oil on canvas 91 x 71
EU0049

Graham, Thomas Alexander Ferguson
1840–1906
John Girdwood (1863–1933)
oil on canvas 70.5 x 57
EU0292

Grant, Francis 1803–1878
*Margaret Stuart Tyndall-Bruce of Falkland
(1788–1869)* 1863
oil on canvas 213 x 127
EU0021

Grant, Thomas F. (attributed to)
active 1868–1879
Edinburgh from Calton Hill
oil on canvas 112 x 185
EU0613

Facing page: Cadell, Francis Campbell Boileau 1883–1937, *The Black Hat*, City of Edinburgh Council (p. 14)

Gray, Gary
At the Bank
oil on canvas 50 x 40
EU0885

Green, Kenneth 1905–1986
Sir Herbert John Clifford Grierson (1866–1960)
1935
oil on canvas 100.5 x 75
EU0302

Greuze, Jean-Baptiste 1725–1805
Interior of a Cottage
oil on panel 63.5 x 80.5
EU0715

Guthrie, James 1859–1930
Marcus Dods (1834–1909) 1906
oil on canvas 106 x 81
EU0409 (P)

Guthrie, James 1859–1930
Sir William Turner (1832–1916) 1912
oil on canvas 132 x 114
EU0094

Haig, George Douglas 1918–2009
Leader in Spate
oil on canvas 85 x 110.5
EU0864

Haig, George Douglas 1918–2009
Pigeons at Frascati, Italy
oil on canvas 84.5 x 150
EU0303

Halliday, John Alexander b.1933
A Wet Day, Kirkcudbright 1968
oil on canvas 50 x 60.5
EU0179

Hals, Frans (after) c.1581–1666
Portrait of a Man Holding a Skull
oil on canvas 91 x 72
EU0442

Harris, Tomás 1908–1964
Mallorca Series No.2 1953
oil on board 44.5 x 36.5
EU1030

Harris, Tomás 1908–1964
Mallorca Series No.3 1953
oil on board 41.5 x 33.5
EU1031

Harris, Tomás 1908–1964
Mallorca Series No.4 1953
oil on canvas 45 x 37.5
EU0266

Harris, Tomás 1908–1964
Mallorca Series No.5 1953
oil on board 52.5 x 43.5
EU0789

Harris, Tomás 1908–1964
Mallorca Series No.7 1953
oil on panel 67 x 70
EU1007

Harris, Tomás 1908–1964
Mallorca Series No.8 1953
oil on panel 67 x 70
EU1008

Harris, Tomás 1908–1964
Mallorca Series No.9 1953
oil on panel 65 x 186
EU1009

Harris, Tomás 1908–1964
Mallorca Series No.10 1953
oil on canvas 133 x 103
EU0791

Hector, James A. H. 1868–1940
Sir Patrick Geddes (1854–1932) 1919
oil on canvas 91.5 x 71
EU0940

Henderson, Keith 1883–1982
Study for 'Waulking Songs'
oil on panel 17.5 x 25
EU0615

Henderson, Keith 1883–1982
Women Singing at a Table (Waulking the Cloth)
oil on canvas 101.6 x 152.4
EU0614

Heyden, Jan van der 1637–1712
Wooded Park Landscape with Deer
oil on panel 22 x 28.7
EU0716

Hobbema, Meindert (attributed to) 1638–1709
A Wooded River Valley with Two Fishermen
oil on panel 46 x 66.5
EU0718

Hobbema, Meindert (style of) 1638–1709
A Woody Lane, with a Thatched Cottage and a Pool 1659
oil on panel 51 x 91
EU0717

Home, Robert 1865–after 1921
Sir Thomas Richard Fraser (1841–1920) 1919
oil on canvas 111 x 85
EU0293

Hope, R.
The Guitarist
oil on panel 24 x 28.5
PCF8

Hunter, George Leslie 1877–1931
Blue Vase
oil on board 66 x 53
EU0073

Hunter, George Leslie 1877–1931
Still Life (Four Creamy Roses in a Blue Vase)
oil on canvas 49 x 34.5
EU0074

Hutchison, William Oliphant 1889–1970
Sir Sydney Alfred Smith (1883–1969) 1953
oil on canvas 117 x 97
EU0045

Hutchison, William Oliphant 1889–1970
Sir Edward Victor Appleton (1892–1965) 1957
oil on canvas 121 x 100
EU0039

Hutchison, William Oliphant 1889–1970
John Baillie (1886–1960)
oil on canvas 77 x 63.5
EU0403

Imrie, Archibald Brown 1900–c.1968
Arthur Cyril William Hutchison (1889–1969)
1955
oil on canvas 76 x 63.5
EU0310

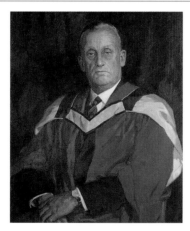

Imrie, Archibald Brown 1900–c.1968
Arthur Cyril William Hutchison (1889–1969)
(copy of an earlier painting) 1958
oil on canvas 76 x 63.5
EU0311

Italian (Roman) School
A Bather
oil on canvas 53 x 43
EU0710

Janssens van Ceulen, Cornelis (attributed to)
1593–1661
James VI and I (1566–1625)
oil on canvas 76 x 63.5
EU0527

Johnstone, Dorothy 1892–1980
September Sunlight 1916
oil on canvas 150 x 106
EU0091

Johnstone, William 1897–1981
Green Fields with Hayricks 1957
oil on canvas 77 x 64
EU0107

Johnstone, William 1897–1981
Red Spring 1958–1959
oil on canvas 80.6 x 139.7
EU0120

Johnstone, William 1897–1981
Black Sitka 1961
oil on canvas 63.5 x 76.2
EU0108

Johnstone, William 1897–1981
Counterswirl, Rain in Ettrick c.1965–1969
oil on canvas 61.5 x 74.2
EU0109

Johnstone, William 1897–1981
East Wind 1969
oil on canvas 139.7 x 246.3
EU0124

Johnstone, William 1897–1981
Morning Haar 1971
oil on canvas 63 x 77
EU0110

Johnstone, William 1897–1981
Untitled c.1971
oil on toilet paper 13.5 x 11.5
EU0135

Johnstone, William 1897–1981
Autumn 1972
oil on board 33 x 23.5
EU0111

Johnstone, William 1897–1981
Autumn 1972
oil on board 27 x 21.5
EU0112

Johnstone, William 1897–1981
Bull with Cows 1972
oil on board 17.5 x 23.5
EU0113

Johnstone, William 1897–1981
Hope Scott 1975
oil on canvas 59 x 49
EU0114

Johnstone, William 1897–1981
Silent Landscape 1975
oil on canvas 137.2 x 243.8
EU0125

Johnstone, William 1897–1981
Portrait Emerging 1976
oil on canvas 88.9 x 90.1
EU0115

Johnstone, William 1897–1981
Border Red c.1976
oil on canvas 69.8 x 90.1
EU0116

Johnstone, William 1897–1981
Fragments of Experience 1979
oil on canvas 133.9 x 243.8
EU0121

Johnstone, William 1897–1981
Terra rossa 1980
oil on canvas 138 x 245
EU0118

Johnstone, William 1897–1981
Diapason c.1980
oil on canvas 167 x 198.5
EU0122

Johnstone, William 1897–1981
The Birth of Venus c.1980
oil on canvas 193 x 137.1
EU0123

Johnstone, William 1897–1981
Abstract Landscape 1981
oil on canvas 120 x 240
EU0119

Johnstone, William 1897–1981
Abstract Composition
oil on board 60.3 x 74.9
EU0106

Johnstone, William 1897–1981
Composition
oil on canvas 69.8 x 90.1
EU0117

Kerr, Henry Wright 1857–1936
William Paterson Paterson (1860–1939) 1903
oil on canvas 75 x 62.5
EU0317

Kerr, Henry Wright 1857–1936
Alexander Martin (1857–1946)
oil on canvas 125 x 89.5
EU0412 (P)

Kerr, Henry Wright 1857–1936
Archibald Kennedy (1847–1938)
oil on canvas 110 x 85
EU0421

Kerr, Henry Wright 1857–1936
The Reverend Thomas Burns
oil on canvas 121 x 95.5
EU0291

Kerr, Henry Wright 1857–1936
William Guy (1859–1950)
oil on canvas 90 x 69.5
EU0312

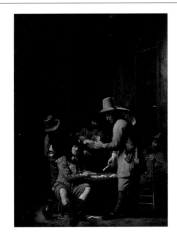

Kick, Simon 1603–1652
Soldiers at Cards
oil on panel 61.5 x 44.5
EU0721

Kininmonth, Caroline 1907–1978
Italian Afternoon
oil on canvas 69.5 x 90
EU0796

Kirkwood, John b.1947
North Sea
oil & mixed media on board 212 x 171
EU1264

Kneller, Godfrey (copy of) 1646–1723
John Locke (1632–1704)
oil on canvas 73.5 x 61.6
EU0027

Knott, Tavernor 1816–1890
William Dick (1793–1866) c.1851
oil on canvas 127 x 101
EU0931

László, Philip Alexius de 1869–1937
Sir Donald Francis Tovey (1875–1940) 1913
oil on board 90 x 69
EU0517

Lauder, Robert Scott 1803–1869
John Wilson (1785–1854)
oil on canvas 228.5 x 152
EU0057

Leeuw, Pieter van der 1647–1679
Landscape with Cattle and Figures 1674
oil on canvas 82.5 x 105.5
EU0722

Lievens, Jan (attributed to) 1607–1674
A Wooded Walk c.1650
oil on canvas 51.5 x 70.5
EU0723

Lingelbach, Johannes (attributed to)
1622–1674
Alehouse Door
oil on canvas 42.5 x 36
EU0724

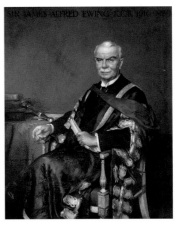

Lintott, Henry John 1877–1965
Sir James Alfred Ewing (1855–1935) 1929
oil on canvas 127 x 101
EU0093

Lintott, Henry John 1877–1965
Joseph Shield Nicholson (1850–1927)
oil on canvas 109 x 83.5
EU0063

Lintott, Henry John (after) 1877–1965
Sir James Alfred Ewing (1855–1935)
oil on canvas 121 x 91
EU0533

Llewellyn, Samuel Henry William
1858–1941
Sir Alexander Grant (1864–1937) 1934–1935
oil on canvas 106 x 86
EU0942

Lorimer, John Henry 1856–1936
James Lorimer (1818–1890) 1878
oil on canvas 127 x 101.5
EU0033

Lorimer, John Henry 1856–1936
John Muir (1838–1914) 1881 & 1889
oil on canvas 127 x 101.5
EU0036

Lorimer, John Henry 1856–1936
Andrew Vans Dunlop (1805–1880) 1883
oil on canvas 74.5 x 62
EU0059

Lorimer, John Henry 1856–1936
Sir Joseph Lister (1827–1912) 1895
oil on canvas 127 x 101
EU0038

Lorimer, John Henry 1856–1936
Archibald Hamilton Charteris (1835–1908)
oil on canvas 134 x 101
EU0406

Lorimer, John Henry 1856–1936
John Stuart Blackie (1809–1895)
oil on canvas 127 x 101.5
EU0031

Facing page: Howe, James, 1780–1836, *The Horse Fair in the Grassmarket, Edinburgh*, City of Edinburgh Council (p. 51)

Lorrain, Claude (after) 1604–1682
Italian Landscape
oil on canvas 102 x 102
EU0551

Lyon, Robert 1894–1978
John MacMurray (1891–1976) 1951
oil on canvas 60 x 50
EU0955

Lyon, Robert 1894–1978
William McGregor Mitchell (1888–1970) 1958
oil on canvas 59.5 x 50
EU0937

Lyon, Robert 1894–1978
John Dover Wilson (1881–1969)
oil on canvas 76.2 x 60.9
EU0973

MacInnes, Ian 1922–2003
George Mackay Brown (1921–1996)
oil on canvas 75 x 65
EU0483

Mackay, Alexander S. 1832–1899
Mary Dick (1791–1883)
oil on canvas 46 x 36
EU0930

Mackie, Charles Hodge 1862–1920
Ella Carmichael Watson (c.1871–1928)
oil on canvas 120 x 95
EU0971

Mackie, George b.1920
Crannoch 1967
oil on canvas 59 x 49
EU0799

MacNee, Daniel 1806–1882
John Hutton Balfour (1808–1884) 1878
oil on canvas 126 x 101
EU0289

MacTaggart, William 1903–1981
Growing Flowers 1959
oil on board 50 x 39.5
EU0428

MacTaggart, William 1903–1981
Building with Spire
oil on board 44.5 x 34
EU1001

MacTaggart, William 1903–1981
Frosty Sunset, Humbie, East Lothian
oil on canvas 91.5 x 102
EU0086

MacTaggart, William 1903–1981
Poppies against a Night Sky
oil on board 64 x 53
EU0089

MacTaggart, William 1903–1981
The Brae Heads
oil on board 49.5 x 60
EU0601

Mainds, Allan Douglass 1881–1945
Vase of Flowers
oil on canvas 38 x 27.5
EU0296

Mann, Catriona b.1955
Boris Semeonoff (1910–1998) 1980
oil on canvas 109.2 x 88.9
EU0965

Martin, David 1736/1737–1798
Joseph Black (1728–1799) c.1770
oil on canvas 73 x 60.5
EU0006

Martin, David 1736/1737–1798
Hugh Blair (1718–1800) c.1775
oil on canvas 75 x 60
EU0029

Martin, David 1736/1737–1798
Robert Trotter (c.1750–1807) 1782
oil on canvas 243.8 x 152.4
EU0061

Maxwell, John 1905–1962
Still Life in the Country 1936
oil on board 63 x 76
EU0286

McClure, David 1926–1998
Fishing Boats 1952
oil on board 36.5 x 44
EU0329

McCulloch, Horatio 1805–1867
Rural Scene
oil on canvas 22 x 25.5
EU0606

McKenzie, George Findlay active 1930–1937
Man Playing a Violin 1930
oil on canvas 50 x 60
EU1037

McKenzie, George Findlay active 1930–1937
Miss Hilda Young 1930
oil on canvas 90.5 x 70
EU1038

McKenzie, George Findlay active 1930–1937
Norman MacCaig (1910–1996) 1937
oil on canvas 90 x 70
EU0605

McLean, John b.1939
Bellahouston, Glasgow 1971
PVA emulsion on canvas 152 x 427
EU0812

McLean, John b.1939
Penicuik, Midlothian 1971
PVA emulsion on canvas 152.5 x 335
EU0813

McLean, John b.1939
Number One (Vertical Painting) 1972
PVA emulsion on canvas 274 x 152.5
EU0811

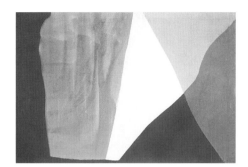

McLean, Talbert 1906–1992
Crudie
oil on canvas 114.5 x 167
EU0865

McLean, Talbert 1906–1992
Dunnichen, Angus
oil & paper on dyed canvas 73 x 92
EU0238

McLean, Talbert 1906–1992
Still Life with a Lamp and Eggs
oil on canvas 65 x 80
EU1041

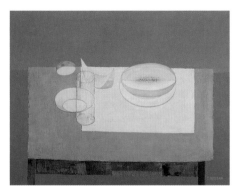

McLean, Talbert 1906–1992
Still Life with a Melon
oil on canvas 69 x 89
EU0239

McNairn, Caroline 1955–2010
Water of Leith
acrylic on canvas 96 x 121
EU0900

McTaggart, William 1835–1910
The Lasswade Road, Edinburgh
oil on canvas 60 x 80 (E)
EU0996

McTaggart, William 1835–1910
Two Children on a Shore
oil on canvas 81 x 62
EU0617

Medina, John 1720–1796
James Thomson (1700–1748) (after John
Patoun) 1774
oil on canvas 76 x 63.5
EU0004

Medina, John Baptist de (style of)
1659–1710
Robert Kerr (1636–1703), 4th Earl and 1st Marquess of Lothian
oil on canvas 73 x 55.5
EU0025

Methuen, Paul Ayshford 1886–1974
George Square, South East Corner, Edinburgh
1958
oil on canvas 49.5 x 64
EU0901

Methuen, Paul Ayshford 1886–1974
George Square, South Side, Edinburgh 1958
oil on canvas 82.5 x 114
EU0599

Methuen, Paul Ayshford 1886–1974
Old College Quadrangle, Edinburgh 1958
oil on canvas 101.5 x 77
EU0072

Meulen, Adam Frans van der
1631/1632–1690
A Cavalcade
oil on canvas 60.5 x 83
EU0725

Miereveld, Michiel Jansz. van (after)
1567–1641
Maurice of Nassau (1567–1625), Prince of Orange 17th C
oil on panel 59.7 x 46.9
EU0212

Miereveld, Michiel Jansz. van (after)
1567–1641
Frederick Count Palatine (1596–1632)
oil on canvas 57.5 x 45
EU0938

Moffat, Alexander b.1943
The Right Honourable Michael Meredith Swann (1920–1990) 1974
oil on canvas 150 x 120
EU0042

Mooney, John b.1948
Cornucopia
acrylic on canvas 182.5 x 229
EU0866

Mooney, John b.1948
Salisbury Crags
oil on canvas 121.5 x 121.5
EU0804

Morrice, Alan Fergusson b.1944
Self Portrait with a Friend
oil on canvas 150 x 120
EU0294

Morrison, James b.1932
Fishing Nets No.1 1959
oil on panel 33 x 74
EU0180

Morrocco, Alberto 1917–1998
*Professor Emeritus Nicholas Kemmer
(1911–1998)* 1980
oil on canvas 84 x 74.5
EU0948

Morrocco, Alberto 1917–1998
Sir John Harrison Burnett (1922–2007) 1987
oil on canvas 113 x 121.5
EU0043

Morrocco, Alberto 1917–1998
John Henderson Seaforth Burleigh (1894–1985)
oil on canvas 127 x 111
EU0404

Morrocco, Alberto 1917–1998
*The Honourable Lord Cameron, John
Cameron (1900–1996)*
oil on canvas 127 x 122
EU0096

Mulier, Pieter the elder (attributed to)
c.1615–1670
Sea Piece
oil on canvas 40 x 57
EU0711

Müller, Morten 1828–1911
Nærøyfjord, Norway 1870
oil on canvas 93.5 x 132
EU0228

Murillo, Bartolomé Esteban (style of)
1618–1682
Figure Subject (diptych, left panel)
oil on canvas 133 x 96
EU0541

Murillo, Bartolomé Esteban (style of)
1618–1682
Figure Subject (diptych, right panel)
oil on canvas 133 x 96
EU0540

Mytens, Daniel I (follower of)
c.1590–before 1647
Jack Gills
oil on canvas 71.5 x 58
EU0026

Nasmyth, Alexander (style of) 1758–1840
Robert Burns (1759–1796)
oil on panel 29.5 x 22
EU0602

Nasmyth, Patrick 1787–1831
Edinburgh Castle from the Southwest
oil on canvas 44.5 x 60
EU0974

Naudé, Pieter Hugo 1869–1941
Dr John Brown (1842–1929)
oil on card 29.5 x 23
PCF10

Neeffs, Peeter the elder c.1578–1656–1661
Interior of a Cathedral
oil on panel 29.5 x 39
EU0726

Nicholson, William 1872–1949
Sir Richard Lodge (1855–1936) 1925
oil on canvas 71 x 80
EU0051

Nicholson, William 1872–1949
Sir Richard Lodge (1855–1936) (copy of an earlier painting) 1925
oil on canvas 71 x 80
EU0950

Facing page: Fergusson, John Duncan, 1874–1961, *The Blue Lamp*, City of Edinburgh Council (p. 29)

Nisbet, Alex b.1952
Tiles 1979
oil on canvas 136.5 x 152.5
EU0902

Oever, Hendrick ten 1639–1716
Canal Landscape with Figures Bathing
oil on canvas 66.7 x 87
EU0727

Oram, Ann b.1956
Duomo, Siena, Italy
oil on canvas 90 x 90
EU0904

Organ, Robert b.1933
The Lot near Saint-Martin-Labouval, France, No.1 1992
oil on canvas 102 x 213
EU0327

Ouless, Walter William 1848–1933
James Bell Pettigrew (1832–1908) 1902
oil on canvas 137 x 102.5
EU0439

Ouless, Walter William 1848–1933
Sir Donald Currie (1825–1909)
oil on canvas 127 x 101.5
EU0032

Ounouh, Mohammed b.1964
Yellow Triangle 1989
acrylic on canvas 101.5 x 137
EU1035

Ounouh, Mohammed b.1964
Birds' Feet 1991
acrylic on board 34 x 27
EU1020

Ounouh, Mohammed b.1964
Red Arrowhead 1991
acrylic on canvas 101.5 x 76
EU1036

Ounouh, Mohammed b.1964
Toasting Fork 1991
acrylic on board 31.5 x 26
EU1021

Ounouh, Mohammed b.1964
White Dog 1991
acrylic on board 34.5 x 25
EU1019

Ounouh, Mohammed b.1964
Fork with Blue Triangle
acrylic on board (?) 30 x 40
EU1026

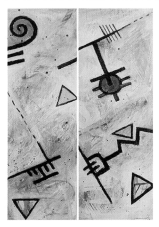

Ounouh, Mohammed b.1964
Two Panels
acrylic on board (?) 40 x 15; 40 x 15 (E)
EU1025

Paget, Henry Mariott 1856–1936
William Prout (1785–1850) (possibly after
John Hayes)
oil on canvas 74.5 x 62
EU0060

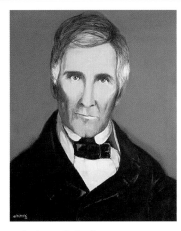

Palacios, Alirio b.1944
Dr José María Vargas (1786–1854) (copied
from a contemporary portrait)
oil on canvas 65 x 52 (E)
EU0970

Panini, Giovanni Paolo c.1692–1765
Roman Ruins with Figures
oil on canvas 114 x 117
EU0994

Panini, Giovanni Paolo c.1692–1765
Roman Ruins with Figures
oil on canvas 96.5 x 124
EU0995

Pannett, Juliet Kathleen 1911–2005
Norman Walker Porteous (1898–2003) 1972
oil on canvas 91 x 71
EU0414

Peploe, Samuel John 1871–1935
Cyclamen
oil on canvas 44 x 39
EU0181

Peploe, Samuel John 1871–1935
White Roses and Grapes
oil on canvas 44 x 39
EU0069

Pettie, John 1839–1893
Disbanded
oil on canvas 92 x 65
PCF16

Philipson, Robin 1916–1992
The Trappers
oil on canvas 49.5 x 59.5
EU0816

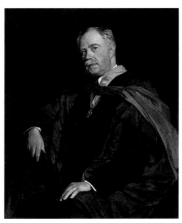

Philpot, Glyn Warren 1884–1937
Sir Ludovic Grant (1862–1936) 1923
oil on canvas 101 x 83
EU0077

Pickersgill, Henry William 1782–1875
Captain Thomas Drummond (1797–1840)
1834
oil on canvas 152 x 116.5
EU0046

Pickersgill, Henry William 1782–1875
*Lyon Playfair (1818–1898), 1st Baron Playfair
of St Andrews*
oil on canvas 90 x 70
EU0440

Pickersgill, Henry William 1782–1875
Sir Roderick Impey Murchison (1792–1871)
oil on canvas 91 x 71
EU0953

Pietro della Vecchia 1603–1678
The Lovers
oil on canvas on panel 71 x 54.5
EU0742

Procaccini, Giulio Cesare 1574–1625
Dead Christ with Angels 1615–1616
oil on paper on panel 28 x 43
EU0729

Pynacker, Adam c.1620–1673
A Forest Glade
oil on canvas 90 x 81.2
EU0730

Raeburn, Henry 1756–1823
Adam Ferguson (1723–1816) c.1790
oil on canvas 127 x 101.5
EU0012

Raeburn, Henry 1756–1823
William Robertson (1721–1793) 1792
oil on canvas 127 x 101.5
EU0011

Raeburn, Henry 1756–1823
*Thomas Elder (1737–1799), Lord Provost of
Edinburgh* 1797
oil on canvas 127 x 101.5
EU0005

Raeburn, Henry 1756–1823
John Robison (1739–1805) c.1798
oil on canvas 127 x 101.5
EU0010

Raeburn, Henry 1756–1823
John Playfair (1748–1819) c.1814
oil on canvas 127 x 101.5
EU0013

Raeburn, Henry 1756–1823
Andrew Dalziel (1742–1806)
oil on canvas 127 x 101.5
EU0015

Raeburn, Henry 1756–1823
Ann Rutherford
oil on canvas 52.5 x 41
Corson P.377

Raeburn, Henry 1756–1823
John Hill
oil on canvas 124 x 99
EU0014

Raeburn, Henry (style of) 1756–1823
John Bruce (1745–1826)
oil on panel 127 x 99
EU0016

Ramsay, Allan (attributed to) 1713–1784
Andrew Fletcher (1692–1766), Lord Milton
oil on canvas 72 x 59.5
EU0435

Ramsay, Allan (follower of) 1713–1784
*John Coutts (1699–1751), Lord Provost of
Edinburgh (1742)* after 1759
oil on canvas 76.2 x 63.5
EU0247

Ramsay, Allan (style of) 1713–1784
David Hume (1711–1776) 1758
oil on canvas 80 x 65
EU0067

Ramsay, Allan (style of) 1713–1784
Joan Kinloch (d.c.1726)
oil on canvas 76 x 59.5
EU0449

Redpath, Anne 1895–1965
Spanish Doorway
oil on board 49.5 x 59.5
EU0529 🐝

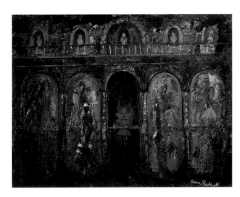

Redpath, Anne 1895–1965
*The Ladies' Garden, Palácio dos Marqueses de
Fronteira, Lisbon*
oil on board 69.5 x 90
EU0500 🐝

Redpath, Anne 1895–1965
Tréboul Harbour, France
oil on board 50 x 60
EU0175 🐝

Reid, George 1841–1913
David Mavor Masson (1822–1907) c.1899
oil on canvas 107 x 83
EU0034

Reid, George 1841–1913
Arthur James Balfour (1848–1930) c.1900
oil on board 121 x 71
EU0037

Reid, George 1841–1913
Alexander Campbell Fraser (1819–1914)
oil on canvas 127 x 101.5
EU0035

Reid, George 1841–1913
Henry Calderwood (1830–1897)
oil on canvas 109 x 90
EU0064

Reid, George 1841–1913
Robert Flint (1838–1910)
oil on canvas 73 x 55.5
EU0410

Reid, George 1841–1913
Robert Rainy (1826–1906)
oil on canvas 134 x 101
EU0415 (P)

Reid, George 1841–1913
Sir John Usher of Norton and Wells (1828–1904)
oil on canvas 121.9 x 81.2
EU0458

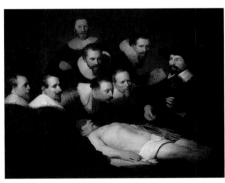

Rembrandt van Rijn (copy after) 1606–1669
The Anatomy Lesson of Dr Tulp
oil on canvas 169.5 x 219.5
EU0464

Reni, Guido (style of) 1575–1642
Ecce Homo
oil on panel 55.5 x 42.5
EU0731

Reynolds, Joshua (style of) 1723–1792
David Steuart Erskine (1742–1829)
oil on canvas 88 x 68.5
EU0008

Robb, William George 1872–1940
A Pastoral
oil on panel 18.5 x 23.5
EU0182

Roberts, Derek b.1947
Study in Red and Blue
acrylic on paper 101 x 76
EU0313

Robertson, Charles Kay d.1939
Sir Herbert Stanley Oakeley (1830–1903) 1884
oil on canvas 124 x 101
EU0522

Robertson, Iain b.1955
Gracenotes
acrylic on canvas 200 x 164
EU1267

Robson, Gavin b.1950
Monumental Object No.22
oil on canvas 122 x 153
EU0833

Rosa, Salvator 1615–1673
Rocky Landscape with Figures
oil on canvas 51 x 92.5
EU0732

Ross, Donald Sinclair (Danny) b.1951
Iona, Land and Seascape 1976
oil on canvas 100 x 156.5
EU0836

Ross, Robert Henry Alison active 1898–1940
Professor Alexander Darroch (1862–1924) 1908
oil on canvas 92 x 72
EU0318

Ross, Robert Henry Alison
active 1898–1940
James Mackinnon (1860–1945)
oil on canvas 74 x 61
EU0411

Ruisdael, Jacob van 1628/1629–1682
A Wood Scene 1649
oil on canvas 61 x 74
EU0733

Rycroft, David b.1969
View of Edinburgh 1992
oil on board 46 x 29.5
EU0552

Sanderson, Robert 1848–1908
Apollo and the Muses
oil on panel 34.5 x 78
EU0216

Scott, David 1806–1849
Mythological Group 1840
oil on canvas 39 x 48.5
EU0620

Scott, James b.1802
William Home (1816–1876), MD, AMS
oil on canvas 91 x 68
EU0448

Scougal, John c.1645–1730
*Sir Thomas Steuart of Kirkfield and Coltness
(1631–1698)* c.1685
oil on canvas 74 x 62
EU0246

Scougal, John (copy after) c.1645–1730
George Heriot (1563–1624) (copy after a
portrait in Heriot's Hospital)
oil on canvas 127 x 93
EU0535

Scougall, David c.1610–c.1680
Sir James Steuart of Coltness (1681–1727)
oil on canvas 73.5 x 61
EU0245

Segers, Hercules Pietersz. (style of)
c.1589–c.1638
Landscape
oil on panel 28.5 x 39
EU0737

Serres, Dominic 1722–1793
*The Landing of William, Duke of Clarence
(later William IV) at Rio di Janeiro in 1790*
oil on canvas 120 x 173
EU0518

Shanks, Duncan b.1937
The Dam Burn 1982
oil on canvas 152.5 x 183
EU0071

Shiels, William 1783–1857
John Dick (c.1769–1844)
oil on canvas 92 x 76
EU0935

Shiels, William 1783–1857
William Dick (1793–1866)
oil on canvas 91 x 76
EU0933

Shojie
Woman
oil on canvas 74 x 50
EU0285

Sim, Agnes
Professor Edward Stebbing (1870–1960)
oil on canvas 87.5 x 67
EU0967

Sinclair, Catherine
The Loaf of Bread
oil on canvas 39.5 x 60
EU0176

Sinclair, Louisa active 19th C
Thomas Chalmers (1780–1847) (copy after
Thomas Duncan)
oil on canvas 125 x 99
EU0405 (P)

Facing page: Raeburn, Henry, 1756–1823, *Admiral Adam Duncan (1731–1804), 1st Viscount Duncan of Camperdown,
1798*, Historic Scotland, Edinburgh (p. 122)

Smart, John 1838–1899
A Cloudy Day, Strathearn, Perthshire 1896
oil on canvas 29 x 39
EU1032

Smith, Colvin 1795–1875
Daniel Ellis (c.1772–1841)
oil on canvas 114 x 88
EU0055

Smith, Colvin 1795–1875
J. Stewart Hepburn (1795–1875)
oil on canvas 91 x 71
EU0050

Smith, Colvin 1795–1875
Mrs Elizabeth Cheape (1768–1857)
oil on canvas 140 x 110 (E)
PCF20

Smith, Colvin 1795–1875
Robert Graham (1786–1845), MD
oil on canvas 74 x 62.5
EU0436

Snyders, Frans 1579–1657
The Boar Hunt
oil on canvas 164.5 x 251
EU0736

Somer, Paulus van I (after) 1576–1621
King James VI and I (1566–1625)
c.1650–1689
oil on canvas 57 x 45
EU0603

Somer, Paulus van I (after) 1576–1621
King James VI and I (1566–1625)
c.1650–1689
oil on canvas 71 x 59.5
EU0604

Spanish School (attributed to)
Portrait of an Unknown Man c.1610–1696
oil on panel 60 x 40 (E)
EU0211

Squire, Geoffrey b.1923
Reverend Thomas Forsyth Torrance (1913–2007)
oil on canvas 93 x 79
EU0420

Steen, Jan 1626–1679
The Doctor's Visit
oil on canvas on panel 69.5 x 55.5
EU0738

Stoop, Dirck (style of) c.1610–c.1686
Catherine of Braganza (1638–1705), Queen Consort of King Charles II 17th C
oil on canvas 72 x 60.5
EU0922

Strachota, Josef Franz b.1911
Sir Thomas Dalling (1892–1982) 1956
oil on canvas 79 x 62
EU0927

Streeton, Arthur 1867–1943
The Borderland 1914
oil on canvas 135.8 x 196.3
EU0844

Sturrock, Alick Riddell 1885–1953
Wooded River Landscape
oil on canvas 40.6 x 50.8
EU0183

Teniers, David II 1610–1690
Peasants Playing Bowls
oil on panel 34.5 x 56.5
EU0739

Teniers, David II (style of) 1610–1690
A Pasticcio
oil on canvas 30 x 45.5
EU0740

Thomson, Adam Bruce 1885–1976
Norman Kemp Smith (1872–1958)
oil on canvas 100 x 85
EU0966

Thomson, John 1778–1840
William Wallace (1768–1843) c.1825
oil on canvas 74 x 59
EU0024

Thomson, John 1778–1840
Crichton Castle, Midlothian
oil on panel 32.5 x 47.5
PCF11

Thomson, John 1778–1840
Hermitage Castle, Scottish Borders
oil on board 24.5 x 35
Corson F.7440

Thomson, John 1778–1840
Innerwick Castle, East Lothian
oil on panel 36.5 x 48.5
PCF12

Thomson, John 1778–1840
Tantallon Castle, North Berwick
oil on panel 35.5 x 47
Corson P.7441

Titian (school of) c.1488–1576
Virgin and Child with St Catherine
oil on panel 49 x 39.5
EU0741

Tong, J. de
Cornelis Petrus Tiele (1830–1902) 1902
oil on canvas 109 x 78
EU0537

unknown artist
Lord John Napier of Merchiston (1550–1617)
1616
oil on canvas 118 x 96.5
EU0001

unknown artist
*William Drummond of Hawthornden
(1585–1649)* 1623
oil on panel 39 x 28.5
EU0482

unknown artist
Robert Leighton (1611–1684) 1662
oil on panel 103.5 x 76.5
EU0082

unknown artist mid 17th C
Unknown Divine
oil on panel 70 x 57
EU0202

unknown artist mid 17th C
Portrait of a Gentleman in Seventeenth-Century Dress (Portuguese Nobleman) (copy of an earlier painting)
oil on canvas 60 x 47
EU0951

unknown artist late 17th C
Queen Henrietta Maria (1609–1669)
oil on canvas 68 x 55.5
EU0944

unknown artist late 17th C
Portrait of an Unknown Man
oil on canvas 73.6 x 60.9
EU0528

unknown artist 17th C
Andrew Cant (d.1728)
oil on canvas 69.5 x 58
EU0526

unknown artist 17th C
Pierre Gassend (1592–1655)
oil on canvas 41.5 x 31.5
EU0939

unknown artist 18th C
Colin Drummond (d.c.1752)
oil on panel 75 x 61.5
EU0009

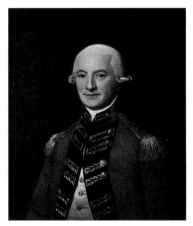

unknown artist
General Sir John Reid (1721–1807) 1803
oil on canvas 74.5 x 62.5
EU0516

unknown artist
Thomas Leckie (1806–1878) c.1830
oil on canvas 34.5 x 29.5
EU0451

unknown artist
Eleanor Ann Ormerod (1828–1901) 1900
oil on canvas 77 x 64.5
EU0022

unknown artist
Andrew Bruce Davidson (1831–1902)
oil on canvas 121 x 93
EU0408

unknown artist
Andrew David Barrowman, Janitor of Old College
oil on canvas 74.5 x 62.5
EU0066

unknown artist
Benedictus Aretius (1522–1574)
oil on panel 64 x 43
EU0207

unknown artist
Donald Ross (d.1883)
oil on canvas 134.5 x 109
EU0058

unknown artist
General John Reid (1721–1807)
oil on canvas 70 x 58.9
EU0083

unknown artist
General Sir Joseph Straton (d.1841)
oil on canvas 52.5 x 42
EU0030

unknown artist
Heinrich Bullinger (1504–1575)
oil on panel 58.5 x 38
EU0204

unknown artist
Highland Dancing Scene
oil on canvas 67 x 82.5
Corson P.378

unknown artist
James Home of Eccles (1681–1737), Advocate
oil on canvas 76 x 59.5
EU0446

unknown artist
John Knox (c.1510–1572)
oil on canvas 69 x 55.5
EU0215

unknown artist
Martin Luther Writing the Prayer Book by the Light of the Gospel
oil on canvas 80 x 100 (E)
EU0423

unknown artist
Portrait of a Man
oil on canvas 46.5 x 34.5
PCF1

unknown artist
Portrait of an Unknown Lady
oil on canvas 72.5 x 58.5
EU0251

unknown artist
Portrait of an Unknown Man (possibly of the Moubray family)
oil on canvas 74 x 63
EU0250

unknown artist
Portrait of an Unknown Woman
oil on canvas 74 x 63
EU0249

unknown artist
Robert Rollock (c.1555–1599)
oil on canvas 73.5 x 60.5
EU0068

unknown artist
Sir David Home (1643–1707), 1st Lord Crossrig
oil on canvas 76 x 61
EU0444

unknown artist
Sir John Goodsir (1814–1867)
oil on canvas 75 x 62.5
EU0941

unknown artist
Sir Walter Scott (1771–1832)
oil on canvas 75 x 62.5
PCF15

unknown artist
The Abduction of Isabella Vere
oil on canvas 45.5 x 61
Corson P.5766

unknown artist
Violet Fairgreave Barrowman
oil on canvas on panel 74 x 62
EU0065

unknown artist
William Carstares (1649–1715)
oil on canvas 75 x 62
EU0017

unknown artist
Young Girl in Green
oil on canvas 75 x 49.5
PCF13

Velde, Adriaen van de 1636–1672
Cattle and Herdsman
oil on panel 30.5 x 38
EU0743

Velde, Willem van de II 1633–1707
Fishing Boats in a Calm 1658
oil on canvas 41.9 x 56.2
EU0744

Facing page: Teniers II, David, 1610–1690, *Peasants Playing Bowls*, The University of Edinburgh Fine Art Collection (p.177)

Veronese, Paolo (studio of) 1528–1588
Venus and Adonis
oil on canvas 82 x 62.5
EU0745

Vos, Paul de (attributed to) 1591–1592 or 1595–1678
The Wolf Hunt
oil on canvas 164 x 243.5
EU0735

Wardman, Clare b.1960
Between Wind and Water
acrylic on canvas 182 x 183
EU1268

Watson, George 1767–1837
General John Reid (1721–1807) 1806
oil on canvas 101.6 x 86.3
EU0523

Watson, George 1767–1837
Thomas Brown (1778–1820) (after Henry Raeburn)
oil on canvas 127 x 101.5
EU0054

Watson, William Smellie 1796–1894
John Donaldson (d.1865)
oil on canvas 127 x 101.6
EU0519

Watson, William Smellie 1796–1894
John Thomson (1805–1841) (style of Thomas Lawrence)
oil on canvas 91 x 71
EU0524

Watt, George Fiddes 1873–1960
Simon Somerville Laurie (1829–1909) 1904
oil on canvas 112 x 86.5
EU0095

Watt, George Fiddes 1873–1960
Malcolm Campbell Taylor (1832–1922) 1917
oil on canvas 105.5 x 77.5
EU0288

Watt, George Fiddes 1873–1960
William P. Paterson (1860–1939)
oil on canvas 101 x 63
EU0413

Weir, William d.1865
The Honourable Henry Erskine (1746–1817)
1782
oil on canvas 127 x 101
EU0534

Whyte, Duncan MacGregor 1866–1953
Cattle on the Shore below Caenn a' Mhara
oil on canvas board 25 x 34
EU0624

Whyte, Duncan MacGregor 1866–1953
No.2, Cottars on 'the Land'
oil on canvas board 29 x 39
EU0625

Whyte, Duncan MacGregor 1866–1953
No.3, Carts on the Shore
oil on canvas board 25 x 33.5
EU0626

Whyte, Duncan MacGregor 1866–1953
No.4, Crofters, Balephuil
oil on canvas 50 x 65
EU0629

Whyte, Duncan MacGregor 1866–1953
No.5, Boats on the Shore
oil on canvas 20.5 x 28.5
EU0630

Whyte, Duncan MacGregor 1866–1953
No.6, Harvesting Potatoes, Red Tam
oil on canvas 36 x 45.5
EU0631

Whyte, Duncan MacGregor 1866–1953
No.7, Neil Eachan
oil on canvas 27.5 x 33
EU0627

Whyte, Duncan MacGregor 1866–1953
No.8, Port Balephuil
oil on canvas 25 x 40
EU0632

Whyte, Duncan MacGregor 1866–1953
No.9, Three Girls
oil on canvas 36.5 x 30
EU0633

Whyte, Duncan MacGregor 1866–1953
Tigh Chaluim (Callum's House)
oil on canvas 31.5 x 39
EU0628

Whyte, John McGregor
No.19, Teampall Pharaig
oil on canvas board 25 x 35
EU0642

Wighton, William
Sir David Brewster (1781–1868)
oil on canvas 101 x 76
EU0530

Willoughby, Trevor 1926–1995
Sir Hugh Norwood Robson (1917–1977) 1979
oil on canvas 100 x 75.5
EU0041

Wilson, Richard 1712/1713–1782
An Italian Landscape c.1751
oil on canvas 50 x 71.5
EU0746

Wingate, James Lawton 1846–1924
An Arran Croft
oil on canvas 24 x 35.5
EU0611

Wright, Allan
Still Life
oil on board 90 x 120
EU0542

Young, A. J.
Mary Dick (1791–1883) 1883
oil on canvas 44.5 x 34.5
EU0928

Young, William Drummond 1855–1924
Sir John Goodsir (1814–1867) (copy of James
Elder Christie) 1889
oil on canvas 111 x 86
EU0455

Żyw, Aleksander 1905–1995
Snow Pattern 1952
oil & tempera on canvas 91 x 72
EU0501

Żyw, Aleksander 1905–1995
Water of Leith 1
oil on canvas 79
EU0854

Paintings Without Reproductions

This section lists all the paintings that have not been included in the main pages of the catalogue. They were excluded as it was not possible to photograph them for this project. Additional information relating to acquisition credit lines or loan details is also included. For this reason the information below is not repeated in the Further Information section.

City of Edinburgh Council

Denune, William c.1712–1750, *Alexander Wilson, Lord Provost (1735–1737)*, 76.8 x 64.2, oil on canvas, CAC1978/286, presented by Mrs W. B. Wilson, not available at the time of photography

Fraser, Alexander (after) 1827–1899, *The Expected Penny*, 41.9 x 34.3, oil on panel, CAC1978/73, unknown acquisition method, not available at the time of photography

Green, Alexander active 19th C, *The Bard of No Regard*, 36.8 x 33, oil on panel, CAC1978/90, presented by William Lightbody, not available at the time of photography

Hardie, Charles Martin 1858–1916, *Sir Walter Scott (1771–1832), as a Boy*, 31.1 x 22.9, oil on panel, HH1804/1958, bequeathed by Mrs M. S. Martin Hardie, 1958, not available at the time of photography

Hardie, Charles Martin 1858–1916, *Tam o' Shanter*, 20.6 x 27.9, oil on panel, CAC1978/97, unknown acquisition method, not available at the time of photography

Harvey, J. M. active 20th C, *Canongate Demolition from Tolbooth Wynd, Edinburgh, 1953*, 46.2 x 31.8, oil on board, HH1738/1957, presented by the artist, 1957, not available at the time of photography

Hendry active early 19th C, *James Grindlay*, 37.8 x 32.8, oil on canvas, HH3129/1967, presented by E. Docherty, 1967, not available at the time of photography

Hope, Robert (attributed to) 1869–1936, *Portrait of a Lady*, 73.6 x 57.1, oil on canvas, CAC377/1964, presented by the Scottish Modern Arts Association, 1963, not available at the time of photography

Innes, Callum b.1962, *Exposed Painting, Pewter/Violet, 1999*, 207.5 x 202.5, oil on canvas, CAC2000/11, purchased from the artist with the assistance of the Jean F. Watson Bequest Fund, the National Fund for Acquisitions and the National Art Collections Fund, 2000, not available at the time of photography

Jack, I. active 1881, *Leith Harbour, 1881*, 88.9 x 121.9, oil on canvas, CAC46/1988, unknown acquisition method, not available at the time of photography

Johnstone, Dorothy 1892–1980, *Study for 'Rest Time in the Life Class'*, 47 x 40.8, oil on board, CAC7(B)/1980, presented by the artist, 1980, not available at the time of photography

Lee, May Bridges 1884–1977, *Erica (b.1909), and Paul Marx (1911–1943)*, 57.7 x 70.5, oil on canvas, CAC1978/202, unknown acquisition method, not available at the time of photography

Mackay, John b.1910, *Professor Sir Donald Tovey (1875–1940), at the Usher Hall, Edinburgh, 1940*, 71.2 x 52, oil on panel, CAC1978/156, presented by the artist, c.1975, not available at the time of photography

McCulloch, Horatio (attributed to) 1805–1867, *Edinburgh from Ravelston, 1841*, 56.2 x 76.5, oil on canvas, HH1493/1953, purchased, 1953, not available at the time of photography

McLea, John Watson active 1840–1860s, *Leith Harbour*, 60.3 x 90.5, oil on canvas, CAC41/1988, unknown acquisition method, not available at the time of photography

McManus, John d.1993, *Old Campaigner*, 91.3 x 61, oil on canvas, CAC1978/423, purchased from the artist, 1974, not available at the time of photography

O'Neill, George Bernard 1828–1917, *The Young Pastry Maker*, 80.7 x 60.7, oil on board, CAC1978/242, unknown acquisition method, not available at the time of photography

Orr, Jack 1890–1961, *Satyr with Dancing Children*, 63.5 x 76.2, oil on canvas, CAC353/1964, presented by the Scottish Modern Arts Association, 1964, not available at the time of photography

Phillips, Thomas 1770–1845, *Sir Walter Scott (1771–1832)*, 91.4 x 64.8, oil on canvas, HH1925/1960, bequeathed by Mrs M. A. Green, 1960, not available at the time of photography

Roia, R. S. active early 20th C, *St Ninian's Church, Leith*, oil on canvas, CAC42/1988, unknown acquisition method, not available at the time of photography

Smeall, William active 1824–1830, *Old Bridge at Ancrum*, 25 x 30.8, oil on canvas, HH1457/1953, presented by Mrs Drummond, 1954, not available at the time of photography

Smeall, William active 1824–1830, *Trinity College Church, Edinburgh and the North Bridge, 1830*, 24 x 33.3, oil on panel, HH1462/1953, presented by Mrs Drummond, 1955, not available at the time of photography

Stewart, William 1823–1906, *The Rivals*, 43.3 x 27.7, oil on panel, MC4380/1961, on long-term loan from Dundee Art Galleries and Museums Collection (Dundee City Council), 1961, not available at the time of photography

Stirling, Calum b.1965, *Portrait of a Former Self, 1987*, 66 x 47.6, acrylic on paper, CAC1987/23, purchased with the assistance of the Jean F. Watson Bequest Fund, 1987, not available at the time of photography

Turner, Margaret D. A. *Lauriston Castle, Edinburgh*, 50.8 x 76.2, oil on canvas, CAC61/1991, presented by Julie Coxon, 1991, not available at the time of photography

unknown artist 18th C, *Portrait of an Unknown Lady (possibly Miss McVey)*, 91.8 x 73.7, oil on canvas, HH1439/1953, presented by Mrs Drummond, 1953, not available at the time of photography

unknown artist *Young Girl Carrying a Basket and a Rose in a Landscape*, c.1815, 28.6 x 24.7, oil on panel, CAC1978/311, unknown acquisition method, not available at the time of photography

unknown artist *Portrait of an Unknown Gentleman*, c.1835, 93 x 73.2, oil on canvas, CAC1978/313, unknown acquisition method, not available at the time of photography

unknown artist *The Caricature*, c.1840, 30.3 x 25.2, oil on canvas, CAC1978/336, unknown acquisition method, not available at the time of photography

unknown artist *Young Girl at the Seaside*, c.1870, 48.9 x 33.1, oil on panel, CAC1978/499, unknown acquisition method, not available at the time of photography

unknown artist 19th C, *Agnes Calder, née Dalrymple, Wife to William Calder, Lord Provost (1810–1811)*, 81.3 x 63.5, oil on canvas, CAC1978/299, unknown acquisition method, not available at the time of photography

unknown artist 19th C, *Girl with a Slate*, 85.2 x 61.2, oil on canvas, CAC1978/318, unknown acquisition method, not available at the time of photography

unknown artist 19th C, *Head of a Young Boy*, 49.8 x 39.7, oil on canvas, CAC1978/330, unknown acquisition method, not available at the time of photography

unknown artist 19th C, *Head of a Young Girl*, 13.3 x 13.3, oil on canvas, CAC1978/326, unknown acquisition method, not available at the time of photography

unknown artist 19th C, *Homework*, 65.4 x 45.2, oil on canvas, CAC1978/337, unknown acquisition method, not available at the time of photography

unknown artist 19th C, *John Stewart of Genogis, Forfar and His Sister Grizel Hamilton Benham (or Stewart)*, 70.5 x 90.5, oil on canvas, CAC1978/305, unknown acquisition method, not available at the time of photography

unknown artist 19th C, *Portrait of an Unknown Gentleman*, 215.4 x 143.5, oil on canvas, CAC1978/312, unknown acquisition method, not available at the time of photography

unknown artist 19th C, *Portrait of an Unknown Gentleman*, 63.5 x 53.3, oil on canvas, CAC35/1992, unknown acquisition method, not available at the time of photography

unknown artist 19th C, *Unidentified Old Town Close*, 41 x 20.5, oil on canvas, CAC1978/357, unknown acquisition method, not available at the time of photography

unknown artist 20th C, *The Lord Provost of Edinburgh with the City Magistrates in the Assembly Rooms, George Street*, 120 x 222.5, oil on canvas, CAC1978/370, unknown acquisition method, not available at the time of photography

unknown artist 20th C, *The Tolbooth, Leith*, oil on canvas, CAC45/1988, unknown acquisition method, not available at the time of photography

unknown artist 20th C, *Three Young Girls on a Cliff Top, c.1950*, 30 x 36, oil on panel, CAC1978/372, unknown acquisition method, not available at the time of photography

Watt, George Fiddes 1873–1960, *Sir Robert Kirk Inches, Lord Provost (1912–1916)*, 238.8 x 148.6, oil on canvas, CAC1978/382, presented to the City, before 1901, not available at the time of photography

Young, Edward Drummond 1877–1946, *John Allen Drummond Young, c.1920*, 52.2 x 41.3, oil on canvas, CAC1978/392, presented by the sitter to the Museum of Childhood, Edinburgh, not available at the time of photography

Facing page: McKenzie, George Findlay, active 1930–1937, *Man Playing a Violin*, 1930, The University of Edinburgh Fine Art Collection (p.160)

Historic Scotland, Edinburgh

unknown artist *Piper*, EDIN047, missing since 1998, not available at the time of photography

University of Edinburgh Fine Art Collection

Aiken, John MacDonald 1880–1961, *Sir George Adam Smith (1856–1942)*, 1929, 91.4 x 76.2, oil on canvas, EU0416, presented by the sitter's family, 1949, not available at the time of photography

Churchill, Martin b.1954, *Old College Dome and Quadrangle*, oil on canvas, EU0770, commissioned to mark the University's quatercentenary, 1983, not available at the time of photography

Czajkowski, Józef 1872–1947, *A Country House in North East Poland*, 48.3 x 33, EU0472, presented to the University of Edinburgh by members of the Polish School of Medicine, 1984, not available at the time of photography

Fleming, John B. 1792–1845, *Landscape*, oil, EU0785, not available at the time of photography

Forbes, Vivian 1891–1937, *Sir Ludovic James Grant (1862–1936)* (copy after Glyn Philpot), 101.6 x 86.3, oil on canvas, EU1034, not available at the time of photography

Geller, William Overend 1804–1881, *John Hunter (1728–1793), Anatomist and Surgeon* (after Joshua Reynolds), oil on canvas, EU0461, not available at the time of photography

Guthrie, James 1859–1930, *Arthur Balfour (1848–1930)*, 145 x 85 (E), oil on canvas, EU1278, donated, 2008, not available at the time of photography

Gwynne-Jones, Allan 1892–1982, *Sir Derrick Melville Dunlop (1902–1980)*, 1964, 78.7 x 71.1, oil on canvas, EU0457, gift from the sitter, 1969, not available at the time of photography

Haig, George Douglas 1918–2009, *Villa Aldobrandini, Frascati, Rome*, EU0788, purchased, 1966, not available at the time of photography

Harris, Tomás 1908–1964, *Mallorca Series No.6*, 54 x 46, oil on board, EU0790, gift from Mrs E. Frankfort and her sister (sisters of the artist), 1977, not available at the time of photography

Hering, George Edwards 1805–1879, *Landscape in Arran*, 101 x 161, oil on canvas, EU0331, purchased by L. D. Macmillan at Lamb's, Queen Street, 1950s; exchanged with the University for a bookcase, 1953, not available at the time of photography

Herkomer, Hubert von 1849–1914, *Robert Bannatyne Finlay (1842–1929)*, 1908, 99 x 81.2, oil on canvas, EU0100, presented by the sitter's family, not available at the time of photography

Lumsden, Ernest Stephen 1883–1948, *Towards Swanston, Edinburgh*, 71 x 91.4, oil in canvas, EU0549, presented by Professor and Mrs Dickens, 1967, not available at the time of photography

Lyon, Robert 1894–1978, *William Lindsay Renwick (1889–1970)*, 76.2 x 60.9, oil on canvas, EU0958, presented by the sitter, 1962, not available at the time of photography

McClure, David 1926–1998, *Hunter's Moon*, 50 x 70 (E), oil, EU0463, purchased, 1962/1966, not available at the time of photography

Mlynarski, Josef 1925–1984, *Cracow University, Poland*, 61 x 45, oil on canvas, EU0806, donated by the Polish School of Medicine, 1976, not available at the time of photography

Morrison, James b.1932, *Raised Beach*, 1967, 58 x 119.5, oil on canvas, EU0805, purchased, 1967, not available at the time of photography

Reid, George 1841–1913, *Peter Guthrie Tait (1831–1901)*, 1882, 68.5 x 49.5, oil on canvas, EU0968, presented by Mrs Tait, not available at the time of photography

Richmond, George 1809–1896, *William Pultney Alison (1790–1859)*, 1847, 63.5 x 48.2, oil on canvas, EU0298, purchased at Christie's, 1973, not available at the time of photography

Ross, Robert Henry Alison active 1898–1940, *Otto Schlapp (1859–1939)*, 1907, 76.2 x 63.5, oil on canvas, EU0964, presented by Dr Robert Schlapp, 1984, not available at the time of photography

Ruisdael, Jacob van 1628/1629–1682, *The Banks of a River*, 1649, 134 x 193, oil on canvas, EU0734, bequeathed as part of the Torrie Collection, 1836; on loan to the National Gallery of Scotland, not available at the time of photography

Sturrock, Alick Riddell 1885–1953, *The Inch House, Edinburgh, Dark Yew Trees*, 62 x 75, oil on canvas, EU0845, presented by Mrs Mary Sturrock, 1972, not available at the time of photography

unknown artist *Dr William Ritchie (1748–1830)*, 78.7 x 63.5, oil on canvas, EU0422, bequeathed by Lady May Elizabeth Bradfute MacLeod, 1963, not available at the time of photography

unknown artist *Sir David Leslie (c.1610–1682), First Lord Newark*, 71.1 x 54.6, oil on canvas, EU0453, offered to the Faculty of Medicine by W. E. Home, RN, Fleet Surgeon, after his and his wife's death, not available at the time of photography

unknown artist *William Dick (1793–1866)*, 61 x 45.5, oil on canvas, EU0934, not available at the time of photography

Utrillo, Maurice 1883–1955, *L'église de Clichy, France*, 25.5 x 32, oil on canvas, EU0105, bequeathed by Hope Scott, 1989, image unavailable due to copyright restrictions

Watson, William Smellie 1796–1894, *Henry George Watson (1796–1879)*, 129.5 x 101.6, oil on canvas, EU0972, presented by the trustees of William S. Watson, 1875, not available at the time of photography

Wright, A. J. *Village Landscape*, 137 x 137, oil on canvas, EU0852, not available at the time of photography

STOLEN

City of Edinburgh Council

Green, Alexander active 19th C, *The Son of Mars*, 28.6 x 21.6, oil on panel, CAC1978/91, presented by William Lightbody

Pratt, William M. 1855–1936, *A Stranger in the Port*, 41.2 x 51.5, oil on canvas, CAC42/1964, presented by the Scottish Modern Arts Association, 1964

Further Information

The paintings listed in this section have additional information relating to one or more of the five categories outlined below. This extra information is only provided where it is applicable and where it exists. Paintings listed in this section follow the same order as in the illustrated pages of the catalogue.

I	The full name of the artist if this was too long to display in the illustrated pages of the catalogue. Such cases are marked in the catalogue with a (…).
II	The full title of the painting if this was too long to display in the illustrated pages of the catalogue. Such cases are marked in the catalogue with a (…).
III	Acquisition information or acquisition credit lines as well as information about loans, copied from the records of the owner collection.
IV	Artist copyright credit lines where the copyright owner has been traced. Exhaustive efforts have been made to locate the copyright owners of all the images included within this catalogue and to meet their requirements. Any omissions or mistakes brought to our attention will be duly attended to and corrected in future publications.
V	The credit line of the lender of the transparency if the transparency has been borrowed. Bridgeman images are available subject to any relevant copyright approvals from the Bridgeman Art Library at www.bridgemanart.com

City of Edinburgh Council

Adam, Patrick William 1854–1929, *A Ballroom*, purchased with the assistance of the Jean F. Watson Bequest Fund and government grant-in-aid, 1989, photo credit: City of Edinburgh Council, City Art Centre

Adam, Patrick William 1854–1929, *The Signet Library, Edinburgh*, presented by the Scottish Modern Arts Association, 1964, photo credit: City of Edinburgh Council, City Art Centre

Adams, William Dacres 1864–1951, *The Cathedral of St Magnus, Kirkwall*, presented by the Scottish Modern Arts Association, 1964

Adamson, Elizabeth A. b.1959, *Gathering Flowers in the Rock Garden*, purchased with the assistance of the Jean F. Watson Bequest Fund and government grant-in-aid, 1986, © the artist, photo credit: City of Edinburgh Council, City Art Centre

Aitchison, Craigie Ronald John 1926–2009, *Silver Birch Trees at Tulliallan, Fife*, presented by the Scottish Arts Council, 1997, © the artist's estate/Bridgeman Art Library

Alexander, Robert L. 1840–1923, *A Tangier Gateway*, presented by the National Art Collections Fund, 1988

Alexander, Robert L. 1840–1923, *Auld Freens*, presented by the Scottish Modern Arts Association, 1964

Alexander, Robert L. 1840–1923, *Feeding the Horse*, presented by J. Kent Richardson

Alexander, Vivien b.1940, *Susan*, purchased from the artist with the assistance of the Friends of the City Art Centre and Museums and the National Fund for Acquisitions, 1991, © the artist

Alison, David 1882–1955, *Sir Thomas Hunter, LLD, WS*, unknown acquisition method

Alison, David 1882–1955, *The Quiet Room*, presented by the Scottish Modern Arts Association, 1964

Alison, David 1882–1955, *Sir James Spittal (1796–1842), Lord Provost of Edinburgh (1833–1837)* (copy after John Watson Gordon), commissioned

Alison, David 1882–1955, *The Interior*, presented by the Scottish Modern Arts Association, 1964, photo credit: City of Edinburgh Council, City Art Centre

Allan, David 1744–1796, *Faith* (triptych, left wing), transferred from the Chapel of St Peter, Roxburgh Place, Edinburgh, 1901

Allan, David 1744–1796, *Hope* (triptych, centre panel), transferred from the Chapel of St Peter, Roxburgh Place, Edinburgh, 1901

Allan, David 1744–1796, *Charity* (triptych, right wing), transferred from the Chapel of St Peter, Roxburgh Place, Edinburgh, 1901

Allan, William 1782–1850, *The Signing of the National Covenant in Greyfriars Kirkyard, Edinburgh*, purchased from the Friends of the Kirk of Greyfriars, 1991, photo credit: City of Edinburgh Council, City Art Centre

Archer, James active c.1860–1870, *A Dog Mourning Its Little Master*, purchased from Mr Spewack, 1961

Armour, Mary Nicol Neill 1902–2000, *The Wee Cumbrae from Corrie*, purchased from the artist with the assistance of the Jean F. Watson Bequest Fund, 1962, © the artist's estate/Bridgeman Art Library

Arnott, Andrew 1963–1995, *Self Portrait*, purchased from the artist with the assistance of the Jean F. Watson Bequest Fund, 1985

J. R. B. *A Hallway*, bequeathed by Diana Maud Stirling King, 2003

Baillie, William James b.1923, *Child's Table*, presented by the Scottish Arts Council, 1984, © the artist

Baillie, William James b.1923, *Cocos Landscape with Palms*, presented by the Royal Scottish Academy, 1975, © the artist

Bain, Donald 1904–1979, *The Pap of Glencoe*, purchased from the artist with the assistance of government grant-in-aid, 1976, © the artist's estate, photo credit: City of Edinburgh Council, City Art Centre

Ballantyne, John 1815–1897, *John Kay, Senior Baillie (1855–1856)*, unknown acquisition method

Balmer, Barbara b.1929, *Shrouded Lunch 2*, purchased from the Royal Scottish Academy Annual Exhibition with the assistance of the Jean F. Watson Bequest Fund and government grant-in-aid, 1987, © the artist

Barker, Joanne b.1963, *Study for 'The Battle of Britain Tapestry'*, purchased from the artist, 1991, © the artist

Barns-Graham, Wilhelmina 1912–2004, *Rocks, St Mary's, Scilly Isles*, purchased from the artist with the assistance of the Jean F. Watson Bequest Fund and government grant-in-aid, 1989, © by courtesy of the Barns-Graham Charitable Trust, photo credit: City of Edinburgh Council, City Art Centre

Barrie, Mardi 1931–2004, *Farmland Autumn*, presented by the Scottish Arts Council, 1997 © the artist's estate

Barrie, Mardi 1931–2004, *Theatre (Château)*, purchased with the assistance of the Jean F. Watson Bequest Fund and government grant-in-aid, 1983 © the artist's estate

Bear, George Telfer 1876–1973, *Poppies*, presented by the Scottish Modern Arts Association, 1964, © the artist's estate

Bear, George Telfer 1876–1973, *Portrait with Still Life*, presented to the City by the artist, 1970, © the artist's estate, photo credit: City of Edinburgh Council, City Art Centre

Beechey, William 1753–1839, *Thomas Coutts (1735–1822)*, unknown acquisition method

Behrens, Reinhard b.1951, *Lost Valley II*, purchased from the artist with the assistance of the Jean F. Watson Bequest Fund and government grant-in-aid, 1985, © the artist

Bell, John active c.1840–1860, *Edinburgh from Craigleith Quarry*, unknown acquisition method, photo credit: City of Edinburgh Council, City Art Centre

Bellany, John b.1942, *Self Portrait with a Razor Shell*, presented by the Scottish Arts Council, 1997, © the artist/Bridgeman Art Library

Bellany, John b.1942, *Bêche-de-mer*, purchased with the assistance of the Jean F. Watson Bequest Fund, 1984, © the artist/Bridgeman Art Library, photo credit: City of Edinburgh Council, City Art Centre

Bellany, John b.1942, *Sweet Promise* (triptych, left wing), purchased from the artist with the assistance of the Jean F. Watson Bequest Fund and the National Fund for Acquisitions, 1995, © the artist/Bridgeman Art Library, photo credit: City of Edinburgh Council, City Art Centre

Bellany, John b.1942, *Sweet Promise* (triptych, centre panel), purchased from the artist with the assistance of the Jean F. Watson Bequest Fund and the National Fund for Acquisitions, 1995, © the artist/Bridgeman Art Library,

Bellany, John b.1942, *Sweet Promise* (triptych, right wing), purchased from the artist with the assistance of the Jean F. Watson Bequest Fund and the National Fund for Acquisitions, 1995, © the artist/Bridgeman Art Library, photo credit: City of Edinburgh Council, City Art Centre

Bellany, John b.1942, *The Obsession*, purchased from the artist with the assistance of the Jean F. Watson Bequest Fund, 1968, © the artist/Bridgeman Art Library, photo credit: City of Edinburgh Council, City Art Centre

Black, Dorothy b.1963, *Gamine*, purchased from the artist with the assistance of the Jean F. Watson Bequest Fund, 1986, © the artist

Black, Dorothy b.1963, *Our Elsie*, commissioned as part of the 'Should Auld Acquaintance Be Forgot' exhibition, 1989, © the artist, photo credit: City of Edinburgh Council, City Art Centre

Black, Dorothy b.1963, *Scales*, gift from the artist, 1989, © the artist

Blackadder, Elizabeth V. b.1931, *Prayer Rug with Flowers*, purchased from the artist with the assistance of the Jean F. Watson Bequest Fund, 1966, © the artist

Blackadder, Elizabeth V. b.1931, *Princes Street Gardens, Edinburgh*, purchased from the artist with the assistance of the Jean F. Watson Bequest Fund, 1966, © the artist, photo credit: City of Edinburgh Council, City Art Centre

Blackadder, Elizabeth V. b.1931, *The Right Honourable Eric Milligan (b.1951), Lord Provost of Edinburgh (1996–2003)*, commissioned, 2007, © the artist

Blyth, Robert Henderson 1919–1970, *Goalmouth*, purchased from the artist, 1965, photo credit: City of Edinburgh Council, City Art Centre

Blyth, Robert Henderson 1919–1970, *Hauling in the Anchor*, gift from Mrs Anna V. Hossack, 1990

Bone, Muirhead 1876–1953, *The Old Racecourse, Ayr*, presented by the Scottish Modern Arts Association, 1964, © estate of Sir Muirhead Bone. All rights reserved, DACS 2012

Bonnar, William (attributed to) 1800–1855, *Mother and Child*, unknown acquisition method

Borthwick, Alfred Edward 1871–1955, *Marjorie*, presented by the Scottish Modern Arts Association, 1964

Borthwick, Alfred Edward 1871–1955, *Sir William J. Thomson (1881–1949), LLD, Lord Provost of Edinburgh (1932–1935)*, commissioned, 1937

Borthwick, Alfred Edward 1871–1955, *Betty*, presented by the

Scottish Modern Arts Association, 1964

Borthwick, Alfred Edward 1871–1955, *Burnhouse*, presented by the Scottish Modern Arts Association, 1964

Borthwick, Alfred Edward 1871–1955, *Head of an Old Man*, presented by the Scottish Modern Arts Association, 1964

Bowie, John Dick 1864–1941, *Robert Miller, Lord Dean of Guild (1890–1898)*, unknown acquisition method

Bowie, John Dick 1864–1941, *Sir Andrew MacDonald (1836–1919), Lord Provost of Edinburgh (1894–1897)*, unknown acquisition method, photo credit: City of Edinburgh Council, City Art Centre

Brackett, Nancy A. b.1907, *Mrs Dunlop and 'Smokey'*, presented by the artist to the Museum of Childhood, Edinburgh

Braes, Lex b.1956, *Nelson Mandela (b.1918), at Nineteen*, purchased with the assistance of the Jean F. Watson Bequest Fund and government grant-in-aid, 1986, © the artist

Braham, Philip b.1959, *The Forest Edge, Augustowska, Poland*, purchased with the assistance of the Jean F. Watson Bequest Fund, 2003, © the artist

Brown, John b.1967, *The Quiet Wood*, purchased from the artist with the assistance of the Jean F. Watson Bequest Fund, 1991

Brown, John b.1967, *International City*, presented to the City of Edinburgh by the Edinburgh International Conference Centre, 1995, photo credit: City of Edinburgh Council, City Art Centre

Brown, Neil Dallas 1938–2003, *Shroud and Barrier*, gift from the Neil Dallas Brown Trust, 2006, © the artist's estate

Brown, William Marshall 1863–1936, *Sardine Fishers, Concarneau, France*, presented by the Scottish Modern Arts Association, 1964, photo credit: City of Edinburgh Council, City Art Centre

Burns, Robert 1869–1941, *John Knox Preaching in St Giles Cathedral to a Congregation Comprising Mary Queen of Scots and Other Noble Personages*, presented by Lord Provost Robert Kirk Inches, 1914

Burns, Robert 1869–1941, *The Valley of the Shadow, Loch Coruisk, Deeside*, presented by the Scottish Modern Arts Association, 1964

Burns, William Alexander 1921–1972, *Ebb Tide*, purchased from the artist with the assistance of the Jean F. Watson Bequest Fund, 1966, photo credit: City of Edinburgh Council, City Art Centre

Burns, William Alexander 1921–1972, *Seahouse 3*, purchased

from the artist with the assistance of the Jean F. Watson Bequest Fund, 1968

Busby, John Philip b.1928, *Silent Landscape*, purchased from the artist with the assistance of the Jean F. Watson Bequest Fund, 1967, © the artist

Busby, John Philip b.1928, *Sky Canticle for June*, presented by the Scottish Arts Council, 1997, © the artist

Busby, John Philip b.1928, *Journey*, presented by the Scottish Arts Council, 1997, © the artist

Bushe, Robbie b.1964, *Cat amongst the Glutton*, purchased from the artist with the assistance of the Jean F. Watson Bequest Fund, 1989 © the artist

Buttersworth, Thomas 1768–1842, *The Arrival of George IV at Leith Harbour, 1822*, purchased with the assistance of the Jean F. Watson Bequest Fund and government grant-in-aid, 1990

Byrne, John b.1940, *Self Portrait*, purchased from the artist with the assistance of the Jean F. Watson Bequest Fund and government grant-in-aid, 1989, © the artist/Bridgeman Art Library

Cadell, Agnes Morrison 1873–1958, *The Orange Hat*, presented by the Scottish Modern Arts Association, 1964, © the artist's estate

Cadell, Francis Campbell Boileau 1883–1937, *The Black Hat*, presented by the Scottish Modern Arts Association, 1964, photo credit: City of Edinburgh Council, City Art Centre © Cadell Estate, courtesy Portland Gallery, London

Cadell, Francis Campbell Boileau 1883–1937, *Iona*, presented by the Scottish Modern Arts Association, 1964, photo credit: City of Edinburgh Council, City Art Centre © Cadell Estate, courtesy Portland Gallery, London

Cadell, Francis Campbell Boileau 1883–1937, *Lady Lavery (1887–1935)*, presented by the Scottish Modern Arts Association, 1964, photo credit: City of Edinburgh Council, City Art Centre © Cadell Estate, courtesy Portland Gallery, London

Cadenhead, James 1858–1927, *Lady with a Japanese Screen and Goldfish (The Artist's Mother)*, presented by the Scottish Modern Arts Association, 1964, photo credit: City of Edinburgh Council, City Art Centre

Cadenhead, James 1858–1927, *Deeside*, presented by the Scottish Modern Arts Association, 1964

Cadenhead, James 1858–1927, *Landscape*, presented by the Scottish Modern Arts Association, 1964

Cairns, Joyce W. b.1947, *War Games*, purchased with the assistance of the Jean F. Watson Bequest Fund, 1987, © the artist, photo credit: City of Edinburgh

Council, City Art Centre

Callender, Robert 1932–2011, *Dawn*, presented by the Scottish Arts Council, 1997, © the artist's estate

Callow, John (imitator of) 1822–1878, *French Fishing Boats*, unknown acquisition method

Cameron, David Young 1865–1945, *Criffel*, presented by the Scottish Modern Arts Association, 1964

Cameron, David Young 1865–1945, *A Garment of War*, presented by the Scottish Modern Arts Association, 1964, photo credit: City of Edinburgh Council, City Art Centre

Cameron, Hugh 1835–1918, *A Summer Idyll*, on long-term loan from Dundee Art Galleries and Museums Collection (Dundee City Council)

Cameron, Hugh 1835–1918, *The Reaper*, presented by the Scottish Modern Arts Association, 1964

Cameron, Hugh 1835–1918, *Children Boating*, presented by Mrs D. K. Wight, 1967

Cameron, Hugh 1835–1918, *Going Visiting*, on long-term loan from Dundee Art Galleries and Museums Collection (Dundee City Council)

Cameron, Mary 1864–1921, *An Edinburgh Halberdier*, unknown acquisition method

Cameron, Mary 1864–1921, *Les joueurs*, presented by the Scottish Modern Arts Association, 1964, photo credit: City of Edinburgh Council, City Art Centre

Campbell, Alexander S. b.1932, *Cattle Trough*, purchased from the artist with the assistance of the Jean F. Watson Bequest Fund, 1966

Campbell, Steven 1953–2007, *Gesturing Hiker with Furnace*, purchased with the assistance of the Jean F. Watson Bequest Fund, 1990, © the artist's estate, photo credit: City of Edinburgh Council, City Art Centre

Carlisle, Fionna b.1954, *Cretan Landscape*, purchased with the assistance of the Jean F. Watson Bequest Fund, 1987, © the artist

Carmichael, Rodick 1931–2008, *Hill Village II*, presented by the Scottish Arts Council, 1997, © the artist's estate

Carmichael, Rodick 1931–2008, *Burning Buddhist III*, presented by the Scottish Arts Council, 1997, © the artist's estate

Carmichael, Stuart b.1960, *Untitled*, purchased with the assistance of the Jean F. Watson Bequest Fund, 1986

Carse, Alexander c.1770–1843, *George IV Landing at Leith, 1822*, acquired by the town of Leith

Carse, Alexander (attributed to) c.1770–1843, *The Barber's Shop*, unknown acquisition method

Carse, William active 1818–1845, *Tam o' Shanter*, presented by

Councillor Robert Gordon

Chalmers, George c.1720–c.1791, *Archibald Macaulay, Lord Provost of Edinburgh (1727–1729, 1737–1738 & 1748–1750)*, presented by Major J. F. Fraser Tytler, 1946, photo credit: City of Edinburgh Council, City Art Centre

Cheape, Malcolm b.1964, *Construction*, purchased with the assistance of the Jean F. Watson Bequest Fund, 1986

Cheyne, E. J. active 19th C, *Portrait of an Unknown Gentleman*, presented by the Scottish Modern Arts Association, 1964

Cheyne, Sally b.1964, *Untitled*, purchased at auction with the assistance of the Jean F. Watson Bequest Fund, 1986, © the artist

Churchill, Martin b.1954, *The Palace Continued*, purchased with the assistance of the Jean F. Watson Bequest Fund, 1985, © the artist

Cina, Colin b.1943, *Running Grey*, presented by the Scottish Arts Council, 1997, © the artist

Clark, William 1731–1801, *Hall of the Old Tolbooth, c.1795*, unknown acquisition method

Clarkson, Kathleen b.1950, *Jetty One*, purchased from the artist, 1972

Clausen, George 1852–1944, *Still Life with Cucumber and Tomatoes*, presented by the Scottish Modern Arts Association, 1964, © Clausen estate

Clays, Paul Jean 1819–1900, *The Port of Leith*, purchased, 1984, photo credit: City of Edinburgh Council, City Art Centre

Collingbourne, Stephen b.1943, *Sunset Strip*, purchased with the assistance of the Jean F. Watson Bequest Fund and the National Fund for Acquisitions, 1989, © the artist

Colombo, Russell b.1947, *Reeker Pike*, purchased with the assistance of the Jean F. Watson Bequest Fund and the National Fund for Acquisitions, 1990, © the artist

Colquhoun, Robert 1914–1962, *Circus Woman*, purchased from the Crane Kalman Gallery with the assistance of government grant-in-aid, 1976, © the artist's estate/Bridgeman Art Library, photo credit: City of Edinburgh Council, City Art Centre

Colquhoun, Robert 1914–1962, *Bitch and Pup*, purchased with the assistance of the Jean F. Watson Bequest Fund and the National Fund for Acquisitions, 1984, © the artist's estate/Bridgeman Art Library

Condie, Robert Hardie 1898–1981, *Winter Landscape*, presented by the Scottish Modern Arts Association, 1964

Connard, Philip 1875–1958, *Self Portrait with Still Life*, presented by the Scottish Modern Arts Association, 1964

Connon, William John b.1929, *Anticoli, Italy*, purchased from the artist with the assistance of the Jean F. Watson Bequest Fund, 1965, © the artist

Convery, Francis b.1956, *Model Resting (Night Class)*, purchased with the assistance of the Jean F. Watson Bequest Fund and the National Fund for Acquisitions, 1995, © the artist, photo credit: City of Edinburgh Council, City Art Centre

Cook, David b.1957, *The Sound of the Drum Is Calling*, presented by the Scottish Arts Council, 1997

Cossaar, Jacobus Cornelis Wyand 1874–1966, *Reredos, St Paul's Cathedral, London* (destroyed during the Second World War), presented by the Scottish Modern Arts Association, 1964

Couling, Arthur Vivian 1890–1962, *Yew Tree Farm, near Coniston, Cumbria*, presented by the Scottish Modern Arts Association, 1964

Coward, Charles R. b.1950, *Landscape Number 3*, purchased from the artist, 1972

Cowie, James 1886–1956, *Mists in the Valley*, presented by the Scottish Modern Arts Association, 1964, © the artist's estate

Crawford, Edmund Thornton 1806–1885, *A Dutch River Scene*, purchased with the assistance of the Jean F. Watson Bequest Fund and the National Fund for Acquisitions, 1982

Crayk, Fred b.1952, *Capital: Lovers*, purchased from the artist with the assistance of the Jean F. Watson Bequest Fund, 1986, © the artist

Crayk, Fred b.1952, *Small Inverleith Park*, presented by the Scottish Arts Council, 1997, © the artist

Crowe, Victoria b.1945, *Beech Tree, Winter*, purchased with the assistance of the Jean F. Watson Bequest Fund and the National Fund for Acquisitions, 2009, © Victoria Crowe

Crowe, Victoria b.1945, *Dr Winifred Rushforth (1885–1983)*, purchased with the assistance of the Jean F. Watson Bequest Fund and the National Fund for Acquisitions, 1982, © Victoria Crowe

Crowe, Victoria b.1945, *The Last Portrait of Jenny Armstrong*, purchased with the assistance of the Jean F. Watson Bequest Fund and the National Fund for Acquisitions, 2007, © Victoria Crowe

Crowe, Victoria b.1945, *Tom Morgan, Lord Provost of Edinburgh (1980–1984)*, commissioned with the assistance of the Jean F. Watson Bequest Fund and the General Purposes Committee, 1988, © Victoria Crowe

Crowe, Victoria b.1945, *Italian Reflections*, purchased with the assistance of the Jean F. Watson Bequest Fund and the National Fund for Acquisitions, 2007, © Victoria Crowe

Crowe, Victoria b.1945, *Dancer and Graffiti*, donated by the artist, 2009, © Victoria Crowe

Crozier, William 1893–1930, *View from the Mound, Edinburgh, Looking West*, presented by the Scottish Modern Arts Association, 1964

Crozier, William 1930–2011, *St James's Park*, purchased with the assistance of the Jean F. Watson Bequest Fund and the National Fund for Acquisitions, 1989, © the estate of William Crozier/ courtesy Flowers Gallery, London, photo credit: City of Edinburgh Council, City Art Centre

Cumming, James 1922–1991, *Charred Table with Lamp and Tins*, purchased from the artist with the assistance of the Jean F. Watson Bequest Fund, 1962, © the artist's estate

Cumming, James (attributed to) 1732–1793, *William MacGregor, an Edinburgh Porter*, purchased, 1984

Cumming, John Begg 1884–1968, *Self Portrait*, presented by the artist's sister, 1976

Cursiter, Stanley 1887–1976, *Synthesis of the Supper Room at an Arts Club Reception*, purchased from Mrs Margaret Hunter, 1979, © estate of Stanley Cursiter 2012. All rights reserved, DACS, photo credit: City of Edinburgh Council, City Art Centre

Cursiter, Stanley 1887–1976, *Tea Room*, purchased from Mrs Margaret Hunter, 1979, © estate of Stanley Cursiter 2012. All rights reserved, DACS, photo credit: City of Edinburgh Council, City Art Centre

Cursiter, Stanley 1887–1976, *A Glass of Milk*, presented by the Scottish Modern Arts Association, 1964, © estate of Stanley Cursiter 2012. All rights reserved, DACS

Cursiter, Stanley 1887–1976, *The Fair-Isle Jumper*, presented by the Scottish Modern Arts Association, 1964, © estate of Stanley Cursiter 2012. All rights reserved, DACS, photo credit: City of Edinburgh Council, City Art Centre

Cursiter, Stanley 1887–1976, *Sir Louis Stewart Gumley (1872–1941), LLD, Lord Provost of Edinburgh (1935–1938)*, commissioned, 1939, © estate of Stanley Cursiter 2012. All rights reserved, DACS

Cursiter, Stanley 1887–1976, *Sir John Ireland Falconer, LLD, WS, Lord Provost of Edinburgh (1944–1947)*, commissioned, 1948, © estate of Stanley Cursiter 2012. All rights reserved, DACS

Cursiter, Stanley 1887–1976, *Sir John Garnett Banks, CBE, LLD, Lord Provost of Edinburgh (1954–1957)*, commissioned, 1958, © estate of Stanley Cursiter 2012. All rights reserved, DACS

Cursiter, Stanley 1887–1976, *Pachmann at the Usher Hall, Edinburgh*, presented by Mrs Margaret Hunter, 1980, © estate of Stanley Cursiter 2012. All rights reserved, DACS

Davidson, Bessie 1879–1965, *Interior*, presented by the Scottish Modern Arts Association, 1964

Davie, Alan b.1920, *Scented Arrow*, purchased, 1986, © the artist, photo credit: City of Edinburgh Council, City Art Centre

Davie, Alan b.1920, *Serpent's Breath*, purchased with the assistance of the Jean F. Watson Bequest Fund, with grants from the National Fund for Acquisitions and the National Art Collections Fund, 1996, © the artist, photo credit: City of Edinburgh Council, City Art Centre

Delacour, William 1700–1767, *View of Edinburgh*, presented by Captain Ramsay of White Hill, 1922, photo credit: City of Edinburgh Council, City Art Centre

Dingwall, Kenneth b.1938, *Shield*, presented by the Scottish Arts Council, 1997, © the artist

Dingwall, Kenneth b.1938, *Calm Grey*, presented by the Scottish Arts Council, 1997, © the artist

Dixon, Arthur Percy active 1884–1917, *Bailie Waterson*, unknown acquisition method

Dobson, Cowan 1894–1980, *Sir Henry Steele (1879–1963), DL, Lord Provost of Edinburgh (1938–1941)*, commissioned, 1942

Dobson, Cowan 1894–1980, *Sir William Lowrie Sleigh, DL, LLD, JP, Lord Provost of Edinburgh (1923–1926)*, commissioned, 1927

Dobson, Henry Raeburn 1901–1985, *Sir Herbert Archbold Brechin, KBE, DLitt, Lord Provost of Edinburgh (1966–1969)*, commissioned, c.1970

Donald, George Malcolm b.1943, *Stuffed Bird*, purchased from the artist with the assistance of the Jean F. Watson Bequest Fund, 1972, © the artist, photo credit: City of Edinburgh Council, City Art Centre

Donald, George Malcolm b.1943, *Blue Dragon Altar*, gift from Sheila Slatkowski, 2009, © the artist

Donald, George Malcolm b.1943, *Red Dragon Altar*, purchased with the assistance of the Jean F. Watson Bequest Fund and the National Fund for Acquisitions, 1990, © the artist

Donaldson, David Abercrombie 1916–1996, *Sir James Wilson Mackay (1912–1992), DLitt, Lord Provost of Edinburgh (1969–1972)*, commissioned, c.1973, © the artist's estate

Donaldson, David Abercrombie 1916–1996, *Sir John Greig Dunbar (b.1907), Lord Provost of Edinburgh (1960–1963)*, commissioned, c.1964, © the artist's estate

Donaldson, David Abercrombie 1916–1996, *The Pink Room, Young Girl*, presented by the Scottish Modern Arts Association, 1964, © the artist's estate

Donaldson, David Abercrombie 1916–1996, *Two Glasgow Girls*, purchased from the artist with the assistance of the Jean F. Watson Bequest Fund and the National Fund for Acquisitions, 1983, © the artist's estate

Dorrat, Gwen Debbie b.1964, *Untitled*, purchased with the assistance of the Jean F. Watson Bequest Fund, 1986

Douglas, William Fettes 1822–1891, *The Bibliophilist's Haunt (Creech's Bookshop)*, purchased with the assistance of the Jean F. Watson Bequest Fund and the National Fund for Acquisitions, 1982

Douglas, William Fettes 1822–1891, *The Village of the Water of Leith from a Window in Rothesay Terrace*, purchased with the assistance of the Jean F. Watson Bequest Fund and the National Fund for Acquisitions, 1980, photo credit: City of Edinburgh Council, City Art Centre

Douthwaite, Pat 1939–2002, *Woman with White Hair*, presented by the Scottish Arts Council, 1997, © the artist's estate

Douthwaite, Pat 1939–2002, *Final Instructions before Take-Off*, purchased from the artist with the assistance of government grant-in-aid, 1977, © the artist's estate

Douthwaite, Pat 1939–2002, *Dr Helen Wright*, purchased with the assistance of the Jean F. Watson Bequest Fund and the National Fund for Acquisitions, 1993, © the artist's estate, photo credit: City of Edinburgh Council, City Art Centre

Douthwaite, Pat 1939–2002, *Suffolk Landscape*, purchased with the assistance of the Jean F. Watson Bequest Fund, 1986, © the artist's estate

Dow, Thomas Millie 1848–1919, *Roses*, presented by the Scottish Modern Arts Association, 1964

Downie, Kate b.1958, *Leith Docks, Perimeter Road, Edinburgh*, purchased from the artist with the assistance of the Jean F. Watson Bequest Fund and the National Fund for Acquisitions, 1990, © the artist

Downie, Kate b.1958, *The Coal Yard*, commissioned, 1988, © the artist, photo credit: City of Edinburgh Council, City Art Centre

Drummond, James 1816–1877, *Sabbath Evening*, unknown acquisition method, photo credit: City of Edinburgh Council, City Art Centre

Drummond, James 1816–1877, *Tam o' Shanter*, presented by the artist

Drummond, Les 1920–1997, *The Bull that Dreamed of Immortality*, donated by Mrs Norma Drummond, 2002, © City of Edinburgh Council

Duguid, Henry Gibson 1805–1860, *Castlehill, Edinburgh, As It Was before Alterations, c.1849*, donated as part of the Whitson Bequest, 1948

Duncan, John 1866–1945, *Hymn to the Rose*, presented by the Scottish Modern Arts Association, 1964, © estate of John Duncan. All rights reserved, DACS 2012, photo credit: City of Edinburgh Council, City Art Centre

Duncan, John 1866–1945, *Tristan and Isolde*, presented by the Scottish Modern Arts Association, 1964, © estate of John Duncan. All rights reserved, DACS 2012, photo credit: City of Edinburgh Council, City Art Centre

Duncan, John 1866–1945, *Aoife*, presented by the Scottish Modern Arts Association, 1964, © estate of John Duncan. All rights reserved, DACS 2012, photo credit: City of Edinburgh Council, City Art Centre

Duncan, John 1866–1945, *Jehanne d'Arc et sa garde Ecossaise*, unknown acquisition method, © estate of John Duncan. All rights reserved, DACS 2012, photo credit: City of Edinburgh Council, City Art Centre

Duncan, John 1866–1945, *The Challenge*, presented by the Scottish Modern Arts Association, 1964, © estate of John Duncan. All rights reserved, DACS 2012, photo credit: City of Edinburgh Council, City Art Centre

Duncan, John 1866–1945, *The Children of Lir*, presented by the Scottish Modern Arts Association, 1964, © estate of John Duncan. All rights reserved, DACS 2012, photo credit: City of Edinburgh Council, City Art Centre

Duncan, John 1866–1945, *The Taking of Excalibur*, presented by the Scottish Modern Arts Association, 1964, © estate of John Duncan. All rights reserved, DACS 2012, photo credit: City of Edinburgh Council, City Art Centre

Durward, Graham b.1966, *Blood Goes on Being Red*, purchased with the assistance of the Jean F. Watson Bequest Fund and the National Fund for Acquisitions, 1986, © courtesy of the artist and Maureen Paley, London, photo credit: City of Edinburgh Council, City Art Centre

Duthie, Philip G. b.1957, *Trembling Veil II*, presented by the Scottish Arts Council, 1997, © the artist

Eardley, Joan Kathleen Harding 1921–1963, *Farmhouse Stove*, presented by the Scottish Arts Council, 1997, © DACS 2012

Eardley, Joan Kathleen Harding 1921–1963, *Seascape*, purchased with the assistance of the Jean F. Watson Bequest Fund and the National Fund for Acquisitions, 1985, © DACS 2012, photo credit: City of Edinburgh Council, City Art Centre

Eardley, Joan Kathleen Harding 1921–1963, *Summer Grasses and Barley on the Clifftop*, purchased from the artist, 1962, © DACS 2012, photo credit: City of Edinburgh Council, City Art Centre

Eardley, Joan Kathleen Harding 1921–1963, *July Fields*, presented by the Scottish Modern Arts Association, 1959, © DACS 2012, photo credit: City of Edinburgh Council, City Art Centre

Edgar, James R. c.1819–1876, *Sir John Melville (1802–1860), WS, Lord Provost of Edinburgh (1845–1859)*, presented by Mrs Maud Melville, 1948

Egan, Felim b.1952, *Land-Score*, presented by the Contemporary Art Society, 1992 © Felim Egan

Emmott, Constance active early 20th C, *From Swanston Bungalow, 1913*, unknown acquisition method

Evans, David Pugh b.1942, *Cheap Rooms*, presented by the Scottish Arts Council, 1997, © the artist

Evans, David Pugh b.1942, *Late Steaming*, purchased with the assistance of the Friends of the City Art Centre and Museums and the Local Museums Purchase Fund, 1983, © the artist

Evans, David Pugh b.1942, *The Bridge*, purchased from the artist with the assistance of the Jean F. Watson Bequest Fund, 1972, © the artist

Ewart, David Shanks 1901–1965, *Sir Ian A. Johnston-Gilbert (1892–1974), CBE, LLD, Lord Provost of Edinburgh (1957–1960)*, commissioned, c.1961

Ewbank, John Wilson c.1799–1847, *The Entry of George IV into Edinburgh from the Calton Hill, 1822*, unknown acquisition method, photo credit: City of Edinburgh Council, City Art Centre

Ewbank, John Wilson c.1799–1847, *The Military Review on the Occasion of George IV's Visit to Edinburgh*, presented by Miss M. S. S. Macfie, 1960, photo credit: City of Edinburgh Council, City Art Centre

Faed, James the younger 1857–1920, *At Cramond, Early Spring*, purchased with the assistance of the Jean F. Watson Bequest Fund and the National Fund for Acquisitions, 1996, photo credit: City of Edinburgh Council, City Art Centre

Faed, Thomas 1826–1900, *Study for 'Sir Walter Scott and His Literary Friends at Abbotsford'*, presented by William Watt, 1967, photo credit: City of Edinburgh Council, City Art Centre

Fairclough, Wilfred 1907–1996, *Olivelli's*, presented by the Scottish Modern Arts Association, 1964, © the artist's estate

Fairgrieve, James H. b.1944, *Cosimo Portulano*, purchased from the artist with the assistance of the Jean F. Watson Bequest Fund, 1969, © the artist

Fairgrieve, James H. b.1944, *Winter Feed*, presented by the Scottish Arts Council, 1997, © the artist

Fairgrieve, James H. b.1944, *Bari, Sea Dog*, purchased from the artist with the assistance of the Jean F. Watson Bequest Fund, 1969, © the artist

Fergusson, John Duncan 1874–1961, *The Blue Hat, Closerie des Lilas*, purchased from Margaret Morris Fergusson, 1962, © The Fergusson Gallery, Perth and Kinross Council, Scotland, photo credit: City of Edinburgh Council, City Art Centre

Fergusson, John Duncan 1874–1961, *The Blue Lamp*, presented by the Scottish Modern Arts Association, 1964, © The Fergusson Gallery, Perth and Kinross Council, Scotland, photo credit: City of Edinburgh Council, City Art Centre

Fergusson, John Duncan 1874–1961, *Villa Gotte Garden*, purchased with the assistance of the Jean F. Watson Bequest Fund and the National Fund for Acquisitions, 1983, © The Fergusson Gallery, Perth and Kinross Council, Scotland

Fergusson, John Duncan 1874–1961, *Study for 'Les Tilleuls, Bécheron, France'*, purchased with the assistance of the Jean F. Watson Bequest Fund and the National Fund for Acquisitions, 1997, © The Fergusson Gallery, Perth and Kinross Council, Scotland

Fergusson, John Duncan 1874–1961, *Les Tilleuls, Bécheron*, purchased with the assistance of the Jean F. Watson Bequest Fund and the Local Museums Purchase Fund, 1978, © The Fergusson Gallery, Perth and Kinross Council, Scotland

Flannigan, Moyna b.1963, *Monuments*, presented by the Scottish Arts Council, 1997, © the artist

Flannigan, Moyna b.1963, *Happy Valley (I)*, purchased with the assistance of the Jean F. Watson Bequest Fund and the National Fund for Acquisitions, 2002, © the artist, photo credit: City of Edinburgh Council, City Art Centre

Fleming, Ian 1906–1994, *Kirn Pier, Winter*, presented by the Scottish Modern Arts Association, 1960, © the artist's estate, photo credit: City of Edinburgh Council, City Art Centre

Fleming, Ian 1906–1994, *Early Morning, Winter*, presented by the Scottish Arts Council, 1997, © the artist's estate

Fleming, John B. 1792–1845, *Robert Andrew Macfie (1811–1893)*, presented by Miss M. S. S. Macfie, 1960

Flockhart, Helen b.1963, *Maire*, purchased with the assistance of the Jean F. Watson Bequest Fund and the National Fund for Acquisitions, 1992, © the artist, photo credit: City of Edinburgh Council, City Art Centre

Foggie, David Simpson 1878–1948, *Dreams*, presented by the Scottish Modern Arts Association, 1964, © the artist's estate

Foggie, David Simpson 1878–1948, *Joanne*, unknown acquisition method, © the artist's estate

Ford, John A. active 1880–1923, *The Right Honourable Ronald Craufurd Munro Ferguson (1860–1934), LLD, MP (1884–1885 & 1886–1914)*, presented by the sitter to the town of Leith

Ford, John A. active 1880–1923, *Malcolm Smith (1856–1935), Provost of Leith (1908–1917), MP (1921–1922)*, presented to the town of Leith by public subscription

Ford, John A. active 1880–1923, *John A. Lindsay (1865–1942), CBE, Provost of Leith (1917–1920)*, presented to the town of Leith by public subscription

Forster, David b.1962, *'For the thorns and bushes laid hold of them as it were with hands, and there they were stuck fast and died miserably'*, purchased from the artist with the assistance of the Jean F. Watson Bequest Fund and the National Fund for Acquisitions, 2005, © the artist

Forster, David b.1962, *'And yet in the midst of the sky there was still a bit of blue'*, purchased from the artist with the assistance of the Jean F. Watson Bequest Fund and the National Fund for Acquisitions, 2005, © the artist

Foulis, James 1770–1842, *James Gillespie of Spylaw (1726–1797), Founder of Gillespie's Hospital*, transferred from the Department of Education, Edinburgh Corporation, c.1975.

Fraser, Alexander 1827–1899, *Barncluith Well, South Lanarkshire*, on long-term loan from Dundee Art Galleries and Museums Collection (Dundee City Council)

Fraser, Alexander 1827–1899, *Cadzow Forest, South Lanarkshire*, presented by the Scottish Modern Arts Association, 1964

Fraser, Alexander b.1940, *Boat Underfoot*, presented by the Scottish Arts Council, 1997, © the artist

Fraser, Alexander b.1940, *More Room*, presented by the Scottish Arts Council, 1997, © the artist

Frazer, William Miller 1864–1961, *Landscape*, unknown acquisition method, © the artist's estate

Frazer, William Miller 1864–1961, *On the Nene, Northamptonshire*, presented by Mrs J. G. Neilson, 1969, © the artist's estate

Fulton, David 1848–1930, *Kyles of Bute*, purchased with the assistance of the Jean F. Watson Bequest Fund, 1985

Gage, Edward 1925–2000, *Fishermen, Falconera, Greece*, purchased from the artist with the assistance of the Jean F. Watson Bequest Fund, 1965, © the artist's estate

Gage, Edward 1925–2000, *Lluch Alcari, Deia, Mallorca, Spain*, purchased from the artist with the assistance of the Jean F. Watson Bequest Fund, 1965, © the artist's estate, photo credit: City of Edinburgh Council, City Art Centre

Gallagher, Mary b.1953, *Flowers from Aberdeen*, purchased at auction with the assistance of the Jean F. Watson Bequest Fund, 1984

Gallagher, Mary b.1953, *Sunflowers*, purchased at auction with the assistance of the Jean F. Watson Bequest Fund, 1984, photo credit: City of Edinburgh Council, City Art Centre

Galt, Alexander Milligan 1913–2000, *Vera*, presented by the Scottish Modern Arts Association, 1964, © by kind permission of the Galt family

Gauld, David 1865–1936, *Spring Morning*, presented by the Scottish Modern Arts Association, 1964, photo credit: City of Edinburgh Council, City Art Centre

Gavin, Charles b.1944, *Los perros cazadores (de Balboa)*, purchased from the artist with the assistance of the Jean F. Watson Bequest Fund, 1986

Gear, William 1915–1997, *Summer Fête*, purchased from the artist with the assistance of the Jean F. Watson Bequest Fund and government grant-in-aid, 1985, © the artist's estate, photo credit: City of Edinburgh Council, City Art Centre

Geddes, Andrew (attributed to) 1783–1844, *Daft Jamie (James Wilson, 1810–1828), One of the Victims of Burke and Hare*, presented by A. E. Haswell Millar, Deputy Director of the National Galleries of Scotland, 1952

Geikie, Walter 1795–1837, *Edinburgh from the South*, purchased with the assistance of government grant-in-aid, 1982, photo credit: City of Edinburgh Council, City Art Centre

Geikie, Walter 1795–1837, *A Hallow Fair Scene*, presented, 1935

Geikie, Walter 1795–1837, *Fisherfolk at Their Boats*, presented, 1935

Geikie, Walter 1795–1837, *Woodland Scene*, presented, 1935

Gibb, Peter James b.1951, *Wave*, purchased from the artist, 1974, © the artist

Gibb, Robert II 1845–1932, *William Law (1799–1878), Lord Provost of Edinburgh (1869–1872)*, presented by Mrs John Law, 1930

Gibbons, Carole b.1935, *Figure in a Landscape*, presented by the Scottish Arts Council, 1997, © the artist

Gibbons, Carole b.1935, *Waiting Figure in a Landscape*, presented by the Scottish Arts Council, 1997, © the artist

Gibroy, C. *Ye Auld Smithy, Roseburn, Edinburgh*, presented by Alexander Murray, 1966

Gibson, Patrick 1782–1829, *View of Edinburgh from the Calton Hill*, presented by James Wilson, 1899, photo credit: City of Edinburgh Council, City Art Centre

Gillespie, Joan b.1954, *Riviera Afternoon*, purchased with the assistance of the Jean F. Watson Bequest Fund and the National Fund for Acquisitions, 1993, © the artist, photo credit: City of Edinburgh Council, City Art Centre

Gillies, William George 1898–1973, *Emma*, on loan from Mrs Diane Fletcher, © Royal Scottish Academy, photo credit: City of Edinburgh Council, City Art Centre

Gillies, William George 1898–1973, *Sisters Emma and Janet*, on loan from Mrs Diane Fletcher, © Royal Scottish Academy, photo credit: City of Edinburgh Council, City Art Centre

Gillies, William George 1898–1973, *Woods at Humbie, East Lothian*, on loan from Mrs Diane Fletcher, © Royal Scottish Academy

Gillies, William George 1898–1973, *The Green Dish*, presented by the Scottish Modern Arts Association, 1964, © Royal Scottish Academy

Gillies, William George 1898–1973, *Interior, Temple Cottage*, on loan from Mrs Diane Fletcher, © Royal Scottish Academy, photo credit: City of Edinburgh Council, City Art Centre

Gillies, William George 1898–1973, *Studio Table*, on loan from Mrs Diane Fletcher, © Royal Scottish Academy, photo credit: City of Edinburgh Council, City Art Centre

Gillies, William George 1898–1973, *Arniston Woods, Midlothian*, on loan from Mrs Diane Fletcher, © Royal Scottish Academy

Gillies, William George 1898–1973, *Back Gardens, Temple*, purchased from the artist, 1967, © Royal Scottish Academy, photo credit: City of Edinburgh Council, City Art Centre

Gillies, William George

1898–1973, *Landscape, 1932*, purchased from the Royal Scottish Academy with the assistance of the Lillie Bequest, the Jean F. Watson Bequest and government grant-in-aid, 1983, © Royal Scottish Academy

Gillies, William George 1898–1973, *Moorfoot*, presented by the National Art Collections Fund, 1988, © Royal Scottish Academy

Gillies, William George 1898–1973, *River Tyne near Haddington, East Lothian*, on loan from Mrs Diane Fletcher, © Royal Scottish Academy

Gillies, William George 1898–1973, *Shadowed Interior*, purchased from the artist with the assistance of the Jean F. Watson Bequest Fund, 1970, © Royal Scottish Academy, photo credit: City of Edinburgh Council, City Art Centre

Gillies, William George 1898–1973, *Studio Table*, on loan from Mrs Diane Fletcher, © Royal Scottish Academy

Gillies, William George 1898–1973, *Temple, Dusk*, purchased from the artist with the assistance of the Jean F. Watson Bequest Fund, 1968, © Royal Scottish Academy, photo credit: City of Edinburgh Council, City Art Centre

Gillies, William George 1898–1973, *Woods at Arniston, Midlothian*, gift from Mrs E. F. Catford, 1992, © Royal Scottish Academy, photo credit: City of Edinburgh Council, City Art Centre

Gillies, William George 1898–1973, *Woods at Temple*, on loan from Mrs Diane Fletcher, © Royal Scottish Academy

Glass, John 1820–1885, *Companions*, presented by Mrs Drummond, 1953

Glass, John 1820–1885, *High School Yards, Edinburgh*, presented by Mrs Drummond, 1953

Glass, John 1820–1885, *Interior of a Highland Cottage*, presented by Mrs Drummond, 1953

Glen, George b.1965, *Beyond the Rock*, purchased from the artist with the assistance of the Jean F. Watson Bequest Fund, 1988

Glen, Graham active 1895–1925, *Meditation*, presented by the Scottish Modern Arts Association, 1964

Gloag, Isobel Lilian 1865–1917, *A Bunch of Flowers*, presented by the Scottish Modern Arts Association, 1964

Gordon, Carola Rosemary Helen b.1940, *The Old Town, Edinburgh*, donated by the artist, 2009, © the artist

Gordon, John Watson 1788–1864, *Mrs Campbell*, donated by Dr Ian H. Barclay, 1994

Gordon, John Watson 1788–1864, *Adam Black (1784–1874), Lord Provost of Edinburgh (1843–1848)*,

unknown acquisition method

Gordon, John Watson 1788–1864, *Sir Walter Scott (1771–1832), at Abbotsford*, unknown acquisition method

Gordon, John Watson 1788–1864, *Sir William Johnston of Kirkhill (1802–1888), Lord Provost of Edinburgh (1848–1851)*, presented by the Royal Scottish Academy, 1975

Goudie, Alexander 1933–2004, *Jack Kane (1911–1999), Dr (h.c.), Lord Provost of Edinburgh (1972–1975)*, commissioned, 1977, © the artist's estate/Bridgeman Art Library

Graham, Thomas Alexander Ferguson 1840–1906, *Boats in a Harbour*, presented by the Scottish Modern Arts Association, 1964

Graham-Gilbert, John 1794–1866, *Charles Lawson of Borthwick Hall (d.1874), Lord Provost of Edinburgh (1862–1865)*, unknown acquisition method

Graham-Gilbert, John (attributed to) 1794–1866, *Portrait of a Lady*, unknown acquisition method

Grant, Francis 1803–1878, *Sir Walter Scott (1771–1832), in His Study*, presented by William Watt, 1967

Grant, Thomas F. active 1868–1879, *The Drongs, Shetlands*, presented by Miss M. S. S. Macfie, 1960

Grant, Thomas F. active 1868–1879, *View from Craigmillar, Edinburgh*, presented by Miss M. S. S. Macfie

Gray, Euan b.1973, *Enchanted Days*, purchased from the artist with the assistance of the Jean F. Watson Bequest Fund, 1996, © the artist

Gray, George active c.1874–1909, *Sunset, Highland Landscape with Cattle*, presented by Bailie Russell

Gray, George active c.1874–1909, *The Tweed at Abbotsford, Melrose*, presented by Bailie Russell

Green, Alfred H. b.c.1822, *A Newhaven Fishwife*, presented by Miss E. M. Mein, 1969, photo credit: City of Edinburgh Council, City Art Centre

Green, Alfred H. b.c.1822, *Mending the Nets, Newhaven, East Sussex*, purchased with the assistance of the Jean F. Watson Bequest Fund and the National Fund for Acquisitions, 1994, photo credit: City of Edinburgh Council, City Art Centre

Grieve, Alec 1864–1933, *Will o' the Wisp*, presented by the Scottish Modern Arts Association, 1964

Gunn, Herbert James 1893–1964, *James Pryde (1866–1941)*, presented by the Scottish Modern Arts Association, 1964, © estate of the artist

Gunn, Herbert James 1893–1964, *Sir Thomas B. Whitson (1869–1948), DL, LLD, Lord Provost of Edinburgh (1929–1932)*, commissioned, c.1932, © estate of

the artist

Gunn, Herbert James 1893–1964, *Sir William Young Darling (1885–1962), Lord Provost of Edinburgh (1941–1944)*, commissioned, c.1944, © estate of the artist, photo credit: City of Edinburgh Council, City Art Centre

Guthrie, James 1859–1930, *Archibald Stodart Walker (1869–1934), MA, MB, OBE*, presented by the Scottish Modern Arts Association, 1964, photo credit: City of Edinburgh Council, City Art Centre

Guthrie, James 1859–1930, *Study of 'Sir John James Burnet (1857–1938), RSA'*, presented by the Scottish Modern Arts Association, 1964

Hadden, Robert active 1876–1889, *View of Portobello from the West*, purchased with the assistance of the Jean F. Watson Bequest Fund and government grant-in-aid, 1983, photo credit: City of Edinburgh Council, City Art Centre

Hähnisch, Anton 1817–1897, *Miss Sarah Lumsden Smith*, presented by Colonel R. J. Maule Horne, 1964

Haig, George Douglas 1918–2009, *Leaderfoot, Scottish Borders*, purchased from the artist with the assistance of the Jean F. Watson Bequest Fund, 1963, © the artist's estate

Haig, George Douglas 1918–2009, *Campo San Vio, Venice*, purchased by the Friends of the City Art Centre and Museums, 1997, © the artist's estate, photo credit: City of Edinburgh Council, City Art Centre

Haig, George Douglas 1918–2009, *Gateheugh*, presented by the Scottish Modern Arts Association, 1964, © the artist's estate, photo credit: City of Edinburgh Council, City Art Centre

Halkerston, Charles 1829–1899, *Princes Street from the Mound, Edinburgh*, purchased with the assistance of government grant-in-aid, 1982, photo credit: City of Edinburgh Council, City Art Centre

Hall, George Wright 1895–1974, *Studio Interior with Figure*, presented by the Friends of the City Art Centre and Museums, 1975

Hall, James W. 1797–1854, *Show Jamie', 1842*, presented by Peter Wood, 1920

Halliday, Dorothy 1923–2001, *Double Portrait*, bequeathed by the artist, 2002, © the artist's estate

Halliday, Dorothy 1923–2001, *MacTavish*, bequeathed by the artist, 2002, © the artist's estate

Hamilton, James Whitelaw 1860–1932, *A West Highland Loch*, presented by the Scottish Modern Arts Association, 1964

Hamilton, James Whitelaw

1860–1932, *At Mayford, Surrey*, presented by the Scottish Modern Arts Association, 1964

Hamilton, James Whitelaw 1860–1932, *Landscape, Kirkcudbright, Dumfries and Galloway*, presented by the Scottish Modern Arts Association, 1964

Hansen, Lys b.1936, *Stance*, purchased with the assistance of the Jean F. Watson Bequest Fund and government grant-in-aid, 1985, © Lys Hansen

Hardie, Charles Martin 1858–1916, *Robert Burns (1759–1796)*, unknown acquisition method

Hardie, Gwen b.1962, *Coupling*, purchased with the assistance of the Jean F. Watson Bequest Fund and government grant-in-aid, 1990, © the artist

Harvey, George (after) 1806–1876, *Robert Macfie (1746–1827)*, presented by Miss M. S. S. Macfie, 1960

Hawkins, James b.1954, *The Shore of the Loch*, purchased from the artist, 1997, © the artist, photo credit: City of Edinburgh Council, City Art Centre

Henderson, Joseph 1832–1908, *The Storm, Ballantrae, South Ayrshire*, presented by the Scottish Modern Arts Association, 1964

Henderson, Keith 1883–1982, *Scottish Landscape*, presented by the Scottish Modern Arts Association, 1964

Hendriksen, Harry b.1937, *Two Cravens*, commissioned, 1981

Henry, George 1858–1943, *Poppies*, presented by the Scottish Modern Arts Association, 1964, photo credit: City of Edinburgh Council, City Art Centre

Henry, George 1858–1943, *The Chalk Pit*, presented by the Scottish Modern Arts Association, 1964

Herdman, Robert Duddingstone 1863–1922, *Borrowed Plumes*, unknown acquisition method

Herdman, Robert Inerarity 1829–1888, *Sir James Falshaw (1810–1889), Bt, Lord Provost of Edinburgh (1874–1877)*, unknown acquisition method

Herdman, William Gawin 1805–1882, *View of the Mound, Edinburgh*, purchased, 1986, photo credit: City of Edinburgh Council, City Art Centre

Herdman, William Gawin 1805–1882, *View of the Lawnmarket, Edinburgh*, bequeathed by Mrs M. A. Green, 1960, photo credit: City of Edinburgh Council, City Art Centre

Highmore, Joseph (attributed to) 1692–1780, *Andrew Bell (1726–1809)*, presented to the City by the publishers of the Encyclopaedia Britannica, 1926

Hill, David Octavius 1802–1870, *In Memoriam: The Calton*, purchased through Dowell's Ltd, Edinburgh, 1964

Hill, David Octavius 1802–1870, *Old Edinburgh, Showing the Castle from Greyfriars Churchyard*, presented by Sir Edward Moss of Middleton, 1909, photo credit: City of Edinburgh Council, City Art Centre

Hislop, Joseph 1884–1977, *Landscape** gift from Joseph Hislop, son of the artist, 1992

Hislop, Margaret 1894–1972, *Girl in Green*, purchased from the artist with the assistance of the Jean F. Watson Bequest Fund, 1965

Hock-Aun-Teh b.1950, *Summer in Beijing, China*, purchased with the assistance of the Jean F. Watson Bequest Fund and government grant-in-aid, 1990

Hodder, Charles D. 1835–1926, *An Old Piper*, presented by Miss A. L. J. Hodder, 1934

Hodges, J. Sidney Willis 1829–1900, *John Coutts (1699–1750), Lord Provost of Edinburgh (1743–1744) (after Allan Ramsay)*, presented by Baroness Burdett Coutts, 1873

Hogg, Alistair b.1966, *Where is Your Superhero Now?*, purchased from the artist with the assistance of the Jean F. Watson Bequest Fund, 1989

Hole, William Brassey 1846–1917, *After Flodden*, unknown acquisition method

Hole, William Brassey 1846–1917, *The Coronation of King James II at Holyrood, 1437*, presented by Sir James Steel, c.1903

Hole, William Brassey 1846–1917, *The Signing of the National Covenant in Greyfriars Churchyard, 1638*, presented by H. E. Moss of Middleton

Hole, William Brassey 1846–1917, *The State Entry of Queen Mary into Edinburgh, 1561*, presented by Sir M. Mitchell Thomson, c.1905

Hole, William Brassey 1846–1917, *The Presentation of a Charter to the Burgesses of Edinburgh by King Robert the Bruce at Cardross, 1329*, presented by the Covenery and Incorporated Trades of Edinburgh, c.1907

Hole, William Brassey 1846–1917, *Queen Mary Brought Captive to Edinburgh from Carberry Hill, 1567*, presented by Lieutenant Colonel James Clark, c.1910

Hole, William Brassey 1846–1917, *Queen Mary's First Farewell to Scotland, 1548*, presented by Lieutenant Colonel James Clark, c.1910

Hole, William Brassey 1846–1917, *News of Flodden*, presented by the Right Honourable James Pickering Gibson, 1906

Hole, William Brassey 1846–1917, *News of the Accession of James VI to the Throne of England, 1603*, presented by Dr Walter B. Blaikie

Hole, William Brassey 1846–1917, *Prince Charles Edward Stuart in Edinburgh, 1745*, presented by the Society of High Constables of

Edinburgh

Holmes, Charles John 1868–1936, *The Head of Wensleydale, Yorkshire*, presented by the Scottish Modern Arts Association, 1964

Home, Bruce James 1830–1912, *Brodie's Close, Edinburgh*, purchased, 1913

Honder, J. L. active 1905, *General Douglas Haig (1861–1928)*, presented by Earl Haig of Bemersyde, 1964

Hone, Nathaniel II 1831–1917, *The Derelict*, presented by the Scottish Modern Arts Association, 1964

Hood, Angus b.1962, *Nobody Worried*, purchased from the artist with the assistance of the Jean F. Watson Bequest Fund, 1985

Hope, Robert 1869–1936, *The Presentation by King James III and Queen Margaret of the Banner Known as the Blue Blanket to the Craftsmen in the Year 1482*, presented by Councillor Inman, 1912

Hope, Robert 1869–1936, *Swanston Farm, Edinburgh*, presented by the National Art Collections Fund, 1988

Hope, Robert 1869–1936, *An Old Herd*, presented by the Scottish Modern Arts Association, 1964

Hope, Robert 1869–1936, *Edinburgh from Craiglockhart*, presented by Alexander Hope and Isabella Hope Henry, c.1937

Hope, Robert 1869–1936, *Edinburgh from the Arboretum*, presented by Alexander Hope and Isabella Hope Henry, c.1937

Hope, Robert 1869–1936, *No.8 Howard Place, Edinburgh, 1914*, presented by the Edinburgh and District Water Trust

Hope, Robert 1869–1936, *No.17 Heriot Row, Edinburgh*, presented by the Edinburgh and District Water Trust

Hope, Robert 1869–1936, *Swanston and Caerketton in Winter, Edinburgh*, presented by the Edinburgh and District Water Trust

Hope, Robert 1869–1936, *Swanston Cottage, Edinburgh*, unknown acquisition method

Hope, Robert 1869–1936, *The Blue Veil*, presented by the Scottish Modern Arts Association, 1964

Hope, Robert 1869–1936, *The Remnant Stall*, presented by the Scottish Modern Arts Association, 1964, photo credit: City of Edinburgh Council, City Art Centre

Hopkins, Louise b.1965, *Relief (739)* (diptych, left wing), purchased with the assistance of the Jean F. Watson Bequest Fund and the National Fund for Acquisitions, 2007, © the artist

Hopkins, Louise b.1965, *Relief (739)* (diptych, right wing), purchased with the assistance of the Jean F. Watson Bequest Fund and the National Fund for Acquisitions, 2007, © the artist

Horne, R. J. Maule *Kilchurn Castle, Argyllshire*

Hornel, Edward Atkinson 1864–1933, *In the Orchard*, presented by the Scottish Modern Arts Association, 1964, photo credit: City of Edinburgh Council, City Art Centre

Hornel, Edward Atkinson 1864–1933, *Seashore Roses*, presented by the Scottish Modern Arts Association, 1964, photo credit: City of Edinburgh Council, City Art Centre

Horsburgh, John A. 1835–1924, *James Pringle (1822–1886), Provost of Leith (1881–1886)*, bequeathed by Christina L. Pringle, 1890

Horsburgh, John A. 1835–1924, *Thomas Hutchison (1796–1852), Provost of Leith (1845–1848)*, presented to the town of Leith by public subscription, c.1887

Horsburgh, John A. 1835–1924, *William Lindsay (1819–1884), Provost of Leith (1860–1866)*, presented to the town of Leith by Mrs Carlow

Hosie, David b.1962, *New Town*, presented by the Scottish Arts Council, 1997, © the artist

Houston, George 1869–1947, *Early Morning*, presented by the Scottish Modern Arts Association, 1964, © the artist's estate

Houston, John 1930–2008, *Beach and Night Sky*, purchased from the artist with the assistance of the Jean F. Watson Bequest Fund, 1968, © the artist's estate, photo credit: City of Edinburgh Council, City Art Centre

Houston, John 1930–2008, *Winter Sea, North Berwick, East Lothian*, purchased from the exhibition 'Scottish Art: 2 Generations' with the assistance of the Jean F. Watson Bequest Fund and government grant-in-aid, 1983, © the artist's estate

Houston, John 1930–2008, *Elizabeth with Yellow Lily*, purchased with the assistance of the Jean F. Watson Bequest Fund and government grant-in-aid, 1983, © the artist's estate, photo credit: City of Edinburgh Council, City Art Centre

Houston, John 1930–2008, *Summer Sea*, purchased from the Royal Scottish Academy with the assistance of the Jean F. Watson Bequest Fund and government grant-in-aid, 1988, © the artist's estate, photo credit: City of Edinburgh Council, City Art Centre

Howard, Ian b.1952, *The Priest, the Beast and the Rest* (triptych, left wing), purchased with the assistance of the Jean F. Watson Bequest Fund, 1985 © the artist

Howard, Ian b.1952, *The Priest, the Beast and the Rest* (triptych, centre panel), purchased with the assistance of the Jean F. Watson Bequest Fund, 1985 © the artist

Howard, Ian b.1952, *The Priest, the Beast and the Rest* (triptych, right wing), purchased with the assistance of the Jean F. Watson Bequest Fund, 1985 © the artist

Howe, James 1780–1836, *All Hallows Fair on the Boroughmuir, Edinburgh*, presented

Howe, James 1780–1836, *The Horse Fair in the Grassmarket, Edinburgh*, purchased, 1980, photo credit: City of Edinburgh Council, City Art Centre

Howson, Peter b.1958, *Study for 'Backstreet Crucifixion'*, purchased with the assistance of the Jean F. Watson Bequest Fund and the National Fund for Acquisitions, 2007, © the artist/ courtesy Flowers Galllery, London

Howson, Peter b.1958, *Regimental Bath*, purchased with the assistance of the Jean F. Watson Bequest Fund and the National Fund for Acquisitions, 1990, © the artist/ courtesy Flowers Galllery, London, photo credit: City of Edinburgh Council, City Art Centre

Hughes, Ian b.1958, *Consumed by Fire*, purchased from the artist with the assistance of the Jean F. Watson Bequest Fund and the National Fund for Acquisitions, 1993, © the artist, photo credit: City of Edinburgh Council, City Art Centre

Hughes, Ian b.1958, *Self Portrait (1)*, gift from the artist, 1993, © the artist, photo credit: City of Edinburgh Council, City Art Centre

Hughes, Ian b.1958, *Self Portrait (2)*, gift from the artist, 1993, © the artist, photo credit: City of Edinburgh Council, City Art Centre

Hughes, Ian b.1958, *Self Portrait (3)*, gift from the artist, 1993, © the artist, photo credit: City of Edinburgh Council, City Art Centre

Hughes, Ian b.1958, *Self Portrait (4)*, gift from the artist, 1993, © the artist, photo credit: City of Edinburgh Council, City Art Centre

Hunter, George Leslie 1877–1931, *Pathway, Loch Lomond*, presented by the Scottish Modern Arts Association, 1964, photo credit: City of Edinburgh Council, City Art Centre

Hutchison, George active 1957, *Old Canonmills as It Was in c.1875*, presented by the artist, 1957

Hutchison, Robert Gemmell 1855–1936, *A Christmas Morning*, on loan from Miss Elizabeth Black

Hutchison, Robert Gemmell 1855–1936, *Sleep*, purchased with the assistance of the Jean F. Watson Bequest Fund and government grant-in-aid, 1983, photo credit: City of Edinburgh Council, City Art Centre

Hutchison, Robert Gemmell 1855–1936, *The New Sabot*, presented by the Scottish Modern

Arts Association, 1964

Hutchison, William Oliphant 1889–1970, *Sir Andrew Murray (1903–1977/1978), OBE, LLD, Lord Provost of Edinburgh (1947–1951)*, commissioned, 1951, © the artist's estate

Hutchison, William Oliphant 1889–1970, *Sir James Miller (1905–1977), LLD, Lord Provost of Edinburgh (1951–1954)*, commissioned, 1956, © the artist's estate

Innes, Callum b.1962, *Exposed Painting, Black/Red Oxide*, purchased with the assistance of the Jean F. Watson Bequest Fund, the National Fund for Acquisitions and the National Art Collection Fund, 2000, © the artist

Irvine, Olivia b.1960, *Figures in an Interior*, purchased from the artist with the assistance of the Jean F. Watson Bequest Fund, 1985, © the artist

Irvine, Olivia b.1960, *Rain*, purchased with the assistance of the Jean F. Watson Bequest Fund and government grant-in-aid, 1990, © the artist, photo credit: City of Edinburgh Council, City Art Centre

Isbister, Arlene b.1966, *From Red (Sister)*, purchased from the artist with the assistance of the Jean F. Watson Bequest Fund, 1990, © the artist

Jacob, Julius I (attributed to) 1811–1882, *Baroness Burdett Coutts (1814–1906)*, presented by the sitter, c.1873

Jenkins, Arthur Henry 1871–1940, *The Scent of the Rose*, presented by Mrs M. Threlfall, c.1978

Johansen, John Christian 1876–1964, *Sir Douglas Haig (1861–1928), FM, in His Study*, presented by Earl Haig of Bemersyde, 1964

Johnstone, Dorothy 1892–1980, *Study for 'Rest Time in the Life Class'*, presented by the artist, 1980, © the artist's estate

Johnstone, Dorothy 1892–1980, *Study for 'Rest Time in the Life Class'*, presented by the artist, 1980, © the artist's estate

Johnstone, Dorothy 1892–1980, *Rest Time in the Life Class*, purchased from the artist with the assistance of the Jean F. Watson Bequest Fund and government grant-in-aid, 1980, © the artist's estate

Johnstone, John 1937–2001, *Dream*, purchased from the artist with the assistance of the Jean F. Watson Bequest Fund, 1965

Johnstone, William 1897–1981, *Untitled*, presented by the Scottish Arts Council, 1997, © the artist's estate

Johnstone, William 1897–1981, *Hugh MacDiarmid (1892–1978) (Christopher M. Grieve)*, purchased from the artist's widow with the assistance of the Jean F. Watson Bequest Fund, 1985, © the artist's

estate

Johnstone, William 1897–1981, *Sanctuary*, purchased from the artist's widow with the assistance of the Jean F. Watson Bequest Fund and government grant-in-aid, 1988, © the artist's estate

Johnstone, William 1897–1981, *Wotan*, purchased from the artist's widow with the assistance of the Jean F. Watson Bequest Fund and government grant-in-aid, 1988, © the artist's estate

Kay, Archibald 1860–1935, *Winter Sunshine*, presented by the Scottish Modern Arts Association, 1964, photo credit: City of Edinburgh Council, City Art Centre

Kay, James 1858–1942, *Harbour and Figures*, purchased with the assistance of the Jean F. Watson Bequest Fund and government grant-in-aid, 1979

Kay, John (style of) 1742–1826, *The Parliament Close and Public Characters of Edinburgh, 50 Years Since*, donated as part of the Whitson Bequest, 1948, photo credit: City of Edinburgh Council, City Art Centre

Keith, Alexander active 1808–1874, *Portrait of a Gentleman (possibly Dr Hill)*, unknown acquisition method

Kenyon-Wade, Corinna b.1961, *Assembly Rooms, Edinburgh*, purchased from the artist with the assistance of the Jean F. Watson Bequest Fund, 1985, © the artist

Kerr, Henry Wright 1857–1936, *Thomas Aitken (1832–1912), Provost of Leith (1887–1893)*, presented to the town of Leith by public subscription, 1893

Knott, Tavernor 1816–1890, *Bailie Robert Cranston (1815–1892)*, presented by Robert Cranston, son of the sitter, 1903

Knox, Jack b.1936, *Square and Constellation*, purchased from the artist with the assistance of the Jean F. Watson Bequest Fund, 1963, © the artist

Knox, Jack b.1936, *Chair with Hat, Île de Ré*, purchased from the artist with the assistance of the Friends of the City Art Centre and Museums and government grant-in-aid, 1988, © the artist, photo credit: City of Edinburgh Council, City Art Centre

Knox, Jack b.1936, *Flower Piece*, bequeathed by the estate of Hazel Heughan, 1993, © the artist, photo credit: City of Edinburgh Council, City Art Centre

Kondracki, Henry b.1953, *The Red Park*, purchased from the artist with the assistance of the Jean F. Watson Bequest Fund, 1997, © the artist, photo credit: City of Edinburgh Council, City Art Centre

Lamb, Henry 1883–1960, *The Elliott Family*, bequeathed by Lord Archibald Elliott, 2009, © estate of Henry Lamb

Lamb, Henry 1883–1960, *Oil Sketch of Lord Elliott*, bequeathed by the sitter, 2009, © estate of Henry Lamb

Lauder, Robert Scott 1803–1869, *John Lauder of Silvermills (1768–1838)*, unknown acquisition method

Lauder, Robert Scott (school of) 1803–1869, *William Macfie of Clermiston (1822–1895)*, presented by Miss M. S. S. Macfie, 1960

Lavery, John 1856–1941, *Miss Esther Joanna Marie McLaren (d.1950) and Mrs Katherine Oliver, née McLaren (c.1870–1966)*, purchased with the assistance of the Jean F. Watson Bequest Fund, 1981, © by courtesy of Felix Rosensteil's Widow and Son Ltd, London on behalf of the estate of Sir John Lavery

Lavery, John 1856–1941, *View of Edinburgh from the Castle*, purchased with the assistance of the Jean F. Watson Bequest Fund and the National Fund for Acquisitions, 1994, © by courtesy of Felix Rosensteil's Widow and Son Ltd, London on behalf of the estate of Sir John Lavery, photo credit: City of Edinburgh Council, City Art Centre

Lawrie, Hamish 1919–1987, *Scalpay Croft, Harris*, purchased from the artist, 1974

Lawson, Thomas b.1951, *Untitled*, presented by the Scottish Arts Council, 1997, © the artist

Le Conte, John 1816–1887, *Cardinal Beaton's House, Cowgate, Edinburgh*, unknown acquisition method, photo credit: City of Edinburgh Council, City Art Centre

Leggett, Alexander 1828–1884, *Sale of Bait: The Arrival of the Mussel Boats, Newhaven*, purchased with the assistance of the Jean F. Watson Bequest Fund and the National Fund for Acquisitions, 2007

Leishman, Robert 1916–1989, *Fountains*, presented by the Scottish Arts Council, 1997, © the artist's estate

Leyde, Otto Theodor 1835–1897, *Sir Thomas Jamieson Boyd, Master of the Edinburgh Merchant Company (1869–1871), Lord Provost of Edinburgh (1877–1882)*, presented by members of the Company of Merchants of the City of Edinburgh, c.1873

Lintott, Henry John 1877–1965, *Sir Alexander Stevenson (1860–1936), LLD, DL, Lord Provost of Edinburgh (1926–1929)*, commissioned, 1931

Lintott, Henry John 1877–1965, *Modo Crepuscolare*, presented by the Scottish Modern Arts Association, 1964, photo credit: City of Edinburgh Council, City Art Centre

Lintott, Henry John 1877–1965, *Near Surrey*, purchased through the Royal Scottish Academy

Exhibition with the assistance of the Jean F. Watson Bequest Fund, 1965

Lintott, Henry John 1877–1965, *Portrait of a Lady*, presented by the Scottish Modern Arts Association, 1964

Lizars, William Home 1788–1859, *The Old Town Guard*, unknown acquisition method

Lizars, William Home (attributed to) 1788–1859, *The Edinburgh Old Town Guard*, unknown acquisition method

Lorimer, John Henry 1856–1936, *The Flight of the Swallows*, presented by the Scottish Modern Arts Association, 1964, photo credit: City of Edinburgh Council, City Art Centre

Low, Bet 1924–2007, *Merge and Emerge*, presented by the Scottish Arts Council, 1997, © Bet Low Charitable Trust

Lucas, Edwin George 1911–1990, *Pentland Hills from Kingsknowe, Winter*, gift from Mr A. Lucas, 2003, © estate of Edwin George Lucas www.EdwingLucas.com

Lucas, Edwin George 1911–1990, *Caley Station, Edinburgh, 1942*, presented by the artist, 1990, © estate of Edwin George Lucas www.EdwingLucas.com

MacArthur, Lindsay Grandison c.1866–1945, *Coasting, Ceylon*, presented by the Scottish Modern Arts Association, 1964

MacArthur, Lindsay Grandison c.1866–1945, *Dawn over Galilee*, presented by the Scottish Modern Arts Association, 1964

Macbeth, Norman 1821–1888, *Mrs Adam Primrose*, presented, 1961

Macbeth, Norman 1821–1888, *William Forrest (1805–1889), ARA*, presented by J. Forrest, 1965

MacBride, William 1856–1913, *The Sheepfold*, presented by the Scottish Modern Arts Association, 1964

MacBryde, Robert 1913–1966, *Woman at Fireplace, No.1*, purchased with the assistance of the Jean F. Watson Bequest Fund and government grant-in-aid, 1988

Macdonald, Arthur active 1895–1940, *The Bell Rock Lighthouse*, donated as part of the Guthrie Bequest, 1926

MacEwan, Geoffrey b.1943, *Lanark Market*, donated by Dr J. Munro, 1998, © the artist

MacGeorge, William Stewart 1861–1931, *Kirkcudbright*, presented by the Scottish Modern Arts Association, 1964, photo credit: City of Edinburgh Council, City Art Centre

Macgillivray, James Pittendrigh 1856–1938, *The Tea Table*, presented by the Scottish Modern Arts Association, 1964, photo credit: City of Edinburgh Council, City Art Centre

MacGoun, Hannah Clarke Preston 1864–1913, *Cupid*, presented by the Scottish Modern

Arts Association, 1964

MacGoun, Hannah Clarke Preston 1864–1913, *St Andrew's Fisherfolk*, presented by the Scottish Modern Arts Association, 1964

MacGregor, William York 1855–1923, *The Quarry* (sketch), presented by the Scottish Modern Arts Association, 1964

MacGregor, William York 1855–1923, *Melrose*, presented by the Scottish Modern Arts Association, 1964, photo credit: City of Edinburgh Council, City Art Centre

Mackenzie, Andrew b.1969, *Ribmarkings*, purchased from the artist with the assistance of the Jean F. Watson Bequest Fund, 1992, © the artist

Mackenzie, William Murray active 1880–1908, *Joppa Saltpans*, purchased with the assistance of government grant-in-aid, 1974

Mackie, Charles Hodge 1862–1920, *'There were three maidens pu'd a flower (by the bonnie banks o' Fordie)'*, purchased with the assistance of the Jean F. Watson Bequest Fund and government grant-in-aid, 1982

Mackie, Charles Hodge 1862–1920, *Study for 'La piazzetta, Venice'*, presented by the Scottish Modern Arts Association, 1964

Mackie, Charles Hodge 1862–1920, *La piazzetta, Venice*, presented by the Scottish Modern Arts Association, 1964, photo credit: City of Edinburgh Council, City Art Centre

Mackie, Charles Hodge 1862–1920, *La musica veneziana*, presented by the Scottish Modern Arts Association, 1964

Mackie, Charles Hodge 1862–1920, *Artis ancilla*, presented by the Scottish Modern Arts Association, 1964

Mackie, Charles Hodge 1862–1920, *In the Borghese Gardens*, presented by the Scottish Modern Arts Association, 1964

Mackie, Charles Hodge 1862–1920, *Margaret Cumming*, presented by the sitter, c.1973

Mackie, Charles Hodge 1862–1920, *St Monans, Fife*, presented by the Scottish Modern Arts Association, 1964

Mackie, Peter Robert Macleod 1867–1959, *Flowers of Springtime*, presented by the Scottish Modern Arts Association, 1964

Maclagan, Philip Douglas 1901–1972, *San Gimignano, Italy, 1925*, presented by Dorothea F. Maclagan, 1981, © the artist's estate

Maclagan, Philip Douglas 1901–1972, *Still Life, Peony and Primrose*, presented by Dorothea F. Maclagan, 1981, © the artist's estate

MacLaren, John Stewart 1860–c.1929, *James Crichton (1808–1889)*, unknown acquisition

method

Maclaurin, Robert b.1961, *In Eastern Territory*, purchased with the assistance of the Jean F. Watson Bequest Fund and government grant-in-aid, 1988, © the artist, photo credit: City of Edinburgh Council, City Art Centre

Maclaurin, Robert b.1961, *Theatrical Scene*, purchased from the artist with the assistance of the Jean F. Watson Bequest Fund, 1984, © the artist

MacNee, Daniel 1806–1882, *Burns and 'Highland Mary'*, presented by the artist

MacNicol, Bessie 1869–1904, *Baby Crawford*, presented by the Scottish Modern Arts Association, 1964, photo credit: City of Edinburgh Council, City Art Centre

MacNicol, Bessie 1869–1904, *Portrait of a Lady (The Green Hat)*, presented by the Scottish Modern Arts Association, 1964, photo credit: City of Edinburgh Council, City Art Centre

MacTaggart, William 1903–1981, *Some Yellow Flowers*, presented by the Scottish Arts Council, 1997, © by permission of the artist's family

MacTaggart, William 1903–1981, *Storm Cloud*, purchased from the artist with the assistance of the Jean F. Watson Bequest Fund, 1966, © by permission of the artist's family, photo credit: City of Edinburgh Council, City Art Centre

MacTaggart, William 1903–1981, *A Glimpse of Stockholm*, presented by the Scottish Modern Arts Association, 1964, © by permission of the artist's family

MacTaggart, William 1903–1981, *Autumn Leaves*, purchased from the artist with the assistance of government grant-in-aid, 1975, © by permission of the artist's family, photo credit: City of Edinburgh Council, City Art Centre

MacTaggart, William 1903–1981, *Still Life with an Oval Table*, purchased with the assistance of the Jean F. Watson Bequest Fund and government grant-in-aid, 1981, © by permission of the artist's family, photo credit: City of Edinburgh Council, City Art Centre

MacTaggart, William 1903–1981, *Telemark, Norway, Revisited*, purchased from the artist with the assistance of the Jean F. Watson Bequest Fund, 1966, © by permission of the artist's family

MacWhirter, John 1839–1911, *Edinburgh from Corstorphine*, presented by the Scottish Modern Arts Association, 1964

Main, Kirkland b.1942, *Shelter*, presented by the Scottish Arts Council, 1997, © the artist

Malcolm, Ellen 1923–2002, *Flower Piece*, purchased from the artist with the assistance of the Jean F.

Watson Bequest Fund, 1965, © the artist's estate

Malietoa, Savea 1914–1994, *Robert Louis Stevenson (1850–1894), in Bed*, presented by James Rough, 1969

Malietoa, Savea 1914–1994, *Samoan Taupou Officiating at the Keva Ceremony*, presented by James Rough, 1969

Mann, Harrington 1864–1936, *Annabel*, presented by the Scottish Modern Arts Association, 1964

Martin, David 1736/1737–1798, *Gilbert Laurie (1729–1809), Lord Provost of Edinburgh (1766–1768 & 1772–1774)*, purchased with the assistance of the Jean F. Watson Bequest Fund and the National Fund for Acquisitions, 2002, photo credit: City of Edinburgh Council, City Art Centre

Massys, Quinten (imitator of) 1466–1530, *The Philosopher*, presented by Miss M. D. Bouthron, 1914

Maxwell, John 1905–1962, *Man with Flowers*, on loan from Ms Veronica Fletcher

Maxwell, John 1905–1962, *The Trellis*, on loan from Ms Veronica Fletcher

Maxwell, John 1905–1962, *Birds against the Sun*, on loan from Ms Veronica Fletcher

Maxwell, John 1905–1962, *Figure and a Bird with a Jug of Flowers*, on loan from Ms Veronica Fletcher, photo credit: City of Edinburgh Council, City Art Centre

Maxwell, John 1905–1962, *The Window*, on loan from Ms Veronica Fletcher

Maxwell, John 1905–1962, *Flowers and Frost Flowers*, presented by the Scottish Modern Arts Association, 1964, photo credit: City of Edinburgh Council, City Art Centre

Maxwell, John 1905–1962, *Garden at Night (Moth)*, on loan from Ms Veronica Fletcher

Maxwell, John 1905–1962, *Harvest Moon*, on loan from Ms Veronica Fletcher

McArtney, Sylvia active 1976, *Waiting for the Tide*, purchased from the artist, 1976

McCall, Charles James 1907–1989, *At the Dressing Table*, purchased from the artist with the assistance of the Jean F. Watson Bequest Fund and government grant-in-aid, 1978, © the artist's estate/Bridgeman Art Library

McCall, Charles James 1907–1989, *London Street in Snow*, presented by the Scottish Modern Arts Association, 1964, © the artist's estate/Bridgeman Art Library

McCance, William 1894–1970, *Kimono Study*, purchased with the assistance of the Jean F. Watson Bequest Fund, the National Fund for Acquisitions, the National Art Collections Fund and the Friends of the City Art Centre and Museums, 1998, © the artist's estate, photo credit: City of Edinburgh Council, City Art Centre

McCarthy, Robin b.1957, *It's all Upside Down*, purchased with the assistance of the Jean F. Watson Bequest Fund and government grant-in-aid, 1989

McCheyne, Alistair 1918–1981, *The Seaside Photographer*, presented, 1982

McClure, David 1926–1998, *Joyce a Firenze*, purchased with the assistance of the Jean F. Watson Bequest Fund and government grant-in-aid, 1989, © the artist's estate

McClure, David 1926–1998, *Boat at Gourdon, France*, purchased from the artist with the assistance of the Jean F. Watson Bequest Fund, 1966, © the artist's estate

McClure, David 1926–1998, *The Mirror II*, purchased from the artist with the assistance of the Jean F. Watson Bequest Fund, 1966, © the artist's estate, photo credit: City of Edinburgh Council, City Art Centre

McClure, David 1926–1998, *Girl Pinning up Her Hair*, donated by Anna V. Hossack, 1990, © the artist's estate

McClure, David 1926–1998, *Bananas and Pansies II*, presented by the Scottish Arts Council, 1997, © the artist's estate

McCulloch, Ian b.1935, *Palm Sunday: Uitenhage*, purchased with the assistance of the Jean F. Watson Bequest Fund and government grant-in-aid, 1986, © the artist, photo credit: City of Edinburgh Council, City Art Centre

McDougall, Lily Martha Maud 1875–1958, *Roses against a Striped Background*, presented by the Scottish Modern Arts Association, 1964

McFadyen, Jock b.1950, *Watney Market, London*, presented by the Contemporary Art Society, 1988, © the artist, photo credit: City of Edinburgh Council, City Art Centre

McGlashan, Archibald A. 1888–1980, *Still Life*, purchased from the artist with the assistance of the Jean F. Watson Bequest Fund, 1962, © the artist's estate

McGlashan, Archibald A. 1888–1980, *The Sleeping Child*, presented by the Scottish Modern Arts Association, 1964, © the artist's estate

McGowan, Gerald b.1949, *Cafeteria*, purchased, 2005, © the artist

McGregor, Robert 1847–1922, *Gathering Stones*, presented by the Scottish Modern Arts Association, 1964, photo credit: City of Edinburgh Council, City Art Centre

McIntyre, Peter 1910–1995, *Dunedin*, presented by the citizens of Dunedin, 1947, © the artist's

estate, photo credit: City of Edinburgh Council, City Art Centre

McKay, William Darling 1844–1924, *Summer at Kilspindie*, presented by the Scottish Modern Arts Association, 1964, photo credit: City of Edinburgh Council, City Art Centre

McLachlan, Thomas Hope 1845–1897, *The Wind on the Hill*, presented by the Scottish Modern Arts Association, 1964

McLaren, Peter b.1964, *Cyclist*, purchased from the artist with the assistance of the Jean F. Watson Bequest Fund, 1986, © the artist

McLaren, Peter b.1964, *Lovers in a Car*, presented to the City of Edinburgh by British Airways, 1989, © the artist, photo credit: City of Edinburgh Council, City Art Centre

McLaurin, Duncan 1848–1921, *Home from the Plough*, presented by the Scottish Modern Arts Association, 1964

McLaurin, Duncan 1848–1921, *Moorland and Mist*, presented by the Scottish Modern Arts Association, 1964

McLean, Bruce b.1944, *Ladder Head*, presented by the Contemporary Art Society, 1992, © the artist

McLean, Bruce b.1944, *Untitled*, bequeathed, 2008, © the artist

McLean, John b.1939, *Whaup*, purchased with the assistance of the Jean F. Watson Bequest Fund and the National Fund for Acquisitions, 1995, © the artist, photo credit: City of Edinburgh Council, City Art Centre

McNab, Janice b.1964, *Chairs 3*, purchased with the assistance of the Jean F. Watson Bequest Fund, The National Fund for Acquisitions and the National Collecting Scheme for Scotland, 2008, © the artist

McNairn, Caroline 1955–2010, *In the Making*, purchased with the assistance of the Jean F. Watson Bequest Fund and government grant-in-aid, 1987, © the artist's estate, photo credit: City of Edinburgh Council, City Art Centre

McNairn, John 1910–2009, *Crail, Fife*, purchased from the artist, 1994, © the artist's estate, photo credit: City of Edinburgh Council, City Art Centre

McNairn, John 1910–2009, *Garden at Broomhill*, purchased from the artist, 1994, © the artist's estate

McNeish, Alexander 1932–2000, *Beach Still Life*, presented by the Scottish Arts Council, 1997

McNeish, Alexander 1932–2000, *The Table*, presented by Nigel McIsaac, 1982

McNeish, Alexander 1932–2000, *Red Rift*, purchased from the artist with the assistance of the Jean F. Watson Bequest Fund, 1964

McNeish, Alexander 1932–2000,

Small Dreaming Stone, purchased from the artist with the assistance of the Jean F. Watson Bequest Fund, 1964

McTaggart, William 1835–1910, *Flotsam and Jetsam*, presented by the Scottish Modern Arts Association, 1964, photo credit: City of Edinburgh Council, City Art Centre

McTaggart, William 1835–1910, *Running for Shelter*, presented by the Scottish Modern Arts Association, 1964, photo credit: City of Edinburgh Council, City Art Centre

McTaggart, William 1835–1910, *Noontide, Jovie's Neuk*, presented by the Scottish Modern Arts Association, 1964, photo credit: City of Edinburgh Council, City Art Centre

McTaggart, William 1835–1910, *The Preaching of St Columba*, presented by the Scottish Modern Arts Association, 1964, photo credit: City of Edinburgh Council, City Art Centre

McTaggart, William (attributed to) 1835–1910, *Portrait of a Boy*, presented by the Scottish Modern Arts Association, 1964

McVeigh, Michael b.1957, *The City Art Centre*, commissioned, 1991, © the artist, photo credit: City of Edinburgh Council, City Art Centre

Mellis, Margaret 1914–2009, *Sea*, purchased with the assistance of the Jean F. Watson Bequest Fund and the National Fund for Acquisitions, 1998, © the estate of Margaret Mellis, photo credit: City of Edinburgh Council, City Art Centre

Melville, Arthur 1855–1904, *Homeward*, purchased with the assistance of the Jean F. Watson Bequest Fund and government grant-in-aid, 1977, photo credit: City of Edinburgh Council, City Art Centre

Melville, Arthur 1855–1904, *A Scene in Tunis*, presented by the Scottish Modern Arts Association, 1964

Michie, David Alan Redpath b.1928, *Public Beach*, purchased from the artist with the assistance of the Jean F. Watson Bequest Fund, 1965, © the artist/ Bridgeman Art Library, photo credit: City of Edinburgh Council, City Art Centre

Michie, David Alan Redpath b.1928, *Accordion, Saxophone and Drum*, bequeathed by Mr Trevor Clark, 2009, © the artist/ Bridgeman Art Library

Michie, David Alan Redpath b.1928, *Dark Garden with a Yellow Border*, purchased from the Royal Scottish Academy with the assistance of the Jean F. Watson Bequest Fund and government grant-in-aid, 1989, © the artist/ Bridgeman Art Library

Miller, John 1911–1975, *Still Life*

with Chrysanthemums, purchased from the artist with the assistance of the Jean F. Watson Bequest Fund, 1964

Miller, Josephine 1890–1975, *The House on the Canal*, presented by the Scottish Modern Arts Association, 1964, photo credit: City of Edinburgh Council, City Art Centre

Miller, Robert b.1910, *Tea in the Garden*, purchased, 1985, photo credit: City of Edinburgh Council, City Art Centre

Milne, John Maclauchlan 1885–1957, *Achmelvich*, presented by the Scottish Modern Arts Association, 1964, © John Maclauchlan Milne, care of Portland Gallery, London, photo credit: City of Edinburgh Council, City Art Centre

Milne, Maggie b.1957, *The Diggers' Triptych* (left wing), commissioned as part of the 'Should Auld Acquaintance Be Forgot' exhibition, 1988, © the artist, photo credit: City of Edinburgh Council, City Art Centre

Milne, Maggie b.1957, *The Diggers' Triptych* (centre panel), commissioned as part of the 'Should Auld Acquaintance Be Forgot' exhibition, 1988, © the artist, photo credit: City of Edinburgh Council, City Art Centre

Milne, Maggie b.1957, *The Diggers' Triptych* (right wing), commissioned as part of the 'Should Auld Acquaintance Be Forgot' exhibition, 1988, © the artist, photo credit: City of Edinburgh Council, City Art Centre

Mitchell, John Campbell 1865–1922, *Landscape, the Plains of Lora*, presented by the Scottish Modern Arts Association, 1964

Mitchell, John Campbell 1865–1922, *Edinburgh from Corstorphine Hill*, presented by the National Art Collections Fund, 1988

Moodie, Donald 1892–1963, *A Frosty Morning*, purchased from the artist with the assistance of the Jean F. Watson Bequest Fund, 1964

Mooney, John b.1948, *Operation without an Aesthetic*, purchased from the Talbot Rice Gallery with the assistance of the Jean F. Watson Bequest Fund and the National Fund for Acquisitions, 1990, © the artist, photo credit: City of Edinburgh Council, City Art Centre

Mooney, John b.1948, *Phoenix I*, presented by the Scottish Arts Council, 1997, © the artist

Morris, Oliver active 1866–1895, *John Traill (1835–1897), Master of Greyfriars Bobby*, presented by Joan Leitch, 1962

Morrison, James b.1932, *Grasses and Trees on Craigs Road*, purchased from the artist with the

assistance of the Jean F. Watson Bequest Fund and government grant-in-aid, 1985, © the artist

Morrison, Neil *Apple*, purchased from the artist with the assistance of the Jean F. Watson Bequest Fund, 1972

Morrocco, Alberto 1917–1998, *The Pub*, presented by the Scottish Modern Arts Association, 1964, © the artist's estate, photo credit: City of Edinburgh Council, City Art Centre

Morrocco, Alberto 1917–1998, *Still Life with Clay Pipe*, purchased from the artist with the assistance of the Jean F. Watson Bequest Fund and government grant-in-aid, 1985, © the artist's estate

Morrocco, Alberto 1917–1998, *Calle de Coseolano Rosas*, presented by the Scottish Modern Arts Association, 1964, © the artist's estate

Morrocco, Leon Francesco b.1942, *Dried Corn*, purchased with the assistance of the Jean F. Watson Bequest Fund, 1966, © the artist/ Bridgeman Art Library

Mosman, William c.1700–1771, *James Stuart, Lord Provost of Edinburgh (1764–1766 & 1768–1770)*, presented by M. V. Erskine Stuart, 1930

Munro, David active 1846–1872, *John Macfie (1783–1852)*, presented by M. S. S. Macfie, 1960

Murray, David 1849–1933, *Woodland Landscape*, unknown acquisition method

Murray, David 1849–1933, *The Half Moon*, presented by the Scottish Modern Arts Association, 1964, photo credit: City of Edinburgh Council, City Art Centre

Murray, Graeme James b.1963, *East of Eden*, purchased from the artist with the assistance of the Jean F. Watson Bequest Fund, 1986, © the artist

Narzynski, Juliusz b.1934, *A Play for Nothing*, purchased with the assistance of the Jean F. Watson Bequest Fund, 1967

Nasmyth, Alexander 1758–1840, *Edinburgh from the Calton Hill*, unknown acquisition method

Nasmyth, Alexander 1758–1840, *The Port of Leith*, presented by the Right Honourable Earl of Rosebery, 1944, photo credit: City of Edinburgh Council, City Art Centre

Nasmyth, Alexander (after) 1758–1840, *Robert Burns (1759–1796)*, unknown acquisition method

Nasmyth, Alexander (attributed to) 1758–1840, *The Old Tolbooth of Edinburgh during Demolition*, presented by Sir William Younger, 1960

Nasmyth, Patrick 1787–1831, *Edinburgh from the Water of Leith*, presented by Councillor James F. Gibson, 1896, photo credit: City of

Edinburgh Council, City Art Centre

Nerli, Girolamo Pieri 1853–1926, *Robert Louis Stevenson (1850–1894), Vailima, Samoa*, donated as part of the Guthrie Bequest, 1926

Nerli, Girolamo Pieri 1853–1926, *A Friend of the Stevenson Household, 1892*, donated as part of the Guthrie Bequest, 1926, photo credit: City of Edinburgh Council, City Art Centre

Newbery, Francis Henry 1855–1946, *Daydreams*, presented by the Scottish Modern Arts Association, 1964, photo credit: City of Edinburgh Council, City Art Centre

Nicholson, William 1872–1949, *The Black Mirror*, presented by the Scottish Modern Arts Association, 1964, © Elizabeth Banks, photo credit: City of Edinburgh Council, City Art Centre

Nicolson, John 1843–1934, *Andrew Lamb's House, Leith*, unknown acquisition method

Nisbet, Pollok Sinclair 1848–1922, *John Knox's House, High Street, Edinburgh, 1885*, presented by Sir Robert and Lady Cranston, 1928

Nisbet, Robert Buchan 1857–1942, *The Bend of the River*, presented by the Scottish Modern Arts Association, 1964

Nixon, Jacqui Miller b.1964, *Frequently Confused*, purchased with the assistance of the Jean F. Watson Bequest Fund, 1987, © the artist

Noble, Robert 1857–1917, *A Misty Morning*, presented by the Scottish Modern Arts Association, 1964, photo credit: City of Edinburgh Council, City Art Centre

Noble, Robert 1857–1917, *Dovecot, East Linton, East Lothian*, presented by the National Art Collections Fund, 1988

Noble, Robert 1857–1917, *Plainstane's Close, Edinburgh, 1878*, unknown acquisition method

Norie, Robert active 1840–1850, *Martello Tower, Leith, Low Water*, purchased with the assistance of the Jean F. Watson Bequest Fund and the National Fund for Acquisitions, 2003

O'Connor, Marcel b.1958, *Two Flags on Purple*, purchased with the assistance of the Jean F. Watson Bequest Fund and the National Fund for Acquisitions, 1994, © the artist

Ogilvie, Elizabeth b.1946, *Sea Journals* (triptych, left wing), purchased with the assistance of the Jean F. Watson Bequest Fund and government grant-in-aid, 1988, © the artist, photo credit: City of Edinburgh Council, City Art Centre

Ogilvie, Elizabeth b.1946, *Sea Journals* (triptych, centre panel), purchased with the assistance of the Jean F. Watson Bequest Fund and government grant-in-aid, 1988, © the artist, photo credit:

City of Edinburgh Council, City Art Centre

Ogilvie, Elizabeth b.1946, *Sea Journals* (triptych, right wing), purchased with the assistance of the Jean F. Watson Bequest Fund and government grant-in-aid, 1988, © the artist, photo credit: City of Edinburgh Council, City Art Centre

Onwin, Glen b.1947, *Subterranean Fire*, donated by the artist, 2007, © the artist

Onwin, Glen b.1947, *Subterranean Water*, purchased from the artist with the assistance of the Jean F. Watson Bequest Fund and government grant-in-aid, 1989, © the artist, photo credit: City of Edinburgh Council, City Art Centre

Oppenheimer, Charles 1875–1961, *A Late Snowfall, Galloway*, presented by the Scottish Modern Arts Association, 1964

Orchardson, William Quiller 1832–1910, *In the Picture Gallery*, presented by the Scottish Modern Arts Association, 1964, photo credit: City of Edinburgh Council, City Art Centre

Owens, H. *Trawler 'GW34'*, donated by Mr H. Stevenson, 2002

Park, Alistair 1930–1984, *Yachting Lake*, presented by the Scottish Arts Council, 1997, © the artist's estate

Park, Alistair 1930–1984, *Blue Little Man*, presented by the Scottish Arts Council, 1997, © the artist's estate

Park, Stuart 1862–1933, *Pink and Yellow Roses*, purchased with the assistance of the Jean F. Watson Bequest Fund and government grant-in-aid, 1979

Paterson, James 1854–1932, *Edinburgh's Playground*, presented by the Scottish Modern Arts Association, 1964, photo credit: City of Edinburgh Council, City Art Centre

Paterson, James 1854–1932, *Sunset, Arthur's Seat, Edinburgh*, purchased with the assistance of the Jean F. Watson Bequest Fund and the National Fund for Acquisitions, 1994, photo credit: City of Edinburgh Council, City Art Centre

Paterson, Toby b.1974, *Citrus Fruit Market*, purchased through the National Collecting Scheme for Scotland with the assistance of the National Fund for Acquisitions, the Art Fund and the Jean F. Watson Bequest Fund, 2006, © the artist

Paton, Joseph Noel 1821–1901, *At Bay*, presented by the Scottish Modern Arts Association, 1964

Patrick, James McIntosh 1907–1998, *Stobo Kirk, Peeblesshire*, presented by the Scottish Modern Arts Association, 1964, © the artist's estate/Bridgeman Art Library, photo credit: City of Edinburgh Council, City Art

Centre

Patterson, Iain b.1946, *For Enver*, presented by the Scottish Arts Council, 1997, © the artist

Patterson, Iain b.1946, *Bindings and Patches*, presented by the Scottish Arts Council, 1997, © the artist

Patterson, Iain b.1946, *New Buds 2*, presented by the Scottish Arts Council, 1997, © the artist

Patterson, Iain b.1946, *New Buds 8*, presented by the Scottish Arts Council, 1997, © the artist

Patterson, Iain b.1946, *Some Other Spring* (panel 1 of 12), presented by the Scottish Arts Council, 1997, © the artist

Patterson, Iain b.1946, *Some Other Spring* (panel 2 of 12), presented by the Scottish Arts Council, 1997, © the artist

Patterson, Iain b.1946, *Some Other Spring* (panel 3 of 12), presented by the Scottish Arts Council, 1997, © the artist

Patterson, Iain b.1946, *Some Other Spring* (panel 4 of 12), presented by the Scottish Arts Council, 1997, © the artist

Patterson, Iain b.1946, *Some Other Spring* (panel 5 of 12), presented by the Scottish Arts Council, 1997, © the artist

Patterson, Iain b.1946, *Some Other Spring* (panel 6 of 12), presented by the Scottish Arts Council, 1997, © the artist

Patterson, Iain b.1946, *Some Other Spring* (panel 7 of 12), presented by the Scottish Arts Council, 1997, © the artist

Patterson, Iain b.1946, *Some Other Spring* (panel 8 of 12), presented by the Scottish Arts Council, 1997, © the artist

Patterson, Iain b.1946, *Some Other Spring* (panel 9 of 12), presented by the Scottish Arts Council, 1997, © the artist

Patterson, Iain b.1946, *Some Other Spring* (panel 10 of 12), presented by the Scottish Arts Council, 1997, © the artist

Patterson, Iain b.1946, *Some Other Spring* (panel 11 of 12), presented by the Scottish Arts Council, 1997, © the artist

Patterson, Iain b.1946, *Some Other Spring* (panel 12 of 12), presented by the Scottish Arts Council, 1997, © the artist

Patterson, Janet b.1941, *Brisbane Garden with Possum*, purchased with the assistance of the Jean F. Watson Bequest Fund and government grant-in-aid, 1989, © the artist

Peploe, Denis Frederic Neal 1914–1993, *An Italian Peasant*, presented by the Scottish Modern Arts Association, 1964, © the artist's estate

Peploe, Samuel John 1871–1935, *A Rocky Shore, Iona*, presented by the Scottish Modern Arts Association, 1964, photo credit: City of Edinburgh Council, City Art

Centre

Peploe, Samuel John 1871–1935, *Still Life*, presented by the Scottish Modern Arts Association, 1964, photo credit: City of Edinburgh Council, City Art Centre

Peploe, Samuel John 1871–1935, *Still Life with Melon and Grapes*, presented by the Scottish Modern Arts Association, 1964

Peploe, Samuel John 1871–1935, *Still Life with Pears and Grapes*, presented by the Scottish Modern Arts Association, 1964, photo credit: City of Edinburgh Council, City Art Centre

Perigal, Arthur the younger 1816–1884, *Edinburgh from the South*, bequeathed by William C. Paterson, 1971

Perrett, E. D. active 19th C, *The Tomb of Tusitala*, presented by the Robert Louis Stevenson Club, 1964

Pettie, John 1839–1893, *Portrait of a Boy with a Cat*, presented by Mr and Mrs James Clark

Philipson, Robin 1916–1992, *Burning in a Wasteland*, purchased from the artist with the assistance of the Jean F. Watson Bequest Fund, 1964, © the artist's estate

Philipson, Robin 1916–1992, *Summer Morning*, presented by the Scottish Arts Council, 2006, © the artist's estate

Philipson, Robin 1916–1992, *Zebra*, purchased with the assistance of the Jean F. Watson Bequest Fund and government grant-in-aid, 1983, © the artist's estate, photo credit: City of Edinburgh Council, City Art Centre

Phillips, Stanley active 20th C, *West Princes Street Gardens, Edinburgh, from the East*, purchased, 1962

Philpot, Glyn Warren 1884–1937, *Sir Thomas Hutchison, Lord Provost of Edinburgh (1921–1923)*, commissioned, c.1923

Pirie, George 1863–1946, *Cock, Hen and Chickens*, presented by the Scottish Modern Arts Association, 1964

Pissarro, Lucien 1863–1944, *Blackpool Valley, 1913*, presented by the Scottish Modern Arts Association, 1964, © the artist's estate

Pollock, Fred b.1937, *Blush*, presented by the Scottish Arts Council, 1997, © the artist

Pope, Perpetua b.1916, *Still Life with Ivy*, presented by the Scottish Modern Arts Association, 1964 © the artist

Potter, Alan b.1949, *The Inquisitor*, purchased from the artist with the assistance of the Jean F. Watson Bequest Fund and government grant-in-aid, 1985, © the artist

Pow, Tom 1909–1996, *Eyemouth, Berwickshire*, purchased from Tom Pow, the artist's son, with the assistance of the Jean F. Watson Bequest Fund and the National Fund for Acquisitions, 1997, © the

artist's estate

Pow, Tom 1909–1996, *Fallen Angels*, purchased from Tom Pow, the artist's son, with the assistance of the Jean F. Watson Bequest Fund and the National Fund for Acquisitions, 1997, © the artist's estate, photo credit: City of Edinburgh Council, City Art Centre

Prehn, Eric Thornton 1894–1985, *Brave New World*, donated by Irina Prehn, 1986

Prehn, Eric Thornton 1894–1985, *Greyfriars Churchyard*, donated by Irina Prehn, 1986

Prehn, Eric Thornton 1894–1985, *Head of Loch Long*, donated by Irina Prehn, 1986

Prehn, Eric Thornton 1894–1985, *Russian Snow Scene*, donated by Irina Prehn, 1986

Prehn, Eric Thornton 1894–1985, *Scottish Landscape with Mountains and Loch*, donated by Irina Prehn, 1986

Pringle, John Quinton 1864–1925, *Muslin Street, Bridgeton, Glasgow*, presented by the Scottish Modern Arts Association, 1964, photo credit: City of Edinburgh Council, City Art Centre

Pringle, John Quinton 1864–1925, *The Loom*, presented by the Scottish Modern Arts Association, 1964, photo credit: City of Edinburgh Council, City Art Centre

Provan, Donald b.1964, *Window View at Sighthill, Edinburgh*, purchased from the Society of Scottish Artists exhibition with the assistance of the Jean F. Watson Bequest Fund and the National Fund for Acquisitions, 1990

Pryde, James 1866–1941, *The Red Bed*, presented by the Scottish Modern Arts Association, 1964, photo credit: City of Edinburgh Council, City Art Centre

Rae, Barbara b.1943, *West Highland Landscape*, purchased with the assistance of the Jean F. Watson Bequest Fund and the National Fund for Acquisitions, 1988, © the artist, photo credit: City of Edinburgh Council, City Art Centre

Raeburn, Henry 1756–1823, *Robert Scott Moncrieff*, on long-term loan from Dean Orphanage

Raeburn, Henry (studio of) 1756–1823, *Sir James Hunter Blair (1741–1787), Lord Provost of Edinburgh (1784–1786)*, purchased from J. Kent Richardson

Ramsay, Allan 1713–1784, *Thomas Shairp of Houston (1724–1781)*, purchased with the assistance of the Jean F. Watson Bequest Fund, the National Fund for Acquisitions and the National Art Collections Fund, 1993

Ramsay, Allan 1713–1784, *John Coutts (1699–1751), Lord Provost of Edinburgh (1742–1743)*, unknown acquisition method

Ramsay, Allan 1713–1784, *Katherine Hall of Dunglass (d.1745)*, purchased with the assistance of the Jean F. Watson Bequest Fund and the National Fund for Acquisitions, 1997, photo credit: City of Edinburgh Council, City Art Centre

Ramsay, Allan b.1959, *Lord Provost Dr John McKay & City Officer Charles Allan*, commissioned, 1990, photo credit: City of Edinburgh Council, City Art Centre

Ranken, William Bruce Ellis 1881–1941, *The Saloon, Moor Park, Hertfordshire*, presented by the Scottish Modern Arts Association, 1964, photo credit: City of Edinburgh Council, City Art Centre

Ranken, William Bruce Ellis 1881–1941, *The Tapestry Panel*, presented by the Scottish Modern Arts Association, 1964

Ranken, William Bruce Ellis 1881–1941, *The Throne Room, Royal Palace, Madrid*, presented by the Scottish Modern Arts Association, 1964

Redfern, June b.1951, *On the Edge of the World*, purchased from the artist with the assistance of the Jean F. Watson Bequest Fund, 1985, © June Redfern. All rights reserved, DACS 2012

Redpath, Anne 1895–1965, *Causewayside, Edinburgh*, purchased with the assistance of the Jean F. Watson Bequest Fund and government grant-in-aid, 1977, © the artist's estate/ Bridgeman Art Library

Redpath, Anne 1895–1965, *Black and White Checks*, presented by the Scottish Modern Arts Association, 1964, © the artist's estate/ Bridgeman Art Library, photo credit: City of Edinburgh Council, City Art Centre

Redpath, Anne 1895–1965, *Shooting Booth, Brittany, France*, purchased from the artist's estate with the assistance of the Jean F. Watson Bequest Fund, 1966, © the artist's estate/Bridgeman Art Library, photo credit: City of Edinburgh Council, City Art Centre

Reed, William Thomas 1845–1881, *Leith Races*, purchased with the assistance of the Jean F. Watson Bequest Fund and government grant-in-aid, 1983, photo credit: City of Edinburgh Council, City Art Centre

Reeves, Philip b.1931, *New Year*, purchased with the assistance of the Jean F. Watson Bequest Fund, 2003, © the artist

Reid, Archibald David 1844–1908, *Landscape with Cattle*, presented by the Scottish Modern Arts Association, 1964

Reid, George 1841–1913, *Dunnotar Castle, Aberdeenshire*, presented by the Scottish Modern Arts Association, 1964

Reid, George 1841–1913, *Duncan McLaren (1800–1886), Lord Provost of Edinburgh (1851–1854)*, unknown acquisition method

Reid, George Ogilvy 1851–1928, *The Granting of a Royal Charter by King James III to the Provost, Bailies and Councillors of the Burgh of Edinburgh in the Year 1482*, presented by Members of the Guildry, 1912

Renton, Joan b.1935, *Olive Trees, Castagne to Carducci, Italy*, purchased from the artist with the assistance of the Jean F. Watson Bequest Fund and the National Fund for Acquisitions, 1992, © the artist

Reynolds, Joshua 1723–1792, *Charles Smith (1688–1768), Merchant and Banker*, purchased with the assistance of the Jean F. Watson Bequest Fund, the National Fund for Acquisitions and the National Art Collections Fund, 1997, photo credit: City of Edinburgh Council, City Art Centre

Rhodes, Carol b.1959, *Town*, purchased through the National Collecting Scheme for Scotland with the assistance of the National Fund for Acquisitions and the Jean F. Watson Bequest Fund, 2006, © the artist

Ritchie, Alexander Hay 1822–1895, *The Execution of Deacon Brodie and George Smith*, unknown acquisition method, photo credit: City of Edinburgh Council, City Art Centre

Roberts, David 1796–1864, *Donaldson's College, Edinburgh*, on long-term loan from Donaldson's College, Edinburgh

Roberts, David 1796–1864, *The Toll House, Edinburgh*, purchased with the assistance of the Jean F. Watson Bequest Fund and government grant-in-aid, 1987

Roberts, Derek b.1947, *Indigo Trail*, presented by the Scottish Arts Council, 1997, © the artist

Roberts, Derek b.1947, *Painting on Green and Black*, purchased from the artist with the assistance of the Jean F. Watson Bequest Fund and the National Fund for Acquisitions, 1993, © the artist, photo credit: City of Edinburgh Council, City Art Centre

Robertson, Eric Harald Macbeth 1887–1941, *Love's Invading*, purchased with the assistance of the Jean F. Watson Bequest Fund and government grant-in-aid, 1981, photo credit: City of Edinburgh Council, City Art Centre

Robertson, Eric Harald Macbeth 1887–1941, *Shellburst*, purchased, 1976

Robertson, Iain b.1955, *Jig*, purchased with the assistance of the Jean F. Watson Bequest Fund, 2009 © the artist

Robertson, James Downie 1931–2010, *Sand and Cliff*,

purchased from the artist with the assistance of the Jean F. Watson Bequest Fund, 1966, © the artist's estate

Robertson, John Ewart 1820–1879, *Robert Andrew Macfie (1811–1893)*, presented by M. S. S. Macfie, 1960

Roche, Alexander Ignatius 1861–1921, *Landscape*, presented by the Scottish Modern Arts Association, 1964

Roche, Alexander Ignatius 1861–1921, *Pittenweem, Fife*, presented by the Scottish Modern Arts Association, 1964, photo credit: City of Edinburgh Council, City Art Centre

Roche, Alexander Ignatius 1861–1921, *Self Portrait*, presented by the Scottish Modern Arts Association, 1964

Roche, Alexander Ignatius 1861–1921, *Sir Robert Cranston (1843–1923), KCVO, VD, Lord Provost of Edinburgh (1903–1906)*, presented by the sitter's fellow citizens, 1907

Roche, Alexander Ignatius 1861–1921, *Tell Me, Shepherds*, presented by the Scottish Modern Arts Association, 1964, photo credit: City of Edinburgh Council, City Art Centre

Roche, Alexander Ignatius 1861–1921, *The Prison Gate, Mogador, Morocco*, presented by the Scottish Modern Arts Association, 1964

Rogers, Henry b.1963, *An Initial Act of Creation*, purchased from the artist with the assistance of the Jean F. Watson Bequest Fund, 1987, © the artist

Ross, John H. *Waverley Station, Edinburgh*, purchased with the assistance of the Jean F. Watson Bequest Fund and the National Fund for Acquisitions, 2007

Rossi, Mario b.1958, *Whirlwind*, presented by the Contemporary Art Society, 1986, © the artist

Russell, Kathleen b.1940, *St Abbs, Berwickshire, Storm*, purchased with the assistance of the Jean F. Watson Bequest Fund, 1965, © Kathleen Russell née Caskey

Russell, Walter Westley 1867–1949, *Camilla*, presented by the Scottish Modern Arts Association, 1964

Russell, Walter Westley 1867–1949, *Joseph Crawhall (1861–1913)*, presented by the Scottish Modern Arts Association, 1964

Sandeman, Margot 1922–2009, *Hawthorn (Mayflower)*, purchased with the assistance of the Jean F. Watson Bequest Fund and government grant-in-aid, 1989

Sanderson, Robert 1848–1908, *Drill Parade, Edinburgh Castle, 1886*, unknown acquisition method, photo credit: City of Edinburgh Council, City Art Centre

Schueler, Jon 1916–1992, *Summer Day: Sleat*, purchased with the

assistance of the Jean F. Watson Bequest Fund and the National Fund for Acquisitions, 1994, © Jon Schueler Estate, photo credit: City of Edinburgh Council, City Art Centre

Schunemann, L. (attributed to) active c.1666–1674, *Sir Alexander Gilmour (1658–1731), Bt of Craigmillar*, unknown acquisition method, photo credit: City of Edinburgh Council, City Art Centre

Scott, David (attributed to) 1806–1849, *Samuel Gilmour*, presented by M. Elizabeth Wilson, 1956

Scougall, David (attributed to) c.1610–c.1680, *Sir James Steuart of Coltness (1608–1681), Lord Provost of Edinburgh (1648–1650 & 1658–1660)*, purchased, 1978, photo credit: City of Edinburgh Council, City Art Centre

Seaton, William active 19th C, *A Man Playing a Penny Whistle*, unknown acquisition method

Sekalski, Józef 1904–1972, *Lobster Pots*, purchased with the assistance of the Jean F. Watson Bequest Fund, 1990

Shanks, Duncan b.1937, *Muddy Pool*, purchased with the assistance of the Jean F. Watson Bequest Fund and government grant-in-aid, 1988, © the artist

Shanks, William Somerville 1864–1951, *Demarco, M. de Munkácsy's Private Model*, presented by the Scottish Modern Arts Association, 1964

Shields, Douglas Gordon 1888–1943, *Glassford Walker*, presented by the Scottish Modern Arts Association, 1941, photo credit: City of Edinburgh Council, City Art Centre

Shields, Douglas Gordon 1888–1943, *Florence Chalmers (d.1993)*, bequeathed by Mrs Florence Chambers, 1993

Shipway, Alan b.1956, *Last Month*, purchased with the assistance of the Jean F. Watson Bequest Fund, 2009, © the artist

Sims, Charles 1873–1928, *Mrs MacWhirter*, presented by the Scottish Modern Arts Association, 1964

Sims, Charles (attributed to) 1873–1928, *Study of a Female Figure*, presented by the Scottish Modern Arts Association, 1964

Sims, Charles (attributed to) 1873–1928, *Study of a Female Nude*, presented by the Scottish Modern Arts Association, 1964

Sims, Charles (attributed to) 1873–1928, *Study of Children Bathing*, presented by the Scottish Modern Arts Association, 1964, photo credit: City of Edinburgh Council, City Art Centre

Sivell, Robert 1888–1958, *Eve*, presented by the Scottish Modern Arts Association, 1958

Smeall, William active 1824–1830, *At Currie, Old Bridge and Old Inn*,

presented by Mrs Drummond, 1953

Smeall, William active 1824–1830, *The Entrance Gate of Trinity College Church, Edinburgh, 1830*, presented by Mrs Drummond, 1953

Smeall, William active 1824–1830, *The Lodge, Trinity College Church, Edinburgh, 1824*, presented by Mrs Drummond, 1953

Smeall, William (attributed to) active 1824–1830, *A Harbour Scene*, presented by Mrs Drummond, 1953

Smeall, William (attributed to) active 1824–1830, *Bakehouse Close, Canongate, Edinburgh*, presented by Mrs Drummond, 1953

Smeall, William (attributed to) active 1824–1830, *Cross Causeway and Buccleuch Church, Edinburgh*, presented by Mrs Drummond, 1953

Smeall, William (attributed to) active 1824–1830, *Old Edinburgh Close*, presented by Mrs Drummond, 1953

Smeall, William (attributed to) active 1824–1830, *Part of Audley House and the Priory of the Holy Trinity, Aldgate, London*, presented by Mrs Drummond, 1953

Smeall, William (attributed to) active 1824–1830, *Shoemaker Close, Edinburgh*, presented by Mrs Drummond, 1953

Smeall, William (attributed to) active 1824–1830, *Study of Boats on Sand*, presented by Mrs Drummond, 1953

Smeall, William (attributed to) active 1824–1830, *Unidentified Old Inn*, presented by Mrs Drummond, 1953

Smith, Colvin 1795–1875, *George Thomson*, presented by Mrs Colvin Smith

Smith, George 1870–1934, *Carting Timber*, presented by the Scottish Modern Arts Association, 1964, photo credit: City of Edinburgh Council, City Art Centre

Smith, Ian McKenzie b.1935, *Tidemark*, presented by the Scottish Arts Council, 1997, © the artist

Smith, Jane Stewart 1839–1925, *Dunbar Close, Edinburgh, 1868*, unknown acquisition method

Smith, Jane Stewart 1839–1925, *View of the High Street, Looking East, from the Lawnmarket, Edinburgh*, unknown acquisition method

Smith, John Guthrie Spence 1880–1951, *John Knox's House, High Street, Edinburgh*, purchased with the assistance of the Jean F. Watson Bequest Fund and government grant-in-aid, 1984, photo credit: City of Edinburgh Council, City Art Centre

Smith, John Guthrie Spence 1880–1951, *Mowbray House, High Street, Edinburgh*, presented by the Scottish Modern Arts Association, 1964

Smith, Marian b.1951, *Still Life*, purchased from the artist, 1973

Souter, John Bulloch 1890–1972, *Sorting Garlic*, presented by the Scottish Modern Arts Association, 1964, © the artist's estate

Standen, Peter b.1936, *View of Princes Street, Edinburgh*, purchased from Edinburgh Printmakers, 1988 © the artist

Stevenson, Fanny Vandergrift Osbourne 1840–1914, *The Bridge at Grez, Forest of Fontainebleau, France*, presented by the Robert Louis Stevenson Club, 1964

Stevenson, Robert active c.1880–1910, *Robert Louis Stevenson (1850–1894)* (after Girolamo Pieri Nerli), presented by John Wilkie, 1967

Stevenson, Robert active 1961, *Swanston Village before Reconstruction, 2 November 1961*, presented by the artist, 1961

Stevenson, Robert Macaulay 1854–1952, *Wooded Landscape*, presented by the Scottish Modern Arts Association, 1964

Strang, William 1859–1921, *Dreams*, presented by the Scottish Modern Arts Association, 1964

Stronach, Ancell 1901–1981, *The Other Wise Man*, presented by the Scottish Modern Arts Association, 1964

Stuart, Robert Easton active 1887–1940, *Maule's Corner after Rain, Edinburgh*, presented by the Scottish Modern Arts Association, 1964, photo credit: City of Edinburgh Council, City Art Centre

Sturrock, Alick Riddell 1885–1953, *A Solway Farm*, presented by the Scottish Modern Arts Association, 1964, photo credit: City of Edinburgh Council, City Art Centre

Sturrock, Alick Riddell 1885–1953, *The Silo*, presented by the Scottish Modern Arts Association, 1964

Sutherland, Alan b.1931, *Sir Duncan M. Weatherstone (1898–1972), MC, TD, LLD, DLitt, Lord Provost of Edinburgh (1963–1966)*, commissioned, c.1967

Sutherland, David Macbeth 1883–1973, *The Demolition of the Crown Hotel, Edinburgh*, purchased, 1982, © the artist's estate

Sutherland, David Macbeth 1883–1973, *Winter Landscape, West Cults, Aberdeen*, presented by the Scottish Modern Arts Association, 1964, © the artist's estate, photo credit: City of Edinburgh Council, City Art Centre

Sutherland, David Macbeth 1883–1973, *Concarneau, Brittany, France*, purchased from the artist with the assistance of the Jean F. Watson Bequest Fund, 1965, © the artist's estate, photo credit: City of Edinburgh Council, City Art Centre

Sutherland, David Macbeth 1883–1973, *Plockton from Duncraig*, purchased from the artist with the assistance of the Jean F. Watson Bequest Fund, 1968, © the artist's estate

Sutherland, George active 19th C, *The International Forestry Exhibition, Edinburgh, 1884*, presented by the executors of the estate of the 11th Marquis of Lothian, 1951

Telford, Zoë b.1964, *Marshland, Rising Mountain*, purchased from the artist with the assistance of the Jean F. Watson Bequest Fund, 1987, © the artist

Thomas, Margaret b.1916, *Castle Nocturne*, purchased from the artist, 1961, © the artist

Thomas, Margaret b.1916, *Christmas*, purchased from the artist, 1961, © the artist

Thoms, Colin 1912–1997, *Strutting Bird*, purchased from the artist's widow with the assistance of the Jean F. Watson Bequest Fund and the National Fund for Acquisitions, 1998, © the artist's estate, photo credit: City of Edinburgh Council, City Art Centre

Thoms, Colin 1912–1997, *Haddington, East Lothian*, presented by the Scottish Modern Arts Association, 1964, © the artist's estate

Thomson, Adam Bruce 1885–1976, *Cedars*, purchased with the assistance of the Jean F. Watson Bequest Fund and government grant-in-aid, 1985 © the artist's estate

Thomson, Adam Bruce 1885–1976, *From My Bedroom Window*, presented by the Scottish Modern Arts Association, 1964 © the artist's estate

Thomson, Adam Bruce 1885–1976, *North Bridge and Salisbury Crags, Edinburgh, from the North West*, presented by the Council of the Society of Scottish Artists, 1935, photo credit: City of Edinburgh Council, City Art Centre © the artist's estate

Thomson, Adam Bruce 1885–1976, *Palm, Pampas Grass and Duncraig*, purchased from the artist with the assistance of the Jean F. Watson Bequest Fund, 1967 © the artist's estate

Thomson, Adam Bruce 1885–1976, *Willow Trees, Cattle and River*, presented by the National Art Collections Fund, 1988 © the artist's estate

Thomson, Jennifer b.1969, *Newhaven Harbour*, purchased from the artist with the assistance of the Jean F. Watson Bequest Fund, 1993, © the artist

Thomson, Jennifer b.1969, *The Fisherman's Choice, Newhaven*, purchased from the artist with the assistance of the Jean F. Watson Bequest Fund, 1993, © the artist

Thomson, John 1778–1840, *Abbotsford, Melrose, 1828*, purchased, 1963, photo credit: City of Edinburgh Council, City Art Centre

Thomson, John 1778–1840, *Craigmillar Castle from the South East, Edinburgh, 1821*, purchased, 1963

Thomson, John 1778–1840, *Edinburgh from Inverleith*, presented by the Scottish Arts Council, 1984, photo credit: City of Edinburgh Council, City Art Centre

Thomson, John 1778–1840, *View of Edinburgh from Craiglockhart*, bequeathed by Mrs M. A. Green, 1960

Thomson, John 1778–1840, *View of Edinburgh from Duddingston*, bequeathed by Mrs M. A. Green, 1960

Thomson, John (attributed to) 1778–1840, *General View of Edinburgh from the Vicinity of Craiglockhart*, bequeathed by Mrs M. A. Green, 1960

Torrance, James 1859–1916, *Still Life, Harness*, presented by the Scottish Modern Arts Association, 1964

Torrance, James 1859–1916, *The Question*, presented by the Scottish Modern Arts Association, 1964

Torrance, James 1859–1916, *The Smile*, presented by the Scottish Modern Arts Association, 1964

Trojanowska, Anna *Red House by a Canal*, purchased with the assistance of the Jean F. Watson Bequest Fund, 1967

Turner, William active 1767–1831, *The Gold Cup, Musselburgh, East Lothian*, purchased with the assistance of the Jean F. Watson Bequest Fund and the National Fund for Acquisitions, 1996

Turner, William active 1767–1831, *The Arrival of the Mail Coach at the 'Black Bull', Edinburgh*, purchased with the assistance of the Jean F. Watson Bequest Fund and the National Fund for Acquisitions, 1991, photo credit: City of Edinburgh Council, City Art Centre

Turner, William 1789–1862, *The Procession of King George IV Entering Princes Street, Edinburgh, August, 1822*, purchased, 1913, photo credit: City of Edinburgh Council, City Art Centre

unknown artist 18th C, *Agrippina Mourning the Ashes of Germanicus*, unknown acquisition method

unknown artist 18th C, *Europa and the Bull*, unknown acquisition method

unknown artist 18th C, *Jove Driving across the Heavens*, unknown acquisition method

unknown artist 18th C, *The Death of Socrates*, unknown acquisition method

unknown artist 18th C, *A Putto Driving a Chariot Led by Two Cheetahs*, unknown acquisition method

unknown artist 18th C, *A River Landscape with Ruins*, unknown acquisition method

unknown artist 18th C, *Landscape with a Hunting Scene*, presented by the Royal Scottish Museum, 1953

unknown artist 18th C, *A Harbour Scene*, presented by the Royal Scottish Museum, 1953

unknown artist 18th C, *Pastoral Landscape with a Ruin*, presented by the Royal Scottish Museum, 1953

unknown artist 18th C, *Portrait of a Gentleman* (possibly Sir George Warrender, c.1658–1721, Bt, Lord Provost of Edinburgh, 1713–1715), presented by Sir Victor Warrender, 1930

unknown artist 18th C, *Portrait of an Unknown Architect* (possibly J. McVey), presented by Mrs Drummond, 1953

unknown artist 18th C, *Portrait of an Unknown Lady in Early Seventeenth-Century Dress*, presented by Councillor Colonel Forbes Mackay, 1895

unknown artist 18th C, *Sir Charles Gilmour (1701–1750), Bt of Craigmillar*, unknown acquisition method

unknown artist 18th C, *The Right Honourable David Steuart, Lord Provost of Edinburgh (1780–1781)*, presented by Colonel F. G. Steuart, 1952

unknown artist 18th C, *Thomas Ruddiman (1714–1747)*, presented by Sylvia Steuart, 1962

unknown artist *'The Comet', Smack*, presented by Reverend J. S. Marshall, 1991

unknown artist *Portrait of an Unknown Lady*, unknown acquisition method

unknown artist *Portrait of an Unknown Gentleman with a Dog*, unknown acquisition method

unknown artist *Portrait of an Unknown Gentleman*, unknown acquisition method

unknown artist *Portrait of an Unknown Gentleman*, unknown acquisition method

unknown artist *Portrait of an Unknown Gentleman*, unknown acquisition method

unknown artist *Two Children Holding a Finch and a Bird's Nest*, unknown acquisition method

unknown artist 19th C, *A Mother and Child in a Bower*, unknown acquisition method

unknown artist 19th C, *A Putto Sailing*, acquired from the Theatre Royal, Shakespeare Square, Edinburgh

unknown artist 19th C, *A Putto Crowning Another with a Garland of Roses*, acquired from the Theatre Royal, Shakespeare Square, Edinburgh

unknown artist 19th C, *A View of the Old Town from the North*, presented by W. Watt, 1949, photo credit: City of Edinburgh Council, City Art Centre

unknown artist 19th C, *Adam White of Fens (1760–1843), First Provost of Leith*, presented to the town of Leith by public subscription

unknown artist 19th C, *Andrew Wemyss (1806–1858), Councillor, Treasurer, Lord Dean of Guild and Benefactor of Trinity Hospital*, unknown acquisition method

unknown artist 19th C, *Ann Taylor Ferguson (1832–1910)*, presented by A. G. W. Ferguson, 1969

unknown artist 19th C, *Bakehouse Close, Canongate, Edinburgh*, presented by Mrs Yacomine, 1934

unknown artist 19th C, *Condemned Covenanters on Their Way to Execution in the West Bow, Edinburgh*, acquired, 1904, photo credit: City of Edinburgh Council, City Art Centre

unknown artist 19th C, *Edinburgh from the South*, unknown acquisition method

unknown artist 19th C, *Edinburgh's City Officers, c.1830*, purchased, 1949

unknown artist 19th C, *Elizabeth Dick Ferguson*, presented by A. G. W. Ferguson, 1969

unknown artist 19th C, *George Meikle Kemp (1795–1844)*, unknown acquisition method

unknown artist 19th C, *George Meikle Kemp (1795–1844) with the Model for the Scott Monument, Edinburgh*, presented by John Taylor, 1953

unknown artist 19th C, *Helen Ferguson (1828–1849)*, presented by A. G. W. Ferguson, 1969

unknown artist 19th C, *Jacob Liebe (b.1779)*, presented by J. R. Scovell, 1986

unknown artist 19th C, *John Allan*, presented by Mrs Drummond, 1953

unknown artist 19th C, *John Macfie (1820–1875)*, presented by M. S. S. Macfie, 1960

unknown artist 19th C, *Low Calton, Edinburgh*, unknown acquisition method

unknown artist 19th C, *Mrs James Waldie, née Margaret Patterson of Coldingham (c.1803–1884)*, presented by Mrs R. Green, 1961

unknown artist 19th C, *Nine Views of the Old Town of Edinburgh: Main Point, West Port* (panel 1 of 9), bequeathed by Mrs M. A. Green, 1960

unknown artist 19th C, *Nine Views of the Old Town of Edinburgh: Foot of Leith Wynd* (panel 2 of 9), bequeathed by Mrs M. A. Green, 1960

unknown artist 19th C, *Nine Views of the Old Town of Edinburgh: Canongate* (panel 3 of 9), bequeathed by Mrs M. A. Green, 1960

unknown artist 19th C, *Nine Views of the Old Town of Edinburgh: Grassmarket* (panel 4 of 9), bequeathed by Mrs M. A.

Green, 1960

unknown artist 19th C, *Nine Views of the Old Town of Edinburgh: Cowgate Port* (panel 5 of 9), bequeathed by Mrs M. A. Green, 1960

unknown artist 19th C, *Nine Views of the Old Town of Edinburgh: Foot of West Port* (panel 6 of 9), bequeathed by Mrs M. A. Green, 1960

unknown artist 19th C, *Nine Views of the Old Town of Edinburgh: In Pleasance* (panel 7 of 9), bequeathed by Mrs M. A. Green, 1960

unknown artist 19th C, *Nine Views of the Old Town of Edinburgh: Foot of Candlemakers Row* (panel 8 of 9), bequeathed by Mrs M. A. Green, 1960

unknown artist 19th C, *Nine Views of the Old Town of Edinburgh: Calton* (panel 9 of 9), bequeathed by Mrs M. A. Green, 1960

unknown artist 19th C, *Portrait of a Boy*, unknown acquisition method

unknown artist 19th C, *Portrait of an Unknown Gentleman Holding a Letter*, unknown acquisition method

unknown artist 19th C, *Portrait of an Unknown Gentleman with a Child and a Dog*, unknown acquisition method

unknown artist 19th C, *Portrait of an Unknown Girl*, unknown acquisition method

unknown artist 19th C, *Robert Burns (1759–1796)*, bequeathed by Mrs M. A. Green, 1960

unknown artist 19th C, *Sir William Arbuthnot (1776–1829), Bt, Lord Provost of Edinburgh (1815–1817 & 1821–1823)*, unknown acquisition method

unknown artist 19th C, *The Edinburgh Town Guard*, presented by Mrs M. S. Irvine, 1915

unknown artist 19th C, *The Entrance to Sir Thomas Dick Lauder's, the Grange, Edinburgh*, unknown acquisition method

unknown artist 19th C, *The Hall, Abbotsford, Melrose*, unknown acquisition method

unknown artist 19th C, *The Netherbow Port, Edinburgh*, presented by Mrs Neil Bayne, 1955

unknown artist 19th C, *The Old Grassmarket from the North, Edinburgh*, c.1850, presented by Mr Tait, 1905

unknown artist 19th C, *Part of Trinity College and Hospital, Edinburgh* (demolished, 1845–1848), unknown acquisition method

unknown artist 19th C, *Part of Trinity College Hospital, Edinburgh* (demolished, 1845–1848), unknown acquisition method

unknown artist 19th C, *Trinity College Church, Edinburgh, from the South West* (demolished, 1845–1848), presented by

Reverend R. A. J. Gossip, 1960

unknown artist 19th C, *Unidentified Old Town Close, Edinburgh*, unknown acquisition method

unknown artist 19th C, *William Nelson (1816–1887)*, presented by the family of the sitter, 1942

unknown artist 19th C, *William Oliphant and His Wife Mary with Their Children: William, Mary, Margaret, John, Elizabeth, Ebenezer, David and Walter, in a Landscape, 1822*, bequeathed by Ada Oliphant, 1963

unknown artist *James Waldie (1831–1915), JP*, presented by Mrs R. Green, 1961

unknown artist 20th C, *Advocate's Close, Edinburgh*, presented by Mrs Neil Bayne, 1955

unknown artist 20th C, *Reid's Close, Edinburgh*, presented by Mrs Neil Bayne, 1955

unknown artist 20th C, *Bailie Waterson*, unknown acquisition method

unknown artist 20th C, *James Waldie (1831–1915), JP*, presented by Mrs R. Green, 1961

unknown artist 20th C, *The Edinburgh City Keys: Robert Paton, City Chamberlain (1895–1925)*, unknown acquisition method

unknown artist *A Dog (possibly 'Greyfriars Bobby')*

unknown artist *Ancient Chapel, Kirkgate, Edinburgh*, unknown acquisition method

unknown artist *Christ*, unknown acquisition method

unknown artist *Johnston Terrace and Castle Wynd, Edinburgh*, unknown acquisition method

unknown artist *Portrait of an Old Man with a Staff*, unknown acquisition method

unknown artist *Richard Mackie (1851–1923), Provost of Leith (1899–1908)*, presented to the town of Leith by public subscription, 1909

unknown artist *The Trawler 'Anworth'*, gift from Mr and Mrs I. Purves, 1997

Urie, Joseph b.1947, *Beauty and the Beast, No.5*, purchased with the assistance of the Jean F. Watson Bequest Fund and government grant-in-aid, 1989, © the artist, photo credit: City of Edinburgh Council, City Art Centre

Vos, Hubert 1855–1935, *Alexander Brand (1836–1931), Provost of Portobello*, purchased, 2003

Walker, Andrew b.1959, *Women on Wheels*, purchased with the assistance of the Jean F. Watson Bequest Fund, 1985, © the artist. Granted for the sole purpose of The Public Catalogue Foundation

Walker, Ethel b.1941, *Stockbridge, Edinburgh*, purchased from the artist with the assistance of the Jean F. Watson Bequest Fund, 1986, © the artist

Walker, George active 1792–1797, *Edinburgh from the South East,*

1797, presented by H. M. Comber, 1947, photo credit: City of Edinburgh Council, City Art Centre

Walker, Richard b.1955, *Table and Flowers*, presented by the Scottish Arts Council, 1997, © the artist

Walls, William 1860–1942, *Cave Dwellers at Play*, presented by the Scottish Modern Arts Association, 1964

Walls, William 1860–1942, *Mountain Goats*, bequeathed by Miss J. H. E. Robinson, 2009

Walton, Edward Arthur 1860–1922, *Shadowed Pastures*, presented by the Scottish Modern Arts Association, 1964, photo credit: City of Edinburgh Council, City Art Centre

Walton, Edward Arthur 1860–1922, *John Kirkhope (1844–1920), Mus.D.*, unknown acquisition method, photo credit: City of Edinburgh Council, City Art Centre

Wane, Marshall active 1889, *James Watt (1806–1881), Provost of Leith (1866–1875)*, presented to the town of Leith by the son of the sitter

Watson, George 1767–1837, *Sergeant Major Patrick Gould, Royal Regiment, Edinburgh Volunteers, 1794*, presented to the City, before 1901

Watson, William Smellie 1796–1894, *John Macfie (1793–1852)*, presented by M. S. S. Macfie, 1960

Watson, William Smellie 1796–1894, *Sir James Forrest of Comiston (1780–1860), Bt, Lord Provost of Edinburgh (1837–1843), and Chairman, Life Association of Scotland*, presented by the Life Association of Scotland Ltd, 1967

Watson, William Stewart 1800–1870, *Holyrood Dairy, Edinburgh, c.1840*, purchased, 1903

Watt, George Fiddes 1873–1960, *William Slater Brown, Lord Provost (1909–1912)*, purchased with the assistance of the Jean F. Watson Bequest Fund and government grant-in-aid, 1988, © the artist's estate, photo credit: City of Edinburgh Council, City Art Centre

Watt, George Fiddes 1873–1960, *Alison Cunningham (1822–1913)*, presented by Lord Guthrie, c.1912, © the artist's estate

Watt, George Fiddes 1873–1960, *Sir Robert Kirk Inches, Lord Provost (1912–1916)*, bequeathed by the estate of Dierdre Inches Carr, 1996, © the artist's estate

Watt, George Fiddes 1873–1960, *Sir John Lorne Macleod (1873–1946), CBE, LLD, Lord Provost (1916–1919)*, commissioned, c.1920, © the artist's estate

Wehrschmidt, Daniel Albert 1861–1932, *Anthony J. O. Maxtone Graham (1900–1971), 16th Laird of Culloquhey and 9th Laird of Redgorton*, presented by the sitter,

c.1957

Wells, T. *'Show Jamie', a Canongate Character*, presented by E. M. Muir, April 1969

Wells, William Page Atkinson 1872–1923, *A Lancashire Village, 1908*, presented by the Scottish Modern Arts Association, 1964, photo credit: City of Edinburgh Council, City Art Centre

Williams, Andrew b.1954, *Deposition II*, presented by the Scottish Arts Council, 1997

Williams, Andrew b.1954, *Study for 'Body Builders, Venice Beach, California, USA'*, purchased with the assistance of the Jean F. Watson Bequest Fund and government grant-in-aid, 1986, photo credit: City of Edinburgh Council, City Art Centre

Williams, Andrew b.1954, *Body Builders, Venice Beach, California, USA*, purchased with the assistance of the Jean F. Watson Bequest Fund and government grant-in-aid, 1986, photo credit: City of Edinburgh Council, City Art Centre

Wilson, Andrew 1780–1848, *Edinburgh, before the Mound Was Completed*, bequeathed by Dr Connie Byrom, 2009

Wilson, William active 1798–1836, *Douglas Cross, Braes of Yarrow*, commissioned by Sir Walter Scott, c.1824

Wingate, James Lawton 1846–1924, *Veiled Moonlight*, presented by the Scottish Modern Arts Association, 1964

Wingate, James Lawton 1846–1924, *Autumnal Sunset*, presented by the Scottish Modern Arts Association, 1964

Wingate, James Lawton 1846–1924, *Harvest in Arran*, presented by the Scottish Modern Arts Association, 1964

Wiszniewski, Adrian b.1958, *Self Portrait*, purchased with the assistance of the Jean F. Watson Bequest Fund and the National Fund for Acquisitions, 1994, © the artist, photo credit: City of Edinburgh Council, City Art Centre

Young, Andrew 1855–1925, *A Select Tea Party*, gift to the City of Edinburgh, c.1972

Young, Edward Drummond 1877–1946, *Corner of the Fife Coast*, gift from Alexandrina Inglis, 1997, © the artist's estate (Hon. Lord Drummond Young)

Young, Edward Drummond 1877–1946, *Satsuma Vase*, presented by the Scottish Modern Arts Association, 1964, © the artist's estate (Hon. Lord Drummond Young)

Young, William Drummond 1855–1924, *John Bennet (1820–1902), Provost of Leith (1893–1899)*, commissioned by the town of Leith, 1899

Zhijun, Suo *Duddingston, Edinburgh*, gift from the artist, 2001

Zhijun, Suo *Old Town of*

Edinburgh from Salisbury Crags, gift from the artist, 2001

Żyw, Aleksander 1905–1995, *Red Figures*, presented by the Scottish Arts Council, 1997

Żyw, Aleksander 1905–1995, *Olivier (Olive Trees)*, presented by the Scottish Arts Council, 1997

Historic Scotland, Edinburgh

Anglo/Chinese School *The Barque 'Loch Broom' of Glasgow*, donated by Captain J. R. K. Taylor

Ansdell, Richard 1815–1885, *The Fight for the Standard*, on loan from The Royal Hospital Chelsea

Belle, Alexis-Simon (attributed to) 1674–1734, *James VIII (1688–1766), 'The Old Pretender'*, purchased by Historic Scotland, possibly from Doig, Wilson & Wheatley

Blair, John 1850–1934, *Edward Brown (d.1802) (after Daniel Orme)*, presented by the sitter's grandson, 1873

British (Scottish) School *The Ship 'Loch Carron' of Glasgow*, presented to Trinity House by Mrs Sybil Burrows

British (Scottish) School mid-19th C, *Thomas Sutherland, Teacher of Mathematics at Trinity House*, presented to the sitter by his students, 1827; donated to Trinity House by his granddaughter

British (Scottish) School *Mrs Colina Mary Grant*, bequeathed by the sitter to the Masters and Members of Trinity House, 1937

British (Scottish) School *The Clipper 'Nonsuch' Making for Sea*

Bury, W. *A View of Portobello, Edinburgh*

Critz, John de the elder (after) 1551/1552–1642, *James VI and I (1566–1625)*

Cromarty, Alexander 1838–1926, *The Barque 'Bencleuch'*, donated by Captain McMillan

Cruikshanks, Francis (attributed to) active 1855–1880, *Mr Robert Thomson, Elected Member of Trinity House, 1873*

Cruikshanks, Francis (attributed to) active 1855–1880, *Mr Thomas Robertson, Secretary to the Corporation (1847–1865)*, purchased

David, Antonio (after) active from 1684, *Princess Maria Clementina Sobieska (1702–1735)*, donated to Historic Scotland by Mrs Stirling

Fairslough, R. B. *The HMS 'Bounty'*

Flemish School *A View of Leith with a Galleon*, purchased by a member of Trinity House from an antique market in Amsterdam; restored by Aitken Dott, 1968

Ford, John A. active 1880–1923, *Charles Kinghorn Mackintosh, Treasurer to the Corporation (1912–1917)*, painted in recognition of services in the First World War, 1919; exhibited at the

Royal Scottish Academy, 1920; purchased by Trinity House
Gordon, John Watson 1788–1864, *John Smith, Master of Trinity House (1833–1856)*
Gordon, John Watson (circle of) 1788–1864, *Captain Walter Smith, Master Member of Trinity House*, presented by the sitter's grandson, 1894
Granges, David des 1611–after 1670, *Charles II (1630–1685)* (after Adriaen Hanneman), on loan from Huw Dalrymple
Hardie, Charles Martin 1858–1916, *Mr Abraham Howling, Master of Trinity House (1901–1902)*, commissioned, 1902; exhibited at the Royal Scottish Academy, 1903; purchased, 2005
Hemy, Bernard Benedict 1845–1913, *A Tug Towing a Sailing Boat*
Hemy, Bernard Benedict 1845–1913, *An Estuary Scene*
Hill, David Octavius 1802–1870, *A View of Leith*
Jamesone, George (attributed to) c.1586–1644, *John Erskine (c.1585–1654), 3rd Earl of Mar, Lord High Treasurer*, on loan from the Earl of Mar and Kellie
Kneller, Godfrey (studio of) 1646–1723, *John Erskine (1675–1732), 6th Earl of Mar*, on loan from the Earl of Mar and Kellie
Lely, Peter (after) 1618–1680, *Charles II (1630–1685)*
Madison, James N. *The Highland Charge of Drummossie Moor (The Battle of Culloden, 16 April 1746)*, on loan from a private lender
McLean, J. W. *The SS 'Venus'*, donated by Mrs Argyle Lindsay, JP, 1920
Miller, William c.1740–c.1810, *Mr Robert Innes, Treasurer of Trinity House (1734–1773)*, purchased by Trinity House, 1773
Mitchell, A. *A View of the Port of Leith with Arthur's Seat in the Distance*
Mitchell, A. *The Port of Leith*, donated by Captain John R. K. Taylor, a member of Trinity House
Monro, Hugh 1873–1928, *James VI (1566–1625)* (after Cornelis Janssens van Ceulen)
Mytens, Daniel I (after) c.1590–before 1648, *Mary, Queen of Scots (1542–1587)*, presented to Trinity House, 1816
Percival, Harold 1868–1914, *The Ship 'Zuleika' of Leith*, donated by Mrs H. Bremner, widow of Captain Bremner, 1940
Raeburn, Henry 1756–1823, *Admiral Adam Duncan (1731–1804), 1st Viscount Duncan of Camperdown*, commissioned by Trinity House, 1798
Raeburn, Henry 1756–1823, *Mr George Smith, Master of Trinity House (1796–1805)*, commissioned by Trinity House
Raeburn, Henry 1756–1823, *Mr John Hay, Master of Trinity House*

(1808–1820)
Raeburn, Henry 1756–1823, *Peter Wood (1749–1846), Whaleship Owner*, donated by the sitter's grandson
Ritchie, Thomas L. active 1837–1865, *Mr Walter Paton, Master of Trinity House (1856–1868)*, commissioned by Trinity House, 1862
Ritchie, Thomas L. active 1837–1865, *Captain Archibald Ritchie, Master Member of Trinity House*, donated to Trinity House by A. R. Gillespie Esq., 1887
Robertson, Charles Kay d.1939, *Mr Francis Riddell*, purchased by Trinity House
Robertson, Nora *Captain William M. Reid, Master of Trinity House (1960–1964)*
Scott, David 1806–1849, *Vasco da Gama Encountering the Spirit of the Storm*, purchased by public subscription, 1849
Somer, Paulus van I (after) 1576–1621, *James VI (1566–1625)*, on loan from the Earl of Mar and Kellie
Stanfield, Clarkson 1793–1867, *A Busy Shipping Lane off Liverpool*
Sutherland, David Macbeth 1883–1973, *Captain Cromarty*, © the artist's estate
unknown artist 17th C, *John Erskine (d.1572), 1st Earl of Mar, Regent of Scotland* (copy after an earlier painting), on loan from the Earl of Mar and Kellie
unknown artist *View of Edinburgh Castle*
unknown artist 18th C, *Louisa Maria von Stolberg-Golden (1753–1824), Countess of Albany* (copy after an earlier painting by an unknown artist), donated by Miss Maria Steuart
unknown artist *View of Newhaven from Forth*
unknown artist *The Warrior*
unknown artist 19th C, *The Lighthouse Tender SS 'Pharos'*
unknown artist *James VI (1566–1625)*, presented by Mrs Stirling
unknown artist *Mary, Queen of Scots (1542–1587)*
unknown artist *'North Carr' Light Vessel*
unknown artist *Prince Henry Stuart, Cardinal York (1724–1807)* (copy after an earlier painting by an unknown artist)
unknown artist *The 'Ben Ledi'*, donated to Captain A. P. Paterson; presented to Trinity House (?)
unknown artist *The Miller's Wharf, London*, donated to Trinity House by Mr Leckie, Minister of Davidson Mains Church
unknown artist *Twin Funnel Paddle Steamer*
Vanson, Adrian (attributed to) –d. before 1610, *James VI (1566–1625)*, purchased by Historic Scotland from the Weiss Gallery, London, 1996
Verity, Colin b.1924, *The*

'Benavon', donated to Captain A. P. Paterson by the sea staff of the Ben Line
Ward, Edward Matthew 1816–1879, *The Last Sleep of Argyll before His Execution, 1685*
Wright, John Michael (attributed to) 1617–1694, *Lady Anne Bruce, Daughter of the 2nd Earl of Elgin, Robert Bruce (c.1660–1716)*, on loan from a private lender
Wright, John Michael (attributed to) 1617–1694, *James VII and II (1633–1701)*, on loan from a private lender
Young, Edward Drummond 1877–1946, *Captain William Wright, Master of Trinity House (1939–1947)*, © the artist's estate (Hon. Lord Drummond Young)
Young, Edward Drummond 1877–1946, *Captain Robert Meikle, JP, Master of Trinity House (1927–1937)*, purchased by Trinity House, © the artist's estate (Hon. Lord Drummond Young)

The University of Edinburgh Fine Art Collection

Aikman, John active c.1712–1731, *William Carstares (1649–1715)*, presented to the University on the death of Mrs Carstares by her executor, Professor Charles Mackie
Aikman, William 1682–1731, *Landscape with a River*
Alison, David 1882–1955, *Adam Cleghorn Welch (1864–1943)*, on loan from the Church of Scotland
Alison, David 1882–1955, *James Walker (1864–1922)*, presented to the sitter in recognition of his 21 years' service as Treasurer of the University Union, 1910; presented to the University by his sister
Alison, David 1882–1955, *Robert William Johnstone (1879–1969)*, bequeathed by the sitter, c.1969
Alison, David 1882–1955, *Sir John Rankine (1846–1922)*
Allan, David (attributed to) 1744–1796, *Professor Francis Home (1719–1813)*, presented to the Faculty of Medicine by W. E. Home, RN, Fleet Surgeon, for acceptance after his death and the death of his wife, 1927
Allan, William 1782–1850, *Fair Maid of Perth*, bequeathed by James C. Corson, 1989
Anderson, J. Alasdair active 1972, *Blair Atholl, Perthshire and Kinross*, donated by the artist to the Talbot Rice Memorial Collection, 1972
Asper, Hans Kaspar (after) 1592–before 1655, *Johannes Œcolampadius (1482–1531)*, given to the University of Edinburgh, before 1696 (?)
Asper, Hans Kaspar (after) 1592–before 1655, *Ulrich Zwingli (1484–1531)*
Backhuysen, Ludolf I 1630–1708, *A Squall: A Lugger Running into Harbour*, bequeathed as part of the Torrie Collection, 1836

Baillie, William James b.1923, *Table with Violins*, © the artist
Baillie, William James b.1923, *Harbour Still Life*, © the artist
Baldi, Lazzaro c.1623–1703, *Battle Piece* (after Giulio Romano), bequeathed as part of the Torrie Collection, 1836
Barclay, John MacLaren 1811–1886, *Anthony Hall* (model for golden boy on the dome of Old College), bequeathed by Helen Mackay
Barrett, John Macdonald *Untitled*, commissioned in memory of Dr Hilde Behrend, after 2000
Barrie, Mardi 1931–2004, *Harbour Evening*, presented to the University (for the new library) by Messrs Steensen, Varming, Mulcahy, heating engineers, 1967, © the artist's estate
Barrie, Mardi 1931–2004, *Harbour Wall*, purchased, 1968, © the artist's estate
Barrie, Mardi 1931–2004, *Off Shore*, purchased, 1967, © the artist's estate
Barrie, Mardi 1931–2004, *Scunthorpe, North Lincolnshire, II*, gift from the artist to the David Talbot Rice Memorial Collection, 1972, © the artist's estate
Beaton, Penelope 1886–1963, *Fruit*, purchased, 1961
Bellany, John b.1942, *Lovers by the Sea*, gift from the artist during his Edinburgh Festival Exhibition, 1995, © the artist/Bridgeman Art Library
Bellucci, Giovanni Battista (attributed to) 1684–1760, *Portrait of an Unknown Man* (possibly Robert Moubray), presented by Robert Durant Trotter, 1946
Berchem, Nicolaes 1620–1683, *A Herdsman Driving Cattle down a Lane*, bequeathed as part of the Torrie Collection, 1836
Berchem, Nicolaes 1620–1683, *Cattle in a Stream, with a Herd Boy Resting*, bequeathed as part of the Torrie Collection, 1836
Beveridge, M. *Welders*
Blackadder, Elizabeth V. b.1931, *Figures at Night*, presented by Mr and Mrs Robertson to the David Talbot Rice Memorial Collection, © the artist
Blackadder, Elizabeth V. b.1931, *Ochre House*, presented to the University (for David Hume Tower) by Messrs Steenson, Varming, Mulcahy, heating engineers, 1967, © the artist
Blackadder, Elizabeth V. b.1931, *Sir David Smith (b.1930)*, acquired, c.1994, © the artist
Blackadder, Elizabeth V. b.1931, *Staffin, Skye*, presented by the Masson Association, © the artist
Blackadder, Elizabeth V. b.1931, *Walltown, Northumberland (Roman Wall)*, purchased, 1961, © the artist
Bond, Marj b.1939, *White House in a Warm Perthshire Valley*, purchased, © the artist

Bond, Marj b.1939, *Three Figures in a Landscape*, purchased, © the artist
Bond, Marj b.1939, *Undulating Perthshire*, purchased, © the artist
Bonnar, Wiliam 1800–1855, *Interior Scene, Woman with a Knife*, bequeathed by James C. Corson, 1989
Borthwick, Alfred Edward 1871–1955, *Andrew Seth Pringle-Pattison (1856–1931)*, bequeathed by the sitter's son, 1974
Borthwick, Alfred Edward 1871–1955, *Sir Francis Albert Ely Crew (1886–1973)* (sketch), presented by Miss Violet Borthwick, 1957
Borthwick, Alfred Edward 1871–1955, *Sir Francis Albert Ely Crew (1886–1973)*, presented by Miss Violet Borthwick, 1957
Borthwick, Alfred Edward 1871–1955, *A Rocky Landscape*
Borthwick, Alfred Edward 1871–1955, *Sir Alexander Gray (1882–1968), CBE, MA, LLD*, bequeathed by the artist
Both, Andries Dirksz. (attributed to) 1611/1612–1641, *A Rocky Landscape with Figures, Sunset*, bequeathed as part of the Torrie Collection, 1836
Both, Jan c.1618–1652, *Landscape with Figures*, bequeathed as part of the Torrie Collection, 1836
Both, Jan c.1618–1652, *Landscape with Mounted Figures*, bequeathed as part of the Torrie Collection, 1836
Bough, Samuel 1822–1878, *Harbour Scene*, purchased
Bourne, Peter b.1931, *The Old Gable*, © the artist
British School 19th C, *Landscape*
Bronckhorst, Arnold (after) c.1566–1586, *George Buchanan (1506–1582)*, given to the University of Edinburgh by the wife of Provost Prince, 1689 (or by Sir Robert Sibbald a few years later)
Bronckhorst, Arnold (after) c.1566–1586, *George Buchanan (1506–1582)*, given to the University of Edinburgh by the wife of Provost Prince, 1689 (or by Sir Robert Sibbald a few years later)
Brown, John Caldwell b.1945, *Hugh MacDiarmid (1892–1978)*, presented by Duval and Hamilton, © the artist
Burns, William Alexander 1921–1972, *Seakirk 1*, donated to the David Talbot Rice Memorial Collection by Mr W. J. Macaulay and Mr W. Jackson, partners in Aitken Dott & Son, Edinburgh
Cadell, Francis Campbell Boileau 1883–1937, *Mountain Landscape*, purchased © Cadell Estate, courtesy Portland Gallery, London
Calderwood, William Leadbetter 1865–1950, *Charles Saroléa (1870–1953)*, bequeathed, 1954
Calvert, Edward 1799–1883,

Alexander Monro 'Secundus' (1733–1817)

Cameron, Hugh 1835–1918, *Dumbiedykes and Jeanie Dean's*, bequeathed by James C. Corson, 1989

Cameron, Mary 1864–1921, *Alexander Inglis McCallum (1845–1921)*

Carlisle, Fionna b.1954, *Professor Sir Kenneth Murray and Lady Noreen Murray (b.1935)*, commissioned, 2009, © the artist

Carrick, Anne b.1919, *Evening Sky over Rum*, © the artist

Carse, Alexander c.1770–1843, *Covenanters in a Glen*, presented by N. C. E. Ashton

Caw, James Lewis 1864–1950, *Sir John Leslie (1766–1832)* (copy after David Wilkie), presented by Dr Carse

Christie, James Elder 1847–1914, *Mary Dick (1791–1883)*, presented by Thomas Dollar, 1894

Cockburn, Tim b.1955, *Law Faculty*, © the artist

Cockburn, Tim b.1955, *Sir Thomas Broun Smith (1915–1988)*, © the artist

Collet, Ruth 1909–2001, *A Conversation*

Convery, Francis b.1956, *Holy Isle*, © the artist

Courtois, Jacques 1621–1676, *A Battle Scene*, bequeathed as part of the Torrie Collection, 1836

Courtois, Jacques 1621–1676, *Skirmish*, bequeathed as part of the Torrie Collection, 1836

Cowie, James 1886–1956, *Hugh Watt (1879–1968)*, presented by Professor Watt, 1952, © the artist's estate

Cowie, James 1886–1956, *The Blue Shirt*, purchased by the University Pictures Committee, 1974, © the artist's estate

Crabb, William 1811–1876, *Sir William Fraser (1816–1898)*, presented by Sir William Fraser's trustees, 1898

Cranach, Lucas the elder (after) 1472–1553, *Philip Melanchthon (1497–1560)*, given to the University of Edinburgh, before 1696 (?)

Crawford, Edmund Thornton 1806–1885, *Watermill*, acquired, 1956

Crome, William Henry 1806–1873, *Wooded Landscape*

Crowe, Victoria b.1945, *John McIntyre (1916–2005)*, presented to the University of Edinburgh by the Very Reverend Professor John McIntyre, 1987, © Victoria Crowe

Crowe, Victoria b.1945, *Dr Ann Matheson*, commissioned, 2009, © Victoria Crowe

Crozier, William 1893–1930, *Via Piero della Francesca, Sansepolcro, Italy*, presented to Cowan House Hall of Residence, George Square by Professor F. W. Ogilvie

Cruikshank, Robert Isaac 1789–1856, *William Patrick of Roughwood (1770–1861)* (after Colvin Smith), presented by Mr Cochrane Patrick

Cuming, William 1769–1852, *Sir John Macpherson (c.1745–1821)* (after Joshua Reynolds)

Cuming, William 1769–1852, *Sir William Fettes (1750–1836)* (after Henry Raeburn)

Cumming, James 1922–1991, *Peat and Paraffin*, bequeathed to Holland House Hall of Residence by J. W. G. H. Ridell of Edinburgh, 1971, © the artist's estate

Cumming, James 1922–1991, *The Invalid*, purchased from Aitken Dott & Son by Professor Giles Robertson with funds subscribed by donors to the Talbot Rice Memorial Collection, 1975, © the artist's estate

Currie, Ken b.1960, *Peter Higgs (b.1929)*, commissioned, 2008, © the artist/ courtesy Flowers Gallery, London

Cursiter, Stanley 1887–1976, *Dr Orlando Charnock Bradley (1871–1937)*, presented to the sitter by his colleagues and students, 1936, © estate of Stanley Cursiter 2012. All rights reserved, DACS

Cursiter, Stanley 1887–1976, *Dr Orlando Charnock Bradley (1871–1937)*, originally presented by the artist to the sitter, © estate of Stanley Cursiter 2012. All rights reserved, DACS

Cursiter, Stanley 1887–1976, *Sir Donald Pollock (1868–1962)*, presented by the sitter, 1942, © estate of Stanley Cursiter 2012. All rights reserved, DACS

Cursiter, Stanley 1887–1976, *Sir Thomas Henry Holland (1868–1947)*, bequeathed by Lady Holland, 1983, © estate of Stanley Cursiter 2012. All rights reserved, DACS

Cursiter, Stanley 1887–1976, *Sir Thomas Henry Holland (1868–1947)*, bequeathed by Lady Holland, 1983, © estate of Stanley Cursiter 2012. All rights reserved, DACS

Cursiter, Stanley 1887–1976, *William Curtis (1876–1961)*, subscribed by colleagues, friends and former students at the Universities of Edinburgh and Aberdeen, and in the Church and presented to Professor Curtis; presented by the sitter to the University's Faculty of Divinity, © estate of Stanley Cursiter 2012. All rights reserved, DACS

Cursiter, Stanley 1887–1976, *Sir Donald Pollock (1868–1962)*, presented by Thorn Electrical Industries Limited, 1967, © estate of Stanley Cursiter 2012. All rights reserved, DACS

Cursiter, Stanley 1887–1976, *Dr John Gillies (1870–1952)*, bequeathed by the sitter's niece, Dr Deidre M. M. Gillies, © estate of Stanley Cursiter 2012. All rights reserved, DACS

Cursiter, Stanley 1887–1976, *Sir Donald Pollock (1868–1962)* (copy of an earlier painting), presented by the executors of the sitter's estate, © estate of Stanley Cursiter 2012. All rights reserved, DACS

Davie, Alan b.1920, *The Golden Palace*, © the artist

Davie, Alan b.1920, *donated by the artist, 1998*, donated by Alan Davie, 1998, © the artist

Davies, Ivor b.1935, *White Landscape with Sky Forms*, purchased by the Scottish Arts Council from the Talbot Rice Art Centre exhibition, 1972; donated, 1997, © Ivor Davies

Delacour, William 1700–1767, *Landscape** (triptych, left wing)

Delacour, William 1700–1767, *Landscape** (triptych, centre panel)

Delacour, William 1700–1767, *Landscape** (triptych, right wing)

Dingwall, Kenneth b.1938, *Between Dark and Dark*, purchased by the University's Picture Committee, 1978, © the artist

Dingwall, Kenneth b.1938, *Calm Grey*, purchased by the Scottish Arts Council from Charlotte Square Gallery, 1977; donated, 1997, © the artist

Dobson, Cowan 1894–1980, *Sir Leybourne Stanley Patrick Davidson (1894–1981)*, presented by Sir Stanley Davidson, 1979

Domenichino (after) 1581–1641, *The Martyrdom of Saint Andrew*, bequeathed as part of the Torrie Collection, 1836

Donald, George Malcolm b.1943, *Gladys Davis (b.c.1940)*, commissioned, 2006, © the artist

Donaldson, David Abercrombie 1916–1996, *Nude (Birth of Venus)*, bequeathed by Hope Scott, 1989, © the artist's estate

Dongen, Kees van 1877–1968, *A Vase of Flowers*, bequeathed by Hope Scott, 1989, © ADAGP, Paris and DACS, London 2012

Dughet, Gaspard 1615–1675, *Land Storm*, bequeathed as part of the Torrie Collection, 1836

Dujardin, Karel 1626–1678, *Halt at an Italian Winehouse Door*, bequeathed as part of the Torrie Collection, 1836

Dujardin, Karel (style of) 1626–1678, *Farrier's Shop*, bequeathed as part of the Torrie Collection, 1836

Duncan, John 1866–1945, *Unicorns*, bequeathed by I. M. Moffat-Pender, © estate of John Duncan. All rights reserved, DACS 2012

Dunn, John active 1768–1841, *William Dick (1793–1866)*, presented by Veterinary Lieutenant Colonel J. H. R. Hallen

Dutch School (attributed to) *Portrait of an Unknown Man with a Jewelled, Plumed Hat*

Dyce, William 1806–1864, *John Small (1828–1886)*

Dyce, William 1806–1864, *Nicholson Bain (c.1787–1840)*, presented by the sitter's daughters

Dyck, Anthony van (style of) 1599–1641, *Alexander Henderson (c.1583–1646)*

Eardley, Joan Kathleen Harding 1921–1963, *Back Street Bookie*, purchased, 1966, © DACS 2012

Eardley, Joan Kathleen Harding 1921–1963, *Bagged Potatoes*, bequeathed by Hope Scott, 1989, © DACS 2012

Eardley, Joan Kathleen Harding 1921–1963, *January Flow Tide*, purchased, 1960, © DACS 2012

Ernst, Max 1891–1976, *Antediluvian Landscape*, bequeathed by Hope Scott, 1989, © ADAGP, Paris and DACS, London 2012

Ewart, David Shanks 1901–1965, *Sir John Fraser (1885–1947)*, commissioned by the University, 1948

Feledi, Tivadar 1852–1896, *Man on a Horse*

Fenwick, Thomas active 1835–1850, *Late Autumn Landscape*, presented by Professor John Orr, c.1957

Ferguson, William active 1835–1850, *A Beach in Coll*, donated to the Department of Physics, 1976

Ferguson, William active 1835–1850, *Near Drem, East Lothian*

Firth, Helen active late 20th C, *Kettle*, purchased

Fleming, John B. 1792–1845, *The Clyde*

Forbes, Phillippa *Major Christopher Henry John Deighton (b.1898)*, presented by the sitter's mother

Fraser, Alexander 1827–1899, *Harvest Scene*

Gear, William 1915–1997, *Untitled*, donated by James Coxon, 1999, © the artist's estate

Gear, William 1915–1997, *October Landscape*, donated by Robert Robertson in memory of his father Giles Robertson, 1997, © the artist's estate

Geddes, Andrew (attributed to) 1783–1844, *Professor James Home (1758–1842)*, presented to the Faculty of Medicine by W. E. Home, RN, Fleet Surgeon, for acceptance after his death and the death of his wife, 1927

Geddes, Andrew (style of) 1783–1844, *Ann Duncan (d.1851), Later Mrs James Home*, presented to the Faculty of Medicine by W. E. Home, RN, Fleet Surgeon, for acceptance after his death and the death of his wife, 1927

Geddes, Andrew (style of) 1783–1844, *George Husband Baird (1761–1840)*, presented to the University, 1864

German School (attributed to) *Martin Bucer (1491–1551)*, given to the University of Edinburgh by the wife of Provost Prince, 1689 (or by Sir Robert Sibbald a few years later)

German School (attributed to) *Theodore Beza (1519–1605)*, given to the University of Edinburgh by the wife of Provost Prince, 1689 (or by Sir Robert Sibbald a few years later)

German School (attributed to) *John Calvin (1509–1564)*, gift, before 1696 (?)

Ghisolfi, Giovanni c.1623–1683, *Architectural Composition*, bequeathed as part of the Torrie Collection, 1836

Ghisolfi, Giovanni c.1623–1683, *Ruins and Figures*, bequeathed as part of the Torrie Collection, 1836

Gillespie *The Lady of Avenil Leaving*, bequeathed by James C. Corson, 1989

Gillies, William George 1898–1973, *St Monans, East Neuk of Fife* (Sketch), purchased from Aitken Dott & Son, 1970, © Royal Scottish Academy

Gillies, William George 1898–1973, *Landscape with a House and a Field*, purchased from the Royal Scottish Academy, 1961, © Royal Scottish Academy

Gordon, Cora Josephine 1879–1950, *Italian Landscape*, bequeathed by Margaret Renwick, 1986

Gordon, John Watson 1788–1864, *Reverend Alexander Brunton (1772–1854)*, presented to the Senatus by a body of subscribers, 1846

Gordon, John Watson 1788–1864, *John Inglis (1810–1891)*

Gordon, John Watson 1788–1864, *HRH Edward, Prince of Wales (1841–1910)*, presented by Miss Macalister Thomson, 1930

Gordon, John Watson 1788–1864, *Sir James Young Simpson (1811–1870)*

Gordon, John Watson 1788–1864, *Alexander Monro 'Tertius' (1773–1859)*, presented by the second Mrs Monro, 1884

Gordon, John Watson 1788–1864, *Andrew Duncan (1744–1828)*

Gordon, John Watson 1788–1864, *George Dunbar (1774–1851)*, purchased, 1928

Gordon, John Watson 1788–1864, *John Lee (1779–1859)*

Gordon, John Watson 1788–1864, *John Lee (1779–1859)*

Gordon, John Watson 1788–1864, *Sir David Baxter of Kilmaron (1793–1872)*

Graham, Thomas Alexander Ferguson 1840–1906, *John Girdwood (1863–1933)*, bequeathed by Annie Webster, 1981

Grant, Francis 1803–1878, *Margaret Stuart Tyndall-Bruce of Falkland (1788–1869)*, presented by Andrew Tyndall Bruce, 1888

Grant, Thomas F. (attributed to) active 1868–1879, *Edinburgh from Calton Hill*

Gray, Gary *At the Bank*

Green, Kenneth 1905–1986, *Sir Herbert John Clifford Grierson (1866–1960)*, presented by Sir Herbert Grierson, 1951, © the artist's estate

McLean, John b.1939, *Number One (Vertical Painting)*, commissioned, 1972, © the artist

McLean, Talbert 1906–1992, *Crudie*, © John & David McLean

McLean, Talbert 1906–1992, *Dunnichen, Angus*, purchased, 1973, © John & David McLean

McLean, Talbert 1906–1992, *Still Life with a Lamp and Eggs*, purchased, 2006, © John & David McLean

McLean, Talbert 1906–1992, *Still Life with a Melon*, purchased, 1972/1973, © John & David McLean

McNairn, Caroline 1955–2010, *Water of Leith*, purchased © the artist's estate

McTaggart, William 1835–1910, *The Lasswade Road, Edinburgh*

McTaggart, William 1835–1910, *Two Children on a Shore*, purchased, c.1956

Medina, John 1720–1796, *James Thomson (1700–1748)* (after John Patoun)

Medina, John Baptist de (style of) 1659–1710, *Robert Kerr (1636–1703), 4th Earl and 1st Marquess of Lothian*, purchased, 1953

Methuen, Paul Ayshford 1886–1974, *George Square, South East Corner, Edinburgh*, commissioned, 1958, © trustees of the Corsham estate

Methuen, Paul Ayshford 1886–1974, *George Square, South Side, Edinburgh*, commissioned, 1958, © trustees of the Corsham estate

Methuen, Paul Ayshford 1886–1974, *Old College Quadrangle, Edinburgh*, commissioned, 1958, © trustees of the Corsham estate

Meulen, Adam Frans van der 1631/1632–1690, *A Cavalcade*, bequeathed as part of the Torrie Collection, 1836

Miereveld, Michiel Jansz. van (after) 1567–1641, *Maurice of Nassau (1567–1625), Prince of Orange*

Miereveld, Michiel Jansz. van (after) 1567–1641, *Frederick Count Palatine (1596–1632)*, given to the University of Edinburgh by the wife of Provost Prince, 1689 (or by Sir Robert Sibbald a few years later)

Moffat, Alexander b.1943, *The Right Honourable Michael Meredith Swann (1920–1990)*, commissioned by the University Court, © the artist

Mooney, John b.1948, *Cornucopia*, donated by the Scottish Arts Council, 1997, © the artist

Mooney, John b.1948, *Salisbury Crags*, purchased, 1979, © the artist

Morrice, Alan Fergusson b.1944, *Self Portrait with a Friend*

Morrison, James b.1932, *Fishing Nets No.1*, bequeathed by Hope Scott, 1989, © the artist

Morrocco, Alberto 1917–1998,

Professor Emeritus Nicholas Kemmer (1911–1998), commissioned and presented by colleagues and friends of Professor Kemmer, 1980, © the artist's estate

Morrocco, Alberto 1917–1998, *Sir John Harrison Burnett (1922–2007)*, commissioned by the University for the sitter's retirement, 1987; presented by the sitter, © the artist's estate

Morrocco, Alberto 1917–1998, *John Henderson Seaforth Burleigh (1894–1985)*, subscribed by colleagues and friends in the University and the Church and presented to Professor Burleigh, 1967; presented to the Faculty of Divinity, © the artist's estate

Morrocco, Alberto 1917–1998, *The Honourable Lord Cameron, John Cameron (1900–1996)*, commissioned, 1975, © the artist's estate

Mulier, Pieter the elder (attributed to) c.1615–1670, *Sea Piece*, bequeathed as part of the Torrie Collection, 1836

Müller, Morten 1828–1911, *Nærøyfjord, Norway*, presented by Miss Ursula Blackwood, 1960

Murillo, Bartolomé Esteban (style of) 1618–1682, *Figure Subject* (diptych, left panel)

Murillo, Bartolomé Esteban (style of) 1618–1682, *Figure Subject* (diptych, right panel)

Mytens, Daniel I (follower of) c.1590–before 1647, *Jack Gills*, presented by Miss Ursula Blackwood, 1960

Nasmyth, Alexander (style of) 1758–1840, *Robert Burns (1759–1796)*, bequeathed by Mrs N. E. Phillips of Aberlady, 1967

Nasmyth, Patrick 1787–1831, *Edinburgh Castle from the Southwest*, bequeathed by Miss Marjory Henderson

Naudé, Pieter Hugo 1869–1941, *Dr John Brown (1842–1929)*, bequeathed by Margaret G. Dick, 1996

Neeffs, Peeter the elder c.1578–1656–1661, *Interior of a Cathedral*, bequeathed as part of the Torrie Collection, 1836

Nicholson, William 1872–1949, *Sir Richard Lodge (1855–1936)*, presented by Miss Margaret B. Lodge, 1959, © Elizabeth Banks

Nicholson, William 1872–1949, *Sir Richard Lodge (1855–1936) (copy of an earlier painting)*, presented, 1925, © Elizabeth Banks

Nisbet, Alex b.1952, *Tiles*, purchased, © the artist

Oever, Hendrick ten 1639–1716, *Canal Landscape with Figures Bathing*, bequeathed as part of the Torrie Collection, 1836

Oram, Ann b.1956, *Duomo, Siena, Italy*, © the artist

Organ, Robert b.1933, *The Lot near Saint-Martin-Labouval, France, No.1*, presented by Eleanor Robertson, 1993, © the artist

Ouless, Walter William

1848–1933, *James Bell Pettigrew (1832–1908)*

Ouless, Walter William 1848–1933, *Sir Donald Currie (1825–1909)*

Ounouh, Mohammed b.1964, *Yellow Triangle*, © the artist

Ounouh, Mohammed b.1964, *Birds' Feet*, © the artist

Ounouh, Mohammed b.1964, *Red Arrowhead*, © the artist

Ounouh, Mohammed b.1964, *Toasting Fork*, © the artist

Ounouh, Mohammed b.1964, *White Dog*, © the artist

Ounouh, Mohammed b.1964, *Fork with Blue Triangle*, © the artist

Ounouh, Mohammed b.1964, *Two Panels*, © the artist

Paget, Henry Mariott 1856–1936, *William Prout (1785–1850)* (possibly after John Hayes), presented by T. J. P. and E. P., 1902

Palacios, Alirio b.1944, *Dr José María Vargas (1786–1854)* (copied from a contemporary portrait), presented by the Venezuelan Ambassador, Snr José Luis Salcedo-Bastardo, 1986

Panini, Giovanni Paolo c.1692–1765, *Roman Ruins with Figures*, bequeathed by Miss Ursula Blackwood, 1960

Panini, Giovanni Paolo c.1692–1765, *Roman Ruins with Figures*, bequeathed by Miss Ursula Blackwood, 1960

Pannett, Juliet Kathleen 1911–2005, *Norman Walker Porteous (1898–2003)*, presented by the sitter, after 1972, © the artist's estate

Peploe, Samuel John 1871–1935, *Cyclamen*, bequeathed by Hope Scott, 1989

Peploe, Samuel John 1871–1935, *White Roses and Grapes*, purchased from Aitken Dott & Son, 1962

Pettie, John 1839–1893, *Disbanded*, bequeathed by James C. Corson, 1989

Philipson, Robin 1916–1992, *The Trappers*, presented by the Edinburgh University Savoy Opera Group, 1963, © the artist's estate

Philpot, Glyn Warren 1884–1937, *Sir Ludovic Grant (1862–1936)*, bequeathed by Ludovic Kennedy, 2009

Pickersgill, Henry William 1782–1875, *Captain Thomas Drummond (1797–1840)*, presented, 1866

Pickersgill, Henry William 1782–1875, *Lyon Playfair (1818–1898), 1st Baron Playfair of St Andrews*, presented by the sitter, 1898

Pickersgill, Henry William 1782–1875, *Sir Roderick Impey Murchison (1792–1871)*, presented by the sitter, 1871

Pietro della Vecchia 1603–1678, *The Lovers*, bequeathed as part of the Torrie Collection, 1836

Procaccini, Giulio Cesare

1574–1625, *Dead Christ with Angels*, bequeathed as part of the Torrie Collection, 1836

Pynacker, Adam c.1620–1673, *A Forest Glade*, bequeathed as part of the Torrie Collection, 1836

Raeburn, Henry 1756–1823, *Adam Ferguson (1723–1816)*, presented by the executors of the estate Sir John Macpherson, 1821

Raeburn, Henry 1756–1823, *William Robertson (1721–1793)*, commissioned

Raeburn, Henry 1756–1823, *Thomas Elder (1737–1799), Lord Provost of Edinburgh*, commissioned, 1797

Raeburn, Henry 1756–1823, *John Robison (1739–1805)*, presented to the Senatus, 1850

Raeburn, Henry 1756–1823, *John Playfair (1748–1819)*, bequeathed by Miss Margaret Playfair, 1857

Raeburn, Henry 1756–1823, *Andrew Dalziel (1742–1806)*

Raeburn, Henry 1756–1823, *Ann Rutherford*, bequeathed by James C. Corson, 1989

Raeburn, Henry 1756–1823, *John Hill*, acquired by the University in satisfaction of estate duty of Mr Henry James Cook (1929–1989)

Raeburn, Henry (style of) 1756–1823, *John Bruce (1745–1826)*, presented by Mrs Tyndall Bruce

Ramsay, Allan (attributed to) 1713–1784, *Andrew Fletcher (1692–1766), Lord Milton*, presented to the Faculty of Medicine by W. E. Home, RN, Fleet Surgeon, for acceptance after his death and the death of his wife, 1927

Ramsay, Allan (follower of) 1713–1784, *John Coutts (1699–1751), Lord Provost of Edinburgh (1742)*, presented by Robert Durant Trotter, 1946

Ramsay, Allan (style of) 1713–1784, *David Hume (1711–1776)*

Ramsay, Allan (style of) 1713–1784, *Joan Kinloch (d.c.1726)*, presented to the Faculty of Medicine by W. E. Home, RN, Fleet Surgeon, for acceptance after his death and the death of his wife, 1927

Redpath, Anne 1895–1965, *Spanish Doorway*, purchased, 1965, © the artist's estate/Bridgeman Art Library

Redpath, Anne 1895–1965, *The Ladies' Garden, Palácio dos Marqueses de Fronteira, Lisbon*, purchased, 1962, © the artist's estate/Bridgeman Art Library

Redpath, Anne 1895–1965, *Tréboul Harbour, France*, bequeathed by Hope Scott, 1989, © the artist's estate/Bridgeman Art Library

Reid, George 1841–1913, *David Mavor Masson (1822–1907)*, presented to the University by the sitter's grandson, Sir Irvine Masson FRS, 1952

Reid, George 1841–1913, *Arthur James Balfour (1848–1930)*

Reid, George 1841–1913, *Alexander Campbell Fraser (1819–1914)*, presented by the sitter's friends and former students, 1890

Reid, George 1841–1913, *Henry Calderwood (1830–1897)*, purchased from Mrs B. Woolrych, 1958

Reid, George 1841–1913, *Robert Flint (1838–1910)*, bequeathed by the sitter, 1922

Reid, George 1841–1913, *Robert Rainy (1826–1906)*, on loan from the Church of Scotland

Reid, George 1841–1913, *Sir John Usher of Norton and Wells (1828–1904)*, presented by the sitter's grandson, 1949

Rembrandt van Rijn (copy after) 1606–1669, *The Anatomy Lesson of Dr Tulp*, presented by Dr Edwin Bramwell

Reni, Guido (style of) 1575–1642, *Ecce Homo*, bequeathed as part of the Torrie Collection, 1836

Reynolds, Joshua (style of) 1723–1792, *David Steuart Erskine (1742–1829)*

Robb, William George 1872–1940, *A Pastoral*, bequeathed by Hope Scott, 1989

Roberts, Derek b.1947, *Study in Red and Blue*, purchased, 1979, © the artist

Robertson, Charles Kay d.1939, *Sir Herbert Stanley Oakeley (1830–1903)*, presented by the University Musical Society, 1983/1984

Robertson, Iain b.1955, *Gracenotes*, donated by the artist, 2008, © the artist

Robson, Gavin b.1950, *Monumental Object No.22*, purchased, 1978, © the artist

Rosa, Salvator 1615–1673, *Rocky Landscape with Figures*, bequeathed as part of the Torrie Collection, 1836

Ross, Donald Sinclair (Danny) b.1951, *Iona, Land and Seascape*, gift from the artist, 1976

Ross, Robert Henry Alison active 1898–1940, *Professor Alexander Darroch (1862–1924)*, bequeathed by Dr Jane Darroch, 1978

Ross, Robert Henry Alison active 1898–1940, *James Mackinnon (1860–1945)*, presented by Sheriff J. A. R. Mackinnon, son of the sitter, 1945

Ruisdael, Jacob van 1628/1629–1682, *A Wood Scene*, bequeathed as part of the Torrie Collection, 1836

Rycroft, David b.1969, *View of Edinburgh*, © the artist

Sanderson, Robert 1848–1908, *Apollo and the Muses*

Scott, David 1806–1849, *Mythological Group*

Scott, James b.1802, *William Home (1816–1876), MD, AMS*, presented to the Faculty of Medicine by W. E. Home, RN, Fleet Surgeon, for acceptance after his death and the death of his wife, 1927

Scougal, John c.1645–1730, *Sir Thomas Steuart of Kirkfield and Coltness (1631–1698)*, presented by Robert Durant Trotter, 1946

Scougal, John (copy after) c.1645–1730, *George Heriot (1563–1624)* (copy after a portrait in Heriot's Hospital), presented by the Governors of Heriot's Hospital, 1864

Scougall, David c.1610–c.1680, *Sir James Steuart of Coltness (1681–1727)*, presented by Robert Durant Trotter, 1946

Segers, Hercules Pietersz. (style of) c.1589–c.1638, *Landscape*, bequeathed as part of the Torrie Collection, 1836

Serres, Dominic 1722–1793, *The Landing of William, Duke of Clarence* (later William IV) *at Rio di Janeiro in 1790*, bequeathed by Professor Emeritus Robert William Johnstone, 1969

Shanks, Duncan b.1937, *The Dam Burn*, presented by the University of Glasgow, 1983, © the artist

Shiels, William 1783–1857, *John Dick (c.1769–1844)*

Shiels, William 1783–1857, *William Dick (1793–1866)*

Shojie *Woman*

Sim, Agnes *Professor Edward Stebbing (1870–1960)*, presented by the sitter's son, c.1970

Sinclair, Catherine *The Loaf of Bread*, bequeathed by Hope Scott, 1989

Sinclair, Louisa active 19th C, *Thomas Chalmers (1780–1847)* (copy after Thomas Duncan), on loan from the Church of Scotland

Smart, John 1838–1899, *A Cloudy Day, Strathearn, Perthshire*, collected by J. M. Ross, 1962 (?)

Smith, Colvin 1795–1875, *Daniel Ellis (c.1772–1841)*, acquired at the request of the Senatus

Smith, Colvin 1795–1875, *J. Stewart Hepburn (1795–1875)*, commissioned by the Senatus, 1866

Smith, Colvin 1795–1875, *Mrs Elizabeth Cheape (1768–1857)*, on loan from Dundee Art Galleries and Museums Collection (Dundee City Council)

Smith, Colvin 1795–1875, *Robert Graham (1786–1845), MD*, presented by Mr Robert Graham, son of the sitter, 1875

Snyders, Frans 1579–1657, *The Boar Hunt*, bequeathed as part of the Torrie Collection, 1836

Somer, Paulus van I (after) 1576–1621, *King James VI and I (1566–1625)*, given to the University of Edinburgh by the wife of Provost Prince, 1689 (or by Sir Robert Sibbald a few years later)

Somer, Paulus van I (after) 1576–1621, *King James VI and I (1566–1625)*, given to the University of Edinburgh by the wife of Provost Prince, 1689 (or by Sir Robert Sibbald a few years later)

Spanish School (attributed to) *Portrait of an Unknown Man*, gift, before 1696 (?)

Squire, Geoffrey b.1923, *Reverend Thomas Forsyth Torrance (1913–2007)*

Steen, Jan 1626–1679, *The Doctor's Visit*, bequeathed as part of the Torrie Collection, 1836

Stoop, Dirck (style of) c.1610–c.1686, *Catherine of Braganza (1638–1705), Queen Consort of King Charles II*, given to the University of Edinburgh by the wife of Provost Prince, 1689

Strachota, Josef Franz b.1911, *Sir Thomas Dalling (1892–1982)*, bequeathed by the sitter, 1982

Streeton, Arthur 1867–1943, *The Borderland*, bequeathed by I. M. Moffat-Pender, 1951

Sturrock, Alick Riddell 1885–1953, *Wooded River Landscape*, bequeathed by Hope Scott, 1989

Teniers, David II 1610–1690, *Peasants Playing Bowls*, bequeathed as part of the Torrie Collection, 1836

Teniers, David II (style of) 1610–1690, *A Pasticcio*, bequeathed as part of the Torrie Collection, 1836

Thomson, Adam Bruce 1885–1976, *Norman Kemp Smith (1872–1958)*, presented by the sitter's friends, 1946 © the artist's estate

Thomson, John 1778–1840, *William Wallace (1768–1843)*, presented by Alexander B. Bell

Thomson, John 1778–1840, *Crichton Castle, Midlothian*, bequeathed by James C. Corson, 1989

Thomson, John 1778–1840, *Hermitage Castle, Scottish Borders*, bequeathed by James C. Corson, 1989

Thomson, John 1778–1840, *Innerwick Castle, East Lothian*, bequeathed by James C. Corson, 1989

Thomson, John 1778–1840, *Tantallon Castle, North Berwick*, bequeathed by James C. Corson, 1989

Titian (school of) c.1488–1576, *Virgin and Child with St Catherine*, bequeathed as part of the Torrie Collection, 1836

Tong, J. de *Cornelis Petrus Tiele (1830–1902)*, presented by the sitter's estate, 1902

unknown artist *Lord John Napier of Merchiston (1550–1617)*, presented by Margaret, Baroness Napier, before 1706

unknown artist *William Drummond of Hawthornden (1585–1649)*, purchased, 1916

unknown artist *Robert Leighton (1611–1684)*

unknown artist mid 17th C, *Unknown Divine*

unknown artist mid 17th C, *Portrait of a Gentleman in Seventeenth-Century Dress*

(Portuguese Nobleman) (copy of an earlier painting)

unknown artist late 17th C, *Queen Henrietta Maria (1609–1669)*, given to the University of Edinburgh by the wife of Provost Prince, 1689

unknown artist late 17th C, *Portrait of an Unknown Man*

unknown artist 17th C, *Andrew Cant (d.1728)*, presented by Mrs White, 1710

unknown artist 17th C, *Pierre Gassend (1592–1655)*, given to the University of Edinburgh by the wife of Provost Prince, 1689 (or by Sir Robert Sibbald a few years later)

unknown artist 18th C, *Colin Drummond (d.c.1752)*

unknown artist *General Sir John Reid (1721–1807)*, bequeathed by the sitter, 1807

unknown artist *Thomas Leckie (1806–1878)*, presented by J. M. Leckie, 1920

unknown artist *Eleanor Ann Ormerod (1828–1901)*, presented, 1900

unknown artist *Andrew Bruce Davidson (1831–1902)*

unknown artist *Andrew David Barrowman, Janitor of Old College*, gift to the University from Philip Knowles, c.1991

unknown artist *Benedictus Aretius (1522–1574)*

unknown artist *Donald Ross (d.1883)*, presented by the sitter's widow and son

unknown artist *General John Reid (1721–1807)*, bequeathed by the sitter, 1807

unknown artist *General Sir Joseph Straton (d.1841)*, presented by Miss Straton Graham of Kirkside, 1894

unknown artist *Heinrich Bullinger (1504–1575)*

unknown artist *Highland Dancing Scene*, bequeathed by James C. Corson, 1989

unknown artist *James Home of Eccles (1681–1737), Advocate*, presented to the Faculty of Medicine by W. E. Home, RN, Fleet Surgeon, for acceptance after his death and the death of his wife, 1927

unknown artist *John Knox (c.1510–1572)*, acquired, 1695 or earlier

unknown artist *Martin Luther Writing the Prayer Book by the Light of the Gospel*, presented by Miss Ursula Blackwood, 1960

unknown artist *Portrait of a Man*

unknown artist *Portrait of an Unknown Lady*, presented by Robert Durant Trotter, 1946

unknown artist *Portrait of an Unknown Man (possibly Moubray)*, presented by Robert Durant Trotter, 1946

unknown artist *Portrait of an Unknown Woman*, presented by Robert Durant Trotter, 1946

unknown artist *Robert Rollock (c.1555–1599)*, acquired, 1696 or

earlier

unknown artist *Sir David Home (1643–1707), 1st Lord Crossrig*, presented to the Faculty of Medicine by W. E. Home, RN, Fleet Surgeon, for acceptance after his death and the death of his wife, 1927

unknown artist *Sir John Goodsir (1814–1867)*

unknown artist *Sir Walter Scott (1771–1832)*, bequeathed by James C. Corson, 1989

unknown artist *The Abduction of Isabella Vere*, bequeathed by James C. Corson, 1989

unknown artist *Violet Fairgreave Barrowman*, gift from Philip Knowles, c.1991

unknown artist *William Carstares (1649–1715)*, presented by Mr John G. Coates, 1957

unknown artist *Young Girl in Green*, bequeathed by Mrs Margaret G. Dick, 1996

Velde, Adriaen van de 1636–1672, *Cattle and Herdsman*, bequeathed as part of the Torrie Collection, 1836

Velde, Willem van de II 1633–1707, *Fishing Boats in a Calm*, bequeathed as part of the Torrie Collection, 1836

Veronese, Paolo (studio of) 1528–1588, *Venus and Adonis*, bequeathed as part of the Torrie Collection, 1836

Vos, Paul de (attributed to) 1591–1592 or 1595–1678, *The Wolf Hunt*, bequeathed as part of the Torrie Collection, 1836

Wardman, Clare b.1960, *Between Wind and Water*, donated by the artist, 2008, © the artist

Watson, George 1767–1837, *General John Reid (1721–1807)*, bequeathed by the sitter

Watson, George 1767–1837, *Thomas Brown (1778–1820)* (after Henry Raeburn), presented by Miss Eleanora Brown, 1846

Watson, William Smellie 1796–1894, *John Donaldson (d.1865)*, presented by Henry Houldsworth of Coltness, 1863

Watson, William Smellie 1796–1894, *John Thomson (1805–1841)*, presented by A. W. Lyon, 1951

Watt, George Fiddes 1873–1960, *Simon Somerville Laurie (1829–1909)*, presented by Mrs Laurie, 1924, © the artist's estate

Watt, George Fiddes 1873–1960, *Malcolm Campbell Taylor (1832–1922)*, presented to the sitter by his students and friends and donated to the University, in accordance with the wishes of the original donors, by the sitter, 1921, © the artist's estate

Watt, George Fiddes 1873–1960, *William P. Paterson (1860–1939)*, © the artist's estate

Weir, William d.1865, *The Honourable Henry Erskine (1746–1817)*, acquired when the University bought the building in

which it had been hung, 1948

Whyte, Duncan MacGregor 1866–1953, *Cattle on the Shore below Caenn a' Mhara*, donated by Mrs Eva MacGregor-Whyte, 1986

Whyte, Duncan MacGregor 1866–1953, *No.2, Cottars on 'the Land'*, donated by Mrs Eva MacGregor-Whyte, 1986

Whyte, Duncan MacGregor 1866–1953, *No.3, Carts on the Shore*, donated by Mrs Eva MacGregor-Whyte, 1986

Whyte, Duncan MacGregor 1866–1953, *No.4, Crofters, Balephuil*

Whyte, Duncan MacGregor 1866–1953, *No.5, Boats on the Shore*, donated by Mrs Eva MacGregor-Whyte, 1986

Whyte, Duncan MacGregor 1866–1953, *No.6, Harvesting Potatoes, Red Tam*, donated by Mrs Eva MacGregor-Whyte, 1986

Whyte, Duncan MacGregor 1866–1953, *No.7, Neil Eachan*, donated by Mrs Eva MacGregor-Whyte, 1986

Whyte, Duncan MacGregor 1866–1953, *No.8, Port Balephuil*, donated by Mrs Eva MacGregor-Whyte, 1986

Whyte, Duncan MacGregor 1866–1953, *No.9, Three Girls*, donated by Mrs Eva MacGregor-Whyte, 1986

Whyte, Duncan MacGregor 1866–1953, *Tigh Chaluim (Callum's House)*, donated by Mrs Eva MacGregor-Whyte, 1986

Whyte, John McGregor *No.19, Teampall Pharaig*, donated by Mrs Eva MacGregor-Whyte, 1986

Wighton, William *Sir David Brewster (1781–1868)*, bequeathed by Mrs James Hope, 1936

Willoughby, Trevor 1926–1995, *Sir Hugh Norwood Robson (1917–1977)*, commissioned posthumously by the University Court

Wilson, Richard 1712/1713–1782, *An Italian Landscape*, bequeathed as part of the Torrie Collection, 1836

Wingate, James Lawton 1846–1924, *An Arran Croft*

Wright, Allan *Still Life*, presented by the artist

Young, A. J. *Mary Dick (1791–1883)*, presented by Thomas Dollar, 1894

Young, William Drummond 1855–1924, *Sir John Goodsir (1814–1867)*

Żyw, Aleksander 1905–1995, *Snow Pattern*, purchased, 1968

Żyw, Aleksander 1905–1995, *Water of Leith 1*, donated by the artist to the Talbot Rice Memorial Collection, 1975

Collection Addresses

Edinburgh

City of Edinburgh Council:

City Art Centre
2 Market Street, Edinburgh EH1 1DE
Telephone 0131 5293993

> City Art Centre
> 2 Market Street, Edinburgh EH1 1DE
> Telephone 0131 5293993
>
> Edinburgh City Chambers
> High Street, Edinburgh EH1 1YJ
> Telephone 0131 2002000
>
> Edinburgh Zoo
> 134 Corstorphine Road, Edinburgh EH12 6TS
> Telephone 0131 3349171
>
> Lauriston Castle
> 2a Cramond Road South, Davidson's Mains,
> Edinburgh EH4 5QD
> Telephone 0131 3362060/3361921
>
> Leith Police Station
> Queen Charlotte Street, Leith, Edinburgh
> EH6 7EY
> Telephone 0131 5549350
>
> Museum of Edinburgh
> Huntly House, 142 Canongate, Royal Mile,
> Edinburgh EH8 8DD
> Telephone 0131 5294143
>
> Stockbridge Care Home
> 2 Haugh Street, Stockbridge, Edinburgh EH4 1LT
> Telephone 0131 3152238
>
> Usher Hall
> Lothian Road, Edinburgh EH1 2EA
> Telephone 0131 2281155
>
> Waverley Court
> 4 East Market Street, Edinburgh EH8 8BG
> Telephone 0131 5297325
>
> Writers' Museum
> Lady Stair's Close, Lawnmarket, Edinburgh
> EH1 2PA
> Telephone 0131 5294901

Historic Scotland, Edinburgh:

Historic Scotland
Longmore House, Salisbury Place, Edinburgh EH9 1SH
Telephone 0131 6688946

> Edinburgh Castle
> Castlehill, Royal Mile, Edinburgh EH1 2NG
> Telephone 0131 2259846
>
> Trinity House
> 99 Kirkgate, Leith, Edinburgh EH6 6BJ
> Telephone 0131 5543289

The University of Edinburgh Fine Art Collection
Museums Support Team, University of Edinburgh, Main
Library, George Square, Edinburgh EH8 9LJ
Telephone 0131 6502882

Facing page: Guthrie, James, 1859–1930, *Archibald Stodart Walker (1869–1934), MA, MB, OBE*, City of Edinburgh Council (p. 41)

Index of Artists

In this catalogue, artists' names and the spelling of their names follow the preferred presentation of the name in the Getty Union List of Artist Names (ULAN) as of February 2004, if the artist is listed in ULAN.

The page numbers next to each artist's name below direct readers to paintings that are by the artist; are attributed to the artist; or, in a few cases, are more loosely related to the artist being, for example, 'after', 'the circle of' or copies of a painting by the artist. The precise relationship between the artist and the painting is listed in the catalogue.

Facing page: Macgillivray, James Pittendrigh, 1856–1938, *The Tea Table*, 1885, City of Edinburgh Council (p. 60)

Acknowledgements

The Public Catalogue Foundation would like to thank the individual artists and copyright holders for their permission to reproduce for free the paintings in this catalogue. Exhaustive efforts have been made to locate the copyright owners of all the images included within this catalogue and to meet their requirements. Copyright credit lines for copyright owners who have been traced are listed in the Further Information section.

The Public Catalogue Foundation would like to express its great appreciation to the following organisations for their kind assistance in the preparation of this catalogue:

Bridgeman Art Library
Flowers East
Marlborough Fine Art
National Association of Decorative & Fine Arts Societies (NADFAS)
National Gallery, London
National Portrait Gallery, London
Royal Academy of Arts, London
Tate

The Public Catalogue Foundation

The Public Catalogue Foundation is a registered charity. It was launched in 2003 to create a photographic record of the entire national collection of oil, tempera and acrylic paintings in public ownership in the United Kingdom.

Whilst our public galleries and civic buildings hold arguably the greatest collection of oil paintings in the world, over 80 per cent of these are not on view. Few collections have a complete photographic record of their paintings let alone a comprehensive illustrated catalogue. What is publicly owned is not publicly accessible.

The Foundation is publishing a series of fully illustrated, county-by-county catalogues that will cover, eventually, the entire national UK collection. To date, it has published over 30 volumes, presenting over 72,000 paintings.

In partnership with the BBC, the Foundation will make its database of the entire UK collection of 200,000 oil paintings available online through a new website called *Your Paintings*. The website was launched in the summer of 2011.

Your Paintings (*www.bbc.co.uk/arts/yourpaintings*) offers a variety of ways of searching for paintings as well as further information about the paintings and artists, including links to the participating collections' websites. For those interested in paintings and the subjects they portray *Your Paintings* is an unparalleled learning resource.

Collections benefit substantially from the work of the Foundation, not least from the digital images that are given to them for free following photography, and from the increased recognition that the project brings. These substantial benefits come at no financial cost to the collections.

The Foundation is funded by a combination of support from individuals, charitable trusts, companies and the public sector although the latter provides less than 20 per cent of the Foundation's financial support.

Supporters

Master Patrons

The Public Catalogue Foundation is greatly indebted to the following Master Patrons who have helped it in the past or are currently working with it to raise funds for the publication of their county catalogues. All of them have given freely of their time and have made an enormous contribution to the work of the Foundation.

Peter Andreae (*Hampshire*)
Sir Henry Aubrey-Fletcher, Bt, Lord Lieutenant of Buckinghamshire (*Buckinghamshire*)
Sir Nicholas Bacon, DL, High Sheriff of Norfolk (*Norfolk*)
Sir John Bather, Lord Lieutenant of Derbyshire (*Derbyshire*)
The Hon. Mrs Bayliss, JP, Lord Lieutenant of Berkshire (*Berkshire*)
Ian Bonas (*County Durham*)

Peter Bretherton (*West Yorkshire: Leeds*)
Michael Brinton, Lord Lieutenant of Worcestershire (*Worcestershire*)
Sir Hugo Brunner, KCVO, JP (*Oxfordshire*)
Mr John Bush, OBE, Lord-Lieutenant of Wiltshire (*Wiltshire*)
Lady Butler (*Warwickshire*)
Richard Compton (*North Yorkshire*)
George Courtauld, DL, Vice Lord Lieutenant of Essex (*Essex*)

The Countess of Darnley, Lord Lieutenant of Herefordshire *(Herefordshire)*
The Marquess of Downshire *(North Yorkshire)*
Martin Dunne, Lord Lieutenant of Warwickshire *(Warwickshire)*
Sir Henry Elwes, KCVO, Lord-Lieutenant of Gloucestershire *(Gloucestershire)*
Jenny Farr, MBE, DL *(Nottinghamshire)*
John Fenwick *(Tyne & Wear Museums)*
Mark Fisher, MP *(Staffordshire)*
Patricia Grayburn, MBE, DL *(Surrey)*
The Earl of Halifax, KStJ, JP, DL *(East Riding of Yorkshire)*
Lord Roy Hattersley, PC *(South Yorkshire: Sheffield*
Algy Heber-Percy, Lord Lieutenant of Shropshire *(Shropshire)*
The Lady Mary Holborow, Lord Lieutenant of Cornwall *(Cornwall)*
Sarah Holman *(Warwickshire)*
Tommy Jowitt *(West Yorkshire)*
Alderman Sir David Lewis, The Rt Hon. The Lord Mayor of London, 2007–2008 *(The City of London)*

Sir Michael Lickiss *(Cornwall)*
Magnus Linklater *(Scotland)*
Lord Marlesford, DL *(Suffolk)*
Dr Bridget McConnell *(Glasgow)*
Lady Sarah Nicholson *(County Durham)*
Malcolm V. L. Pearce, MP *(Somerset)*
Sir John Riddell, Lord Lieutenant of Northumberland *(Northumberland)*
Venetia Ross Skinner *(Dorset)*
The Most Hon. The Marquess of Salisbury, PC, DL *(Hertfordshire)*
Julia Somerville *(Government Art Collection)*
Tim Stevenson, OBE, Lord Lieutenant of Oxfordshire *(Oxfordshire)*
Phyllida Stewart-Roberts, OBE *(East Sussex)*
Lady Juliet Townsend, Lord Lieutenant of Northamptonshire *(Northamptonshire)*
Leslie Weller, DL *(West Sussex)*
Sir Samuel C. Whitbread, KCVO, Lord Lieutenant of Bedfordshire *(Bedfordshire)*

Financial support

The Public Catalogue Foundation is particularly grateful to the following organisations and individuals who have given it generous financial support since the project started in 2003.

National Sponsor

Christie's

Benefactors (£10,000–£50,000)

The 29th May 1961 Charitable Trust
Arts Council England
The Barbour Trust
Binks Trust
City of Bradford Metropolitan District Council
Deborah Loeb Brice Foundation
The Bulldog Trust
A. & S. Burton 1960 Charitable Trust
Christie's
City of London Corporation
The John S. Cohen Foundation
Covent Garden London
Creative Scotland
Department for Culture, Media and Sport

Sir Harry Djanogly, CBE
Mr Lloyd Dorfman
Dunard Fund
The Elmley Foundation
Fenwick Ltd
Fidelity UK Foundation
Marc Fitch Fund
The Foyle Foundation
J. Paul Getty Jr Trust
Hampshire County Council
The Charles Hayward Foundation
Peter Harrison Foundation
Mr Robert Hiscox
Hiscox plc
David Hockney, CH, RA
ICAP plc

Sir Idris Pearce
Roger Neville Russ Peers
The Pennycress Trust
Perkins Family
The Lord & Lady Phillimore
Mrs Margaret Pollett
Simon & Ursula Pomeroy
The Portland Family
Portsmouth City Council
George Pragnell Ltd
The Prince Philip Trust Fund for the
    Royal Borough of Windsor and
    Maidenhead
Provident Financial plc
Mr John Rank
Rathbone Investment Management
    Ltd
The Hans and Märit Rausing
    Charitable Trust
Roger & Jane Reed
Renaissance North East
Renaissance South East
Renaissance South West
Michael Renshall, CBE, MA, FCA
Sir John Riddell
Sir Miles & Lady Rivett-Carnac
Rockley Charitable Trust
Rolls-Royce plc
The Roper Family Charitable Trust
Rothschild Foundation
Royal Cornwall Museum
Graham & Ann Rudd
Sir Nigel Rudd
Russell New
The J. S. & E. C. Rymer Charitable
    Trust
The Earl St Aldwyn
The Sammermar Trust
Scarfe Charitable Trust
Andrew & Belinda Scott
The Trustees of the Finnis Scott
    Foundation
Shaftesbury PLC
Mr W. Sharpe
The Shears Foundation
Robert Shields, DL
Smith & Williamson

South West of England Regional
    Development Agency
Caroline M. Southall
Stuart M. Southall
Southampton City Council
The Jessie Spencer Trust
Hugh & Catherine Stevenson
Mrs Andrew Stewart-Roberts, OBE
Mr Michael Stone
Mr Peter Stormonth Darling
The Stratford-upon-Avon Town
    Trust
Strutt and Parker
Suffolk County Council, through the
    Association for Suffolk Museums
Surrey County Council
The John Swire 1989 Charitable
    Trust
The Tanner Trust
Tennants Auctioneers
Tesco Charity Trust
The Thistle Trust
Prof. Caroline Tisdall
Trusthouse Charitable Foundation
Gladwyn Turbutt
TWM Business Partners
Tyne & Wear Museums
University College Falmouth
University of Derby
University of Essex
David & Grizelda Vermont
Wakefield Metropolitan District
    Council
Robert & Felicity Waley-Cohen
The Peggy Walker Charitable Trust
The Walland Trust Fund
John Wates Charitable Trust
Leslie Weller, DL
The Welton Foundation
West Sussex County Council
Mr & Mrs David Wigglesworth
Wilkin & Sons Ltd
Mr & Mrs Jo Windsor
Peter Wolton Charitable Trust
Michael J. Woodhall, FRICS
Sir Philip Wroughton
Mrs Angela Yeoman

First published in 2012 by The Public Catalogue
Foundation, Printed Catalogue Division,
8 Frederick's Place, London, EC2R 8AB

ISBN 978-1-904931-86-7

Edinburgh I photography:
Andy Phillipson

Designed by Sally Jeffery

Printed in Hong Kong by Paramount Printing
Company Limited